WELSH SLATE CRAFT

Welsh Crafts Series:

1. THE FLANNEL MAKERS
A Brief History of the Welsh Woollen Industry
J. Geraint Jenkins

2. DRE-FACH FELINDRE
AND THE WOOLLEN INDUSTRY
J. Geraint Jenkins

3. WELSH SLATE CRAFT
Alun John Richards

4. TRADITIONAL SPOONCARVING IN WALES
Gwyndaf Breese

5. THE CORACLE
J. Geraint Jenkins

6. CHEESE-MAKING IN WALES
Eirwen Richards

7. THE THIRSTY DRAGON
Brewing beer, distilling whisky
and cider and mead-making in Wales
Lyn Ebenezer

WELSH
CRAFTS

Welsh Slate Craft

A brief account of slate working in Wales

Alun John Richards

Gwasg Carreg Gwalch

Published by Gwasg Carreg Gwalch in 2006.
All rights reserved. No part of this publication
may be reproduced or transmitted, in any form
or by any means, without prior permission.

ISBN: 1-84527-029-0

Gwasg Carreg Gwalch,
12 Iard yr Orsaf, Llanrwst, Conwy,
Cymru (Wales) LL26 0EH
Tel: 01492 642031 Fax: 01492 641502
e-mail: books@carreg-gwalch.co.uk website: www.carreg-gwalch.co.uk
Printed and published in Wales.

Acknowledgements:
Dr David Gwyn
Griff R. Jones
Dr Gwynfor Pierce Jones
Dr Dafydd Roberts
Richard M. Williams
Emrys Evans, Blaenau Ffestiniog for his first-hand knowledge
of the techniques and Welsh terms of the quarrymen

Special thanks to:
V. Irene Cockroft, great-great-great-granddaughter of
G.E. Magnus, pioneer of slate enamelling

All images are the property of the author or Gwasg Carreg Gwalch, except as below
(page references), the use of which is acknowledged with thanks:
Amgueddfa Ceredigion: 33C
Caban, thanks to Jean Napier: 25C, 29AB, 50, 51, 54CD, 62, 63, 71
Gwynfor P. Jones: 13, 59
Inigo Jones Ltd: 24, 25AB, 54A, 60B, 61, 72, 73, 74, 76
The late Dafydd Price: 60A
William Rice: 48ABC
Royal Commission on Ancient & Historic Monuments in Wales: 47B

Contents

Introduction 7

Grey gold...10

Quarrying methods 15

Winning the slate 19

Slate for everything 22

Roofing the world..27

Slate and education..30

The golden years..49

The locust years..55

A workers' aristocracy 59

The great (and not so great) little trains of Wales......64

Gilding the lily 72

Slate art..78

Slate of the future..82

Sites mentioned 87

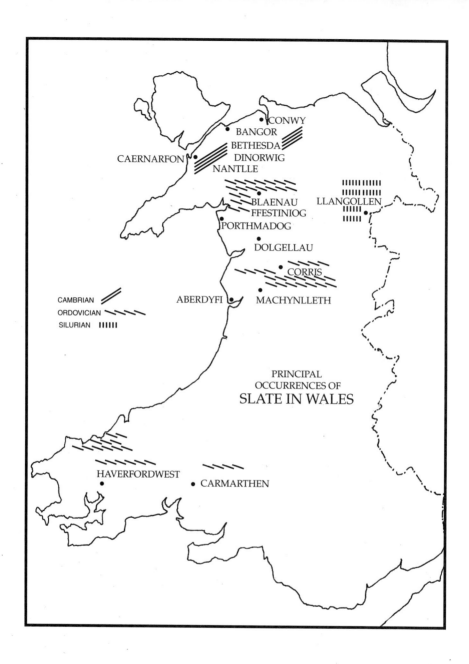

CONWY
BANGOR
BETHESDA
CAERNARFON DINORWIG
NANTLLE

BLAENAU
FFESTINIOG LLANGOLLEN
PORTHMADOG

DOLGELLAU

CORRIS

CAMBRIAN
ORDOVICIAN   ABERDYFI   MACHYNLLETH
SILURIAN

PRINCIPAL
OCCURRENCES OF
SLATE IN WALES

HAVERFORDWEST
CARMARTHEN

Introduction

Hundreds of millions of years ago, when life on earth had scarcely begun, the sediments and oozes of seas and lakes from hundreds of millions of years earlier were forming the earliest rocks.

While continents drifted, seas boiled and volcanoes erupted, the uneasy planet tossed these primeval rocks, pressing and relentlessly squeezing. Unimaginable forces and immeasurable temperatures caused the layers from which the rocks were formed to fuse into a solid mass. Then, as the relentless crushing continued unremittingly, the very grains of the rock were forced into alignment.

This torment, which itself lasted millions of years, metamorphosised the rock into a hard substance that was readily cleavable into thin sheets. It had a strength unmatched by any other natural material and indeed unmatched by any man-made product until the discovery of steel.

This slate, as we call it, had strength, ease of working, stability, longevity, a high specific heat and an attractive appearance, making it such a fundamentally useful substance that if it had not existed, someone

The rock face in a slate opening in one of Llechwedd's caverns

7

Man-hauled barges on the Teifi at Cilgerran quarries.
(etching by W. Hughes, 1810)

would have had to invent it.

Slate occurs very widely throughout the world but places where it is workable are few. Slate occurs in much of Wales, but good material is mostly limited to the following five areas:

1. Northern Caernarfonshire, where the slate is of the Cambrian series formed almost 500 million years ago. It is the hardest and most durable, and notably occurs at Bethesda and Llanberis. Working it were the 'Superquarries' of Penrhyn and Dinorwig, as well as many minor workings. The veins of slate continue into the Nantlle valley and beyond, with lesser exposures in the intervening Gwyrfai valley. The same veins extend in the opposite direction to the northern coast on a much reduced scale, and across into the lower Conwy valley. The Cambrian series also underlies much of Meirionnydd, mostly at depths that makes extraction uneconomic. Even so there were minor workings between Maentwrog and the river Mawddach.

2. Northern Meirionnydd, where the Ordovician slate famously was and

still is worked at Blaenau Ffestiniog. Here there are five veins of the world's finest roofing slate. To geologists it is 'younger' than the Cambrian but it is still over 450 million years old, from a time when there was still just one super continent, 'Gondwana', on which land life was just emerging.

3. Southern Meirionnydd, where this same Ordovician rock is found in a great swathe running from the coast at Tywyn almost to the borders of England. Much of it, particularly around Corris, made world-quality slab.

4. The valley of the river Dee around Corwen and Llangollen, where there is Silurian slate, more 'recent' still than the Ordovician, at 400 million years old. Less durable than some forms, it yielded and still yields excellent slab product.

5. Pembrokeshire and extending into Carmarthenshire, where there are limited occurrences of Ordovician slate which, prior to the availability of better material from northern Wales, made a relatively important industry. One feature of Pembrokeshire is the Llangolman slate on the Carmarthenshire border. Unlike any other Welsh slate it is composed of volcanic ash. Its green colour and grainy texture enabled its producers to develop a niche market that could compete against larger producers tied to traditional slate.

Commercially exploitable slate of various series was also to be found in isolated occurrences in Anglesey, Breconshire, and Radnorshire.

1
Grey gold

In the Iron Age slate was used to line burial chambers. In later times a slab would span a doorway, or a longer one would serve as a makeshift bridge. Minor uses included scrapers for preparing hides, and baking stones (for 'Welshcakes').

The Romans used slate as a building material – for flooring and, taking advantage of its impermeability, for water tanks. However, being used to Mediterranean tiles, the Romans failed to recognise its potential for roofing, which became its main and best-known application.

Slate roofing was used in the twelfth century, but only for prestigious buildings such as churches, castles and the very grandest of houses. In general it was only used near to where it was produced, which at that time was mainly Cilgwyn near Caernarfon, and around the area where Llanberis and Bethesda are today.

Over the next three or four centuries slate was increasingly mentioned in manuscripts, and slate sources became more diverse: along the Afon Conwy (*afon*: river), in Denbighshire, in southern Meirionnydd, and in south-western Wales. In fact there were also small and unrecorded diggings all over mid-Wales; here, whenever a building needed roofing, a 'slater' would extract rock from which he would make the slates that were required. Even the larger quarries were still 'cottage industries' – literally so in the case of some diggings on the south side of Llyn Padarn, where blocks were taken by boat to be made into slates at home.

By the sixteenth century, workings outside northern Caernarfonshire were coming into their own: Aberllefenni, north of Machynlleth, was making regular shipments, and a little later, as towns such as Chester, Shrewsbury and Birmingham grew, workings in north-eastern Wales sent frequent cartloads to the English Midlands. By the seventeenth century the Pembrokeshire quarries were developing a significant Irish trade. With slate becoming a freely traded commodity, commercial matters were increasingly handled by specialist merchants who came to exercise great influence in the industry.

By the latter part of the eighteenth century, in the more abundant areas at least, slate was beginning to be dug on an organised and quasi-industrial basis, with quarries developing a payroll system and a supervisory hierarchy. Landowners themselves operated some workings,

Ladders at Penyrorsedd quarry

but most were operated on leased ground by working proprietors or outside investors.

The first of these new lessee firms was in Blaenau Ffestiniog, which until then had not been a prime slate area. A working-owner type of operation, it was set up by Methusalem Jones, an ex-quarryman and publican who put together a team and took a lease on the bleak Diffwys sheepwalk in 1765, allegedly in response to a dream of rich pickings. His digging became the mother quarry of Blaenau, and although he himself would not enjoy its riches, others would certainly do so.

At the same time diggers working on the Penrhyn estate on the northern side of Mynydd Elidir, near what later became the village of Bethesda, were building up a respectable trade, operating under 'Take Notes', supposedly paying a royalty on each ton they raised. Unfortunately, the owner of the Penrhyn estate, John Pennant, had some difficulty in ascertaining how much each digger was raising. Indeed, as nearly all the diggers were called Humphreys or Williams, each with a raft of fathers, sons, brothers, uncles and nephews with the same name, he did not really know one digger from another. Accordingly he put everyone on a flat rate lease and arranged for a Reeve to buy in all their 'make' and forward it to an agent in Liverpool. This spared them the sort of difficulty faced by the Diffwys outfit, where they

Ancient roof: Clynnog Fawr church

sometimes had to send someone to London (on foot) to sell the slates that they sent round by sea.

By the time John Pennant died in 1781 and Richard Pennant took over, the tenants were doing very well indeed out of the leasing/selling arrangements. For tenants to do well was anathematic to Pennant's new status as Lord Penrhyn, so he immediately abrogated the leases and amalgamated the workings into one combined quarry, leaving the tenants in a situation not unlike that of the slaves on the Pennants' West Indian plantations.

On the opposite side of Mynydd Elidir, Assheton Smith, the owner of the Vaynol estate, was also tired of his agents chasing his diggers all around the mountain trying to collect royalties. In 1787, therefore, he arranged the amalgamation of the diggings into the one big Dinorwig quarry.

Encouraged by the success of these landowner quarries, a syndicate of Caernarfon lawyers and businessmen decided that the diggers operating on Crown land on Cilgwyn Common could be similarly organised. Forming the Cilgwyn Company in 1800, they took a lease on nearly all the ground between the Nantlle and the Gwyrfai valleys. Pennant and Assheton Smith had had enough difficulty persuading the men working on their lands to accept wages rather than the royalty system, but the Cilgwyn Company encountered even greater reluctance on the part of the Cilgwyn diggers. This reluctance was understandable since the Crown Agent had long ceased trying to collect any rents. These diggers had therefore been 'freeloading' for years. Because of their failure to collect dues, and as a result of over-reaching themselves by buying up quarries in adjoining areas, the Cilgwyn Company, the first investment-driven slate operation in Wales, was not a success.

Glanrafon quarry

The Napoleonic wars brought difficulties. The army took most of the available horses, and the price of fodder for those that remained rocketed, while the Navy's demands created a shortage of timber and iron. Most serious for the slate industry was the tax on coastal shipments, a tax purportedly imposed to protect them from French raiders.

Even into the 1820s when the country was settling down into a semblance of peacetime prosperity, Welsh slate cargoes were still being rendered uncompetitive by the wartime tax.

In 1823 Samuel Holland famously walked from Liverpool to Blaenau Ffestiniog in order to sack and supplant the drunken manager of his father's quarry. In a bare two years he built it up to such an extent that financier Nathan Rothschild formed the Welsh Slate Company and made Holland an offer that 'he could not refuse'.

At £28,000 (a value of about £1.75 million today) this offer was an absurd amount of money, particularly with the tax eating up profits. The Welsh Slate Company shareholders persuaded Rothschild that he should 'spend more time with his family' and installed Lord Palmerston – then the Foreign Minister – in his place. As soon as Palmerston discovered that the slate tax was crippling the business, the tax was repealed.

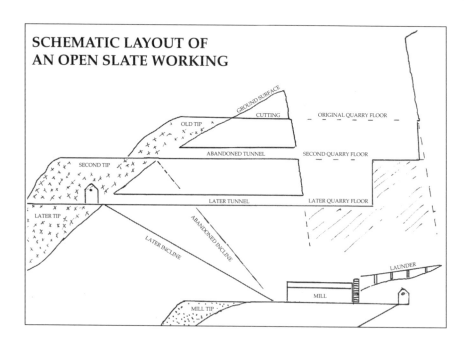

SCHEMATIC LAYOUT OF
AN OPEN SLATE WORKING

*Rosebush terrace and pit quarry (Pembrokeshire). Rubbish to each side, dressing 'walls'
on terraces, mill and mill waste below.*

2
Quarrying methods

With the repeal of the Slate Tax in 1831, Welsh slate was set to become a bone fide industry, serving a market that was national and fast becoming international. With a runaway demand and an almost annual increase in prices, investment in quarries boomed, which financed development and improvements of every kind.

A quarry normally started with an outcrop being identified and proved; then, according to the dip of the vein and the lie of the land, it was worked by one of three methods:

1. Digging into a hillside in a traditional quarrying manner.
2. Where the ground was level, as in a valley floor, digging down to form a pit.
3. By mining underground where following a dipping vein would involve having to remove increasing depths of overburden.

As an open quarry progressed into a hillside, the working face became higher and higher, which, once it exceeded about 100 feet, caused problems of safety and of breakages of rock. The solution was to work on a series of terraces at some 60-70 foot vertical intervals. This not only kept the height of the face within bounds, but also enabled many work gangs to operate simultaneously. At Penrhyn and Dinorwig a number of gangs worked on each of some twenty levels, enabling thousands of men to be employed.

In early times rock was prised from the face by crowbars, or by driving wedges into cracks or natural joints. Wooden wedges or quicklime could be wetted to force joints open. In fact some Pembrokeshire coastal workings used the tide to do this. From the late eighteenth century gunpowder was increasingly used, shots being placed in holes that were laboriously drilled by repeated impact from a spear-like tool called a Jwmpah.

Drilling, besides being laborious, was a highly skilled job since depth, angle and positioning of the shot holes had to be planned to dislodge the maximum amount of rock with the least possible shattering.

Unusable rock, which could be three-quarters or more of what came off the face, was dumped, preferably clear of any future working, whilst good 'make' was trammed away, more often than not by incline.

Ideally all movement of slate was downward, which enabled the weight of down-going loaded wagons to up-haul empty ones, by use of two tracks with a drum and an endless rope. Upward movement required power: hand-windlass, horse-whim, water-wheel or, later on, steam or electricity. The simplest way of raising the quarry 'make' was by water-balance. Like a gravity incline used for lowering loads, this also had two tracks, but one carried a wheeled water tank. The weight of this tank when full was enough to pull a loaded wagon up the other track, but when the tank was emptied it was light enough for a descending empty truck to raise it back to the top of the incline. A variation that was in much use at Penrhyn and to a limited extent at Nantlle was the vertical water-balance, which operated on the same principle, but in a shaft.

At places like Nantlle, slate was won by digging directly down into the valley floor, and working from galleries in the resultant pit. Besides the burden of pumping, all material – rubbish and good rock alike – had to be raised to the surface, which was traditionally done by hoists wound by men or horses.

In a continually expanding pit, incline ramps would get in the way, so chain inclines were developed. In these, loads suspended from a sheave on a fixed running rope were hauled by steam, by electricity or by water wheel. A variation of the chain incline much used in the Nantlle valley was the 'Blondin'. Here, instead of the rope descending to the pit bottom, it was stretched on towers on either side of the pit. A sheave could be positioned anywhere along it, enabling loads to be raised from different points.

The final and most interesting method of working was underground, where the vein was mined by tunnelling into it and working 'to the rise'. Just as with the terrace working of open quarries, the work area could be expanded by a series of tunnels entering the vein at successive levels. The excavation upward would eventually reach the level above, and would ultimately result in a vast sloping void. This work was simultaneously repeated horizontally so as to create a series of chambers separated by a wall of rock (a pillar) which supported the overlying ground.

As with open quarries, much work was done on the quarrying face high above the floor, but the dank conditions meant that a worker could not support himself by wrapping a rope around one thigh, but had to use a cruelly cutting iron chain. Workers would be in stygian darkness relieved only by the flicker of a candle (which, like explosives, fuses, tools and tool sharpening, the men had to buy for themselves). They were constantly threatened by rock falls from the roof, which, invisible in the gloom fifty or more feet above, they could only inspect for safety by climbing precariously balanced ladders.

Today, all underground slate working has ceased. Powerful diggers make the removal of overburden economic so whereas at Blaenau almost all extraction was underground, now it is all open work, most of it consisting of 'untopping' old workings and quarrying the walls of good rock (pillars) that had been left to support the roofs of chambers.

'Yr ebill mawr': Jwmpah drill

Loading a block onto a truck

Eighteenth century slating

*Reconstructed
eighteenth century roof*

Traditional names for sizes of Roofing Slates. (inches) Typical 'Computed' weight per 1200 'Best' Quality*				
		t	c	q
Empresses	26 x 16	4	0	0
Princesses	24 x 14	3	5	0
Duchesses	24 x 12	2	15	0
Small Duchesses	22 x 12	2	10	0
Narrow Duchesses	22 x 11	2	5	0
(or Marchionesses)				
Broad Countesses	20 x 12	2	5	0
Countesses	20 x 10	1	15	0
Small Countesses	18 x 10	1	12	2
Viscountesses	18 x 9	1	7	2
Wide Ladies	16 x 10	1	7	2
Broad Ladies	16 x 9	1	5	0
Ladies	16 x 8	1	2	2
Small Ladies	14 x 8	1	0	1
Narrow Ladies	14 x 7	0	17	2
Doubles	12 x 6	0	14	0
Singles	10 x 5	0	9	3

3
Winning the slate

At one time slates were sold by weight in random sizes, and usually had a pointed or rounded top with a single hole for a fixing peg. They were thick, rough, and crudely trimmed and, being uneven, needed to be packed with moss to remain weatherproof. Only for the most prestigious structures such as cathedrals could large, flat and rectangular slate be afforded.

Improved techniques and a need for standard sizes during the eighteenth century gave rise to the modern rectangular, two-nail shape. Initially these were as small as ten-by-five inches ('Singles') or twelve-by-six inches ('Doubles').

As production methods improved, larger sizes became practicable and by the early 1800s Penrhyn quarry was offering these new sizes in the well-known 'Female Nobility' names. These sizes, which were soon adopted throughout the industry, eventually ranged from 'Narrow Ladies' (fourteen-by-seven inches) up to 'Empresses' (twenty-six-by-sixteen inches). Even bigger sizes were available to special order but these were not named.

Since it took no longer to lay a big slate than a small one, and called for fewer battens, the larger sizes commanded a proportionally higher price: doubling the size might well increase the price threefold. Therefore it paid the quarry to make slates in the largest size possible that could be got out of any particular block. Price was also determined by 'quality', which in practice mainly meant thickness. Again, since thinner slates cost less to transport and allowed the use of lighter roof-timbers, a buyer would be prepared to pay more for them. Prices were declared annually, having been set by the 'market leaders' Penrhyn and Dinorwig (at prices that largely suited themselves). These two, working the best veins, could make an abundance of large sizes in the best quality and then, having secured their profit on these, could afford to offer the smaller sizes and lower qualities at clearance prices. This was very bad news for the many quarries whose rock came away in smaller blocks and yielded mainly thick and less than perfect slates.

Eventually some seventeen sizes, each in up to three qualities, plus 'Rags', 'Ton slates' and other low value items were listed, so a quarry

19

might find itself carrying big stocks but having to turn away orders for popular and profitable varieties.

Traditionally the men winning the rock and making the slates were not paid wages; instead, every four weeks, a gang of four to six men would negotiate a 'bargain' with the Letting Steward whereby they would work a particular stretch of face and would be paid on a scale according to the perceived difficulty and expected yield. Since the Letting Steward was the bosses' man, negotiation tended to be somewhat one-sided and allegedly could be influenced by bribes, favours or chapel membership.

Typically two men would do the actual quarrying while two would make the slates. Having carefully studied the lie of the rock and its grain and pillaring lines, the rock men would prise or blast material from the face to provide the maximum yield of good block.

Rejected material would be taken to the tip by 'rubblers'. It is sobering to think that every ounce of the quarter of a billion tons of waste that still lies on the northern hillsides of Wales was manhandled piece by piece by these rubblers.

One of the slate-making half of the gang would select a block and split it to obtain a handy-sized parallel-faced piece some $2\frac{1}{2}$ inches thick, which would produce the largest, flattest and thinnest possible slates. In a nearby dressing shed, this block would be halved and halved again with hammer and broad chisel until a number of irregularly shaped slates were obtained. His partner would take these and dress them to rectangles by marking with a measuring stick and chopping over a fixed straightedge with a crank-handled knife. Later, in Meirionnydd and anywhere else that Ordovician or Silurian slate was worked, trimming was done with rotative dressing machines driven by hand-crank or treadle.

From the mid-nineteenth century, slate makers were moved from the open-fronted sheds where they had worked, to a mill building where the dressers could be powered. The power would be shared with the saws. Originally only used for slab work, saws were increasingly being used in slate making to square off the blocks so that a minimum of trimming was called for after splitting. Such 'Integrated Mills' which had maybe a score of saws and as many dressers, were very much a feature of the Blaenau Ffestiniog area.

Quarries such as Penrhyn and Dinorwig generally found that their hard, brittle Cambrian rock shattered if it was mechanically dressed, so although they made some use of treadle guillotines, they largely relied on hand dressing until the late twentieth century, when semi-automatic machines capable of handling the harder material became available. By this time the saw-benches adapted from timber practice were long gone, and had been replaced by high-speed, electrically driven diamond saws.

Despite attempts going back a hundred and fifty years or more, the splitting of the slate has never been satisfactorily mechanised.

Original Greaves hand-wheel-operated dresser

4
Slate for everything

At one time, the main use for slate besides roofing was the marking of graves. This was originally with slabs roughly chiselled to shape and laid flat on the ground, with crudely incised initials and perhaps a date. Later, as the art of incising, cutting and shaping improved, these horizontal slabs became upright stones with inscriptions and increasingly elaborate decoration. The serried ranks in chapel cemeteries, varying from the simple slab to the complex tomb, which reflect in death the status in life of those memorialised, epitomise Wales more than any daffodil or dragon.

The introduction of sawing in the eighteenth century enabled slab to be readily produced in rectangular or other precise shapes, which opened up a whole new market for slate. The first saws were hand-held sand saws, resembling a two-man timber saw, but having a toothless blade. The cutting action was derived from wet sand introduced into the kerf (the cut made by the saw). The work piece was always laid flat on one split face so that the cut was long but shallow. For detail work, carpenter-type handsaws were used.

By the early nineteenth century sand saws were being driven by water wheels, and shortly afterwards began to be supplanted by much faster and more efficient toothed circular saws. By mid-century these had been almost universally adopted, enabling the industry to meet a demand that rapidly grew as new slab products were devised. When planers, polishers, lathes, routers and other machines became available, there seemed no limit to the uses to which slate could be put.

The same huge housing programmes of the time that created a demand for roofing slates also created a market for flooring, steps, sills, lintels, larder slabs and mantelpieces; since there were fireplaces in almost every room, these latter were needed in quantity. Farming called for sties and stalls as well as feed bins and cisterns, and industry required vats and tanks as well as laboratory benches and tool-room tables. Slate virtually became the plastic of the nineteenth century.

The great Victorian expansion of sea trade created a need for warehouse flooring at the ports – flooring that could withstand iron-wheeled trucks, resist spillages and be readily cleaned. Increasing public health awareness also produced a demand for impermeable surfaces for

Example of palm tree motif
(Carmarthenshire)

Carved pilaster head

dairies and for food preparation. Slate proved ideal for these applications, especially when its high specific heat helped to keep produce cool. With its ease of cleaning, it was used for such diverse purposes as mortuary slabs and gentlemen's urinals, although lavatory seats were less popular!

Increasing prosperity brought a market for ever more elaborate items. Fireplaces that had until then consisted of just a shelf and two sides became complex fabrications. Even modest homes incorporated architectural embellishments of some complexity. With the growth of life insurance, gravestones became a riot of finials and flounces. One macabre slate artefact was the reusable coffin, which gave dignity to the burial of the poor and the destitute. Often highly ornamental, they were supplied without bottoms, so that they could be recovered from the grave and reused.

All this was good news for the quarries, although the per-ton return on bulk slab was less than on roofing slates; nevertheless it was much cheaper to produce. In addition, slab was not normally the subject of predatory pricing by the big quarries and, unlike roofing slate where buyers demanded 'Bangor' or 'Porthmadog', the slab market was not source-sensitive.

Converting crude slab into artefacts made it even more profitable, and some quarries therefore did this themselves, particularly for simpler items such as mantelpieces. Most was done by independent manufacturing merchants however. Some, such as Crawia, were sited alongside railways lines, but were more usually at ports. Bangor and Caernarfon each had something like half a dozen such firms; Porthmadog had at least two; there were others at Pwllheli, Port Penrhyn and Port Dinorwig, and as many as three at Aberystwyth. A great deal of slate work was also done in towns and cities in various parts of the UK. It was this slab trade that drove forward the mechanisation of the quarries and furthered the development of slate-working machinery.

Although the Welsh slate industry was justifiably criticised for clinging to outdated methods, the later twentieth century was as innovative as the mid-nineteenth, adopting such techniques as wiresawing, high-speed machinery, laser measurement, computer control and water-jet cutting.

There have also been some unlikely technology transferences. For example, the rock-cutting technique devised to re-site the Abu Simbel temple in Upper Egypt was applied to slate winning at Aberllefenni.

Besides the mechanical engineering developments in the quarries, civil engineering was equally bold and innovative: huge projects such as Glan y Don bridge at Oakeley quarry, and the inclines systems that cascade down the mountains at Blaenau and at South Snowdon, were designed and built 'in house' by the respective quarries. In addition, the pioneering work in the generation and application of electrical power developed by Moses Kellow of Croesor quarry and Martyn Williams Ellis of Llechwedd, was of a world importance.

Bringing slab to Aberllefenni mill

24

Transferring slab from Corris Railway to Cambrian Railways at Machynlleth

Aberllefenni mill

Two quarrymen freeing a block of slate underground at Oakeley quarry

Food safe

Slate wheel for the crushing of bark at tannery near Llanbedr

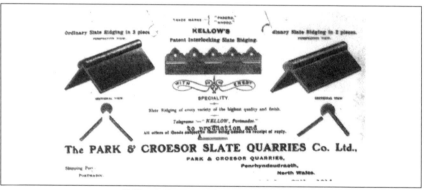

Kellow's Patent Ridging, Parc quarry

Doors of drying room, enamelling department, Rhiw'r Gwreiddyn quarry, Corris

5
Roofing the world

The early slaters who dug and made their own roofing slates found themselves with a mixed bag of random sizes. On site they would sort through them, picking the biggest to form the first (lower) course of the roof. Subsequent courses would be formed of gradually decreasing sizes, and the spacing of the battens to which the slates were pegged would be adjusted to maintain an overlap appropriate to the local weather pattern. Pitching the roof steeply required less overlap, but increased the roof area. Selecting an economical pitch called for careful judgment. As slates were often far from flat, skill was needed to select them so that they would nest with their neighbours with the minimum of moss packing. Finally at the ridge the very smallest slates would be used. Small slates would also be used in roof valleys, often jammed tight without pegs.

This was fine as long as building remained a small-scale occupation, but with the large scale building developments in the nineteenth century, a uniform easily-laid product became a practical as well as a commercial necessity.

The availability of Welsh slate in standard sizes and dependable

Loading slate at Port Dinorwig

qualities brought worldwide recognition and acceptance. There might be dispute in America, Argentina or Australia as to the relative merits of 'Bangor' slate versus 'Portmadog' but there was universal consensus about the importance of the slate being Welsh.

A dozen ports right around the coast from Conwy to Cardigan and beyond prospered from sending roofing slate to every country from Muscovy to Madagascar. At these ports dynasties of mariners and shipbuilders were backed by foundries, sawmills, sail and rope makers, chandlers, insurers, shipbrokers and schools of navigation (the latter often run by sea captains' wives).

However none of these ports surpassed Porthmadog, where ships that were designed, built, owned, manned and insured in the port carried Blaenau Ffestiniog slate across every ocean. In fact, so great was the avalanche of slate that thundered daily down the Ffestiniog Railway that all the ships which the ports on Bae Ceredigion (*bae*: bay) could supply were needed to deal with the constant struggle to clear the clogged quaysides.

Eventually, as wooden sailing ships became cheaply available from Canada and as these were in turn supplanted by iron-hulled steamships,

Possibly the first drumhouse in Blaenau Ffestiniog Holland's quarry with all wood drumgear, pictured c. 1970.

local shipbuilding died out. The increasing size of ocean-going vessels diverted the trade to ports such as Liverpool, although ship repairing survived, and Port Dinorwig retained its reputation as a centre of excellence for the maintenance of the most prestigious steam yachts into the second half of the twentieth century.

Oakeley slate en route to LMS station, Blaenau Ffestiniog

Slate wagons at F.R. Diffwys station, Blaenau Ffestiniog

6
Slate and education

Almost a century before the Education Act of 1870 put an obligation on local authorities to provide free schooling for all, the British and Foreign Schools Society had been set up in London by the Quaker Joseph Lancaster.

These 'British' schools readily appealed to the chapel-going Welsh workers, since unlike the 'National' schools they had no connection with the Church and its English/Boss/Landowner associations.

Neither of these 'penny per child per week' school movements could have functioned without writing slates. Lancaster calculated that to provide a class of sixty with paper, quills and ink for a year would cost £99, but five dozen slates could be had for £1. Even this modest sum, he suggested, could be further reduced by salvaging slates from demolished buildings. Providing each scholar with a hundred slate pencils per year would cost a further £2.

Writing slates and their soft slate stick pencils had been in use in the fourteenth century, but the growth of educational initiatives created a vast market which, despite hygienic fears of pupils cleaning them with spit, did not die out until the mid-twentieth century.

Besides founding the schools, for a time Lancaster also manufactured and exported slates and pencils, until commercial factories caught up with demand. He charged 2/- (10p) per dozen for slates and 1/- (5p) per hundred for the pencils, and achieved the former price by making the items a tiny six-by-three inches, as opposed to the standard eleven-by-seven.

The first mass production writing slate factory was established at Port Penrhyn in 1798, but Penrhyn was producing writing slates by hand long before that. Thomas Pennant observed in 1778 that they had twenty-five to thirty men making framed writing slates and had sold 133,000 in the previous year, using 3000 cubic feet of timber.

In the course of the nineteenth century the demand grew rapidly so that the Port Penrhyn factory was followed by many others. These factories were usually at ports, which saved carriage on the timber. (At one time Bangor had five factories making ciphering slates, as they were correctly known.)

Votty & Bowydd quarry had their own writing slate works on site, but this was exceptional; where a quarry did have its own factory, it was more likely to be sited in the neighbouring settlement, so that women (who were very unwelcome on quarry premises) and older and less fit men could be employed. When Votty & Bowydd built their second (Newborough) Mill it was sited in Blaenau Ffestiniog itself. Bryneglwys quarry likewise had a small works in nearby Abergynolwyn village. Similarly, Glandinorwig, which, though independent, was very much an offshoot of Dinorwig quarry, had their three works sited in nearby Deiniolen. Their machinery eventually included a reciprocating gang-saw to reduce logs to planks (such as can be seen at the Slate Museum), three circular saws to convert the planks into frame components, machines to plane, mortise, tenon, groove and drill (to enable the slate to be hung from a nail), as well as a machine to wire the sides together and another to round off the corners. The slates themselves were made from slab, using four saws, four polishers and a machine for scribing the squared pattern on the reverse of standard school slates. The painting in of the scribed pattern was the only non-mechanised part of the whole operation. It is curious that despite the closure of Dinorwig Railway in the early 1840s (alongside which the works were sited) the works survived until the end of the century, and were the first substantial slate works of any kind to operate without a rail connection.

Writing Slate factory, Bangor

In contrast, in 1861 the still flourishing Inigo Jones factory was sited alongside the Nantlle Railway close to Groeslon village in order to make writing slates from Nantlle material. Despite benefiting greatly from the 1870 Elementary Education Act, they switched from this fiercely competitive trade to the more profitable one of enamelling.

A model using a writing slate at the Victorian School Museum, Llangollen

A slate blackboard at the Lloyd George museum in Llanystumdwy

Enamelled fireplace and detail,
Tudor Slate Works.
By kind permission of Inigo Jones

Detail of an enamelled slate chimneypiece painted by Alfred Worthington.
Courtesy of Amgueddfa Ceredigion, Aberystwyth

Abereiddi slate quarry, Pembrokeshire

Vivian quarry, Llanberis

Chwarel Cors y Bryniau, Rhosgadfan (Alexandra quarry)

Oakeley quarry, Blaenau Ffestiniog

Old mill sheds at Llechwedd, Blaenau Ffestiniog

Dinorwig, Llanberis

Bridge, Braich quarry, Fron

Powder house, Dinorwig

Prince of Wales quarry barracks, Cwm Pennant

*Prince of Wales
quarry mill,
Cwm Pennant*

*Slate clapper bridge,
Croesor*

Quarrymen's window (detail) St David's church, Blaenau Ffestiniog

Slate slabs on wagons,
Welsh Slate Museum, Llanberis

Slate gatepost near Cilgwyn quarry

Slate fence, Museum of Welsh Life, St Fagans

Old quarry tips and train at Blaenau Ffestiniog's town centre today

Layers of Welsh slate from different quarries at Millenium Centre, Cardiff

Industrial heritage remembered at Dyffryn Nantlle

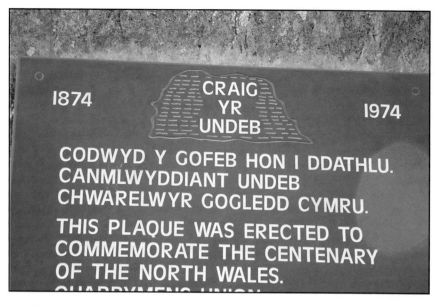

The Quarrymen's Union remembered at Craig yr Undeb ('the rock of the union'), Llyn Padarn.

Quarrymen in front of their 'Caban' – the lunchtime hut which was the scene of many political and cultural discussions.

The Penrhyn strike memorial at Bethesda – the longest industrial dispute in the history of the world.

The quarrymen's memorial at Blaenau Ffestiniog

Memorial to Kate Roberts (1891-1985), a leading Welsh writer and daughter of a quarryman.

Cae'r Gors, Rhosgadfan – the home of Kate Roberts

Quarryman's cowshed from Waunfawr at the Museum of Welsh Life, St Fagans

Inside Rhiwledyn, a quarryman's cottage at the Museum of Welsh Life, St Fagans

A typical quarryman's cottage at Rhosgadfan

Multiple gravestones, Carmarthenshire

Local culture and heritage celebrated by Croesor schoolchildren

Mr V. Bickford, Berwyn quarry with 2m diamond saw.

Diamond saw at Penrhyn quarry

Cutting slate slabs at Llechwedd quarry today

Llechwedd quarry

Dressing slates at Llechwedd

45

Enamelled slate table by G. E. Magnus for Great Exhibition 1851.
By kind permission Mrs N. Edwards

Inside Fron Haul terrace at the Welsh Slate Museum, Llanberis

*Ynysypandy mill,
Cwm Ystradllyn*

*Glanrafon quarry,
Cwm Gwyrfai*

Moeltryfan quarry incline

Rosebush quarry (Pembrokeshire)

Modern day slate craft by William Rice of Blaenau Ffestiniog

7
The golden years

In just a few decades Welsh slate went from being a rural craft to becoming a national industry that served a global market.

Shortly after the 1831 repeal of the Slate Tax, the expansion of the railway began to create a huge demand for slates to roof the stations, the depots, the goods and engine sheds, the signal boxes and the lineside huts, as well as the houses of tens of thousands of railway employees.

The railways generated a galloping prosperity which resulted in the building of countless works and factories. This caused an unprecedented urban growth, fuelling a demand for houses, shops, pubs and public buildings of every kind, almost all of which required slate roofs. With goods of all kinds being exported, and increasing affluence demanding exotic imports, docks proliferated, which in turn created a demand for more houses and offices, as well as for slate-roofed and floored warehouses.

In addition, the re-roofing of Hamburg with Welsh slate after the great fire of 1842 generated a market not only in the German states, but all over Europe. At the same time this British and Continental prosperity was reflected in America and in the then colonies, which created their own insatiable demands for slate.

This was the apogee of the great maritime towns of Caernarfon, Bangor and Porthmadog as well as lesser ones such as Conwy, Pwllheli, Barmouth, Aberdyfi, Aberystwyth and Cardigan. It was the era when the private harbours of Port Dinorwig and Port Penrhyn became industrial complexes. Besides handling and processing slate, the ports had foundries, some of which, such as De Wintons of Caernarfon, became major engineering enterprises, providing technical support for the quarries and mills. They built trucks, winding drums, water wheels, winches and even steam engines. Notably, they made slate-processing equipment such as sawing tables and dressing machines, almost always to designs by that arch-inventor, J. W. Greaves of Llechwedd quarry, Blaenau Ffestiniog.

As the quarries prospered, their workers' housing needs expanded, as did the requirement for pubs, bakeries, flourmills, tobacco and soap factories and, of course, chapels and churches, all of which generated

Glan-y-don bridge, Blaenau Ffestiniog

further demand for slate.

The defining year of this Golden Age was probably 1861. The boost in trade and industry generated by the Great Exhibition of 1851 had been dampened by the Crimean War, but by this time was really taking off. However, the slate industry was sceptical, having 'seen it all before': an upturn had always been followed by a downturn. Yet this time round the 'boom and bust' suddenly became a 'boom and boom'. The industry was on the cusp of an extraordinary episode; never before had prices and output consistently climbed year by year without setback.

Life for the worker at the time is illustrated by the No. 3 Fron Haul exhibit, one of the houses from Tanygrisiau near Blaenau Ffestiniog that were re-erected at the Welsh Slate Museum. Although this housing would be a slum by today's standards, the occupants would have counted themselves lucky: despite being without drainage or running water, they were much better housed than many of the hovel dwellers in that then explosively expanding area. Somewhere they would have had a fragment of ground to plant potatoes and perhaps keep a pig. They might have squeezed a lodger in somewhere or, if the husband was a top rockman, there might even have been a live-in maid, possibly a young relative gaining experience before seeking a position 'in service' in Liverpool.

50

They would have begun to enjoy factory-made clothing, boots and other necessities at a fraction of the price of the old locally-made articles. Steamships were starting to bring in foodstuffs at affordable prices from the colonies. Their relative prosperity is indicated by their possession of a long-case clock, which would have cost the equivalent of several thousand pounds in modern money. Yet in the quarries, the seeds of dissent that led to Y Streic Fawr (the Big Strike) had already been sown.

No matter how many fresh rock faces were started, fresh bargains let, or completely new diggings begun, production fell behind demand – there were instances of people seeking slate in their back gardens! The new railway links proved vital, as there were neither the ships nor the port capacity to meet such frenzied output.

Prices were upped, but still buyers stampeded. Slates of the lowest grades that had been dead stock for decades were off-loaded at inflated prices, while waiting lists for 'Bests' stretched to two years. Forward price projections were extrapolated exponentially, bringing new entrants and new money into the industry. Patches of barren ground changed hands for royal ransoms.

In the meantime, while customers felt that the slate owners were extorting money out of them, the quarrymen were thinking along much the same lines. Industrial relations were complex: the Bargain system meant that the quarrymen were effectively independent contractors who resented any imputation that they were mere wage slaves, and the small owner-manager quarry differed from one controlled from a distant boardroom or by a big landowner.

The North Wales Quarrymen's Union was formed in 1874, but this differed from the normal trade union in that the 'them and us' were not master and man, but rather the big proprietors versus the men and the small owners. In fact the union officials were almost all owners or managers of small quarries. Even so, industrial muscle was now there to be flexed and the last thing that a slate master wanted was an

Splitting a block

51

Dinorwig quarry hospital, a pioneer user of X-rays

Slate resting bench at the Dinorwig quarry hospital

interruption of the frantic scramble for output.

No such bonanza could last. Every price rise made tiles and foreign slates more competitive, a situation that the makers and importers naturally exploited, but besides this, galvanised sheet was now available to cover sheds and warehouses at a fraction of the cost of slate or tile.

Within three years of the formation of the Union the bubble had burst. In an avalanche of cancelled orders, demand went into a free fall that the repeated slashing of prices failed to check, and quarry owners almost welcomed strikes to save on wages and to clear accumulating stocks.

The 1880s were very difficult: some quarries amalgamated, others closed, and men were laid off. Some left for the coal mines of southern Wales, while others took their skills to America and elsewhere, helping to develop indigenous industries.

There was a recovery in the early 1890s, which was particularly strong in Blaenau Ffestiniog, where by then three main line railways fought for their business (the Great Western Railway, the London & North Western Railway and, via the Ffestiniog Railway, the Cambrian). Whilst other quarrying areas did not quite match Blaenau's jackpot, activity on Moel Tryfan blossomed, and everywhere employment rose close to an all-time high. By the end of the century the half-million-ton output was five times the 1831 total and despite the increasing tonnages transported by rail, there was still enough to keep all the local ports frantically busy.

Beneath the surface, however, there was discord. In the mid-1880s there had been strikes at Dinorwig and at Penrhyn, and in the 1890s at Llechwedd in Blaenau, but their effects were not felt much outside their particular districts. Then in November 1900 came Y Streic Fawr, the Penrhyn dispute – the Götterdämmerung of the Welsh slate industry.

There had been disputes before; there would be disputes again, but there was nothing as cataclysmic as when Penrhyn quarry came to a three year near-standstill.

Although only a few thousand men in a somewhat obscure occupation in a remote part of Wales were involved, few industrial disputes became such a national cause celebre, and none, not even the General Strike of 1926, would rend a community to such an extent nor leave such enduring scars.

The quarrying families whose lives are illustrated by the No. 2 Fron Haul exhibit would see forty years of rising standards collapse into three years of terrible hardship.

No. 2 Fron Haul
at the Welsh Slate Museum, Llanberis

A union solidarity poster in the window of
the striker at No. 3:
'There is no Traitor in this house.'

Turning slate on a lathe at Inigo Jones works

Minfford Interchange Ffestiniog Railway/Cambrian Railways

Setting up an air drill. Note supervisor carrying 'Big Lamp' which was effectively his badge of office.

'Wild car' on Graig Ddu Incline, Blaenau Ffestinog

8
The locust years

The beginning of the twentieth century was a time of great change. It saw the end of the last British colonial war, the end of mankind as an earth-bound species, the end of a world dominated by Europe, but above all it saw the end of the Victorian era. Sadly, it also saw the end of Welsh slate as a great world-dominant industry.

The Penrhyn stoppage of 1900-1903 is often blamed for the decline of the Welsh slate industry. Admittedly it caused a shortfall in production that other Welsh quarries could not fill, forcing buyers to seek alternative suppliers or alternative materials and encouraging customer countries to develop their own slate industries, but in fact in 1899 the sales by Welsh quarries totalled less than the 1898 figure and even had the Penrhyn dispute not spiralled out of control in November 1900, tonnages that year would still have shown a further drop. Penrhyn events merely gave a push to an industry already on the brink of decline.

Investors had been frightened off by the market collapse of the 1870s, and short leases inhibited long-term planning, so that despite being in the most innovative era in the history of man, slate working methods had not changed for fifty years or more. Besides this, many quarries were being choked by their own rubbish, so that it was often more profitable to lease one's quarry as a tip for a neighbour, than to operate it.

Even the most modern quarry, Glanrafon, the sole new opening of any consequence in the final thirty years of the nineteenth century, was in a run-down state that only massive new investment could rectify.

With closures and a continuation of the amalgamations begun in the latter years of the old century, the industry slowly assumed a 'leaner and meaner' aspect, and a decade or so after the end of the Penrhyn dispute it was beginning to look to the future with some confidence.

Then in 1914 came war. Immediately all building work stopped, which virtually eliminated the home market. Overseas, the German market vanished and on much of the rest of the Continent destruction rather than construction was the order of the day. In any case, as many ships were requisitioned for war purposes and others were being sunk (including quarry-owned vessels) such overseas orders as there were, could not be delivered.

Because of operating in a 'non-essential' industry, quarries could not get supplies. Indeed some of their own equipment was commandeered (for example, the engine winding the big incline at Llechwedd was seized to power munitions-making at the Ffestiniog Railway's Boston Lodge works). Most quarries closed or just ticked over, the men going to the forces or to ordnance factories.

By 1919 the pent-up demand for repairs at home, and for rebuilding in France and Belgium, overwhelmed an industry whose worn-out plant could not be replaced and a quarter of whose workers had been killed or wounded.

Price increase followed price increase (stocks of slate were so valuable that they almost needed armed guards) and then in 1922 the bubble burst, and such producers as had survived the war fell into a deep recession.

For the most part the larger quarries rode it out, buoyed by further amalgamations, and some very small units stumbled on hand to mouth, from day to day, until by the late 1930s some stability was achieved.

Then came World War II – again bringing almost complete shut down. Once more, men went to the forces or to the munitions factories, some of which were set up in quarries. Other quarries were taken over to store explosives or, famously, art treasures. Those quarries that remained open, which were staffed by young boys and older men, had a steady demand for slate for bomb damage repairs.

At the war's end in 1945, the industry was even more run down than it had been in 1918 and was even less able to meet the backlog for repairs, let alone for new buildings. Controls ensured that there would be no run-away price inflation, but also ensured that such slate as was available was reserved for repairs. These regulations helped to ensure speedy restoration of blitzed towns, but meant that the building industry elsewhere became accustomed to using tiles, while it also prevented quarry owners from charging enough to enable them to pay competitive wages.

Regrettably there was no spare slate to meet the huge demand from the Continent to repair bomb damage. This demand was eagerly met by Spanish quarries, which set them on the road to domination of the world slate market.

The decline of the Welsh industry from around 1950 was not so much due to lack of orders but lack of men. Mercifully the Second World War had not wrought the comprehensive slaughter of the earlier conflict, but

*Wagon being raised on Blondin,
Penyrorsedd quarry c. 1976*

Blondin Towers, Penyrorsedd quarry

men were no longer prepared to toil long and dangerously in the rain and snow at the top of a mountain, or in a dusty, draughty, virtually unheated shed, making less money than their daughters, who were sitting in nice warm factories with 'music while you work', canteens and decent toilets.

Quarrying still provided job satisfaction, which was absent from repetitive factory or clerical work, but as the No. 1 Fron Haul exhibit shows, erstwhile luxuries, such as TV, indoor plumbing, and fitted kitchens were now considered necessities, but job satisfaction was a luxury that could not be afforded.

Had the rewards been better, men might have been persuaded to stay in the industry, but even after the end of controls, there were not the profits to pay better wages or to buy machines that could have lightened the work, and the once-proud Union became just a little offshoot of the Transport and General Workers' Union.

Following almost seventy years of amalgamation, rationalisation and decline, the 1960s saw a levelling out of the rate of closures – if only because they were running out of places to close. Cilgwyn, which could trace its ancestry back to the thirteenth century, had closed in 1956; its great cavernous pits suffered the indignity of becoming Gwynedd County Council's rubbish tip. The 1960s saw Penmachno, Dorothea and Rhos close. Having swallowed several neighbours, the great Oakeley quarry at Blaenau Ffestiniog closed. Even Alexandra on Moel Tryfan, that consummate weatherer of economic fire, storm and tempest, was forced to close.

At the end of that decade came the hammer blow: Dinorwig, the largest slate employer and the second largest slate producer on the planet, ceased production.

The last days of rails at Penrhyn quarry, 1963

Derelict fan house,
Croesor quarry, 1976

Steps at Abercwmeiddaw quarry
c. 1980

9

A workers' aristocracy

Timber grown on bleak, north-facing slopes was very much in demand by carpenters and shipwrights as its quality was superior to that nurtured on sunnier, gentler ground and, in similar fashion, generations of people moulded in the bleakness of adversity in Bethesda or Blaenau, Corris or Cwm Penmachno or wherever slate has been wrested from the recalcitrant rock, formed dynasties as honourable and noble as any of those who lent their name to their roofing products.

Slate quarrying used to be the most hazardous of industrial occupations, more dangerous than coal mining, with dirt, dust and disease reducing life-expectancy to a level only marginally better than seafaring. It was usually conducted in the remotest, bleakest and most inhospitable of locations.

Hard though the work was, getting to work was often even harder. Men routinely walked many miles each way daily, and then possibly faced a climb or descent of many hundreds of feet to their workplaces

Staff of Treflan quarry, 1926

*Handling a block at
Bwlch y Slaters quarry, 1960s*

where they would spend up to twelve hours of almost unremitting toil – either in the worst of the weather on a terrace, or in a pit, or in the dankness and candle-gloom of a troglodytic chamber.

Others whose homes were further away might spend the week on site sharing a barracks with fleas, and worse. These men would set out at perhaps 2 or 3 o'clock on a Monday morning to walk a dozen miles or more across the open mountain, perhaps in rain, sleet or snow, carrying their provisions for the week. They might then spend the entire working day on the rock face soaked through, hoping that there would be enough dry kindling and

Workers at Inigo Jones works

peat in the barracks to make a fire in the evening. It might not be until they arrived home on Saturday afternoon that they could change out of wet clothes and get a proper wash. Yet despite conditions that were appalling even by nineteenth century standards, poetry and choral music was produced in the course of barrack evenings.

Quarrymen's lives were ruled by loyalties – loyalty to the bargain gang, to their Caban (eating place), or to the quarry itself; loyalty to their families, friends and to the community and above all to their chapel.

The chapel completely dominated the community that so often bore its name. Even those who did not attend Sabbath services were fiercely partisan in their support of the Baptist, Wesleyan, Presbyterian or Congregational connection. The Established Church played little part in ordinary peoples' lives, partly because although services might be in Welsh, it was thought of as being 'English'. Besides, although some owners were themselves Nonconformists, the Church was nevertheless regarded as a bosses' foundation. Indeed some churches, such as Llandegai, were paid for by owners, and had congregations largely comprised of supervisory staff or those sycophantically seeking elevation to such status.

The chapel was not just for Sunday services; usually every evening there would be study groups, debates, band or choir practice, youth

Three slate workers, showing the different stages of the 'dressing'

61

Block on trucks, underground at Oakeley quarry

organisations and so on. To hold the office of deacon or elder in the chapel carried a status that far transcended any secular hierarchy, even outranking that of chairman of a Caban, who was the overseer of the rigid protocol that ruled the quarry meal-breaks. Inter-Caban literary or musical contests were not unknown, and in big quarries 'Bonciau' (terraces) would compete, culminating in a quarrymen's eisteddfod, often held in a mill. To have won an award at even a minor eisteddfod put one high in the pecking order.

It is remarkable that after a long and exhausting day men would find the energy to turn out for chapel or other cultural activities. Even so, some managed to 'moonlight'; for instance Conglog quarry for a time was worked by men after they had finished their day's work at Rhosydd quarry.

Besides all these activities, almost every household would have a vegetable patch to tend and probably poultry or an animal to feed, which, even with the entire household pitching in, took further time. Indeed agriculture was very close to quarrymen's hearts, which is not surprising, as almost all of them would have come from farming stock. In some instances, men living at a distance lodged with farmers, helping out in lieu of rent, often only going home on the quarterly *tâl mawr* (big pay) Saturdays.

Women were employed in off-site factories and there have been notable examples of women as hands-on owners, but in general women were barred entirely from the quarries themselves, and even female clerks were unknown until the First World War.

Women were vital to the life of quarry communities. They kept the men fed and laundered on pittances that could vanish at times of layoff or dispute, and they raised families in the desperate overcrowding of late nineteenth century Blaenau, or in tiny, bleakly isolated settlements such as Rhiw-bach or Treforus. Even when living in 'proper' villages such as Rhosgadfan, their often self-built cottages were a poor protection from savage winter storms.

Although the medical facilities at the big quarries were the best, it was the women who nursed the sick and kept men on their feet, when unfitness for work meant destitution, and widowhood could mean starvation for them and their children.

Above all, it was the women who turned hovels into homes and who survived on short commons so that the wage earners and the children could be nourished.

In a Caban, underground at Oakeley quarry

10
The great (and not so great) little trains of Wales

In the early days of the quarries, much slate reached the coast by pack animal. Carting, where possible, was less expensive but it could still exceed the cost of production, and the rough roads caused many breakages. In winter, rains made the roads impassable and in summer the carters sought richer pickings by bringing in the harvest. Any slate producer who could transport his product cheaply, quickly, smoothly and reliably, would have a decisive competitive edge.

In 1801 Penrhyn quarry achieved all these criteria by building the Penrhyn Railroad, using the same small-truck, edge rail equipment that was then coming into use for internal quarry movement. A few dozen horses pulling trains replaced hundreds pulling carts. Penrhyn's trains of trucks travelling with set-your-watch regularity to Port Penrhyn at almost trifling cost, put those who were still carting to the coast at a serious disadvantage. Any still transporting their product to a beach or makeshift shipping point by convoys of pack animals tended by young girls, were right out of the running.

Dinorwig, the other 'super quarry', continued to upgrade their roads extensively and expensively, which obviated the use of rowing boats on Llyn Padarn to transport slate, but little else. It was 1824 before they got around to hastily cobbling together their Dinorwig Railway in an effort to catch up with the rapidly expanding Penrhyn.

This threw into panic the quarry-owners of the neighbouring Nantlle valley. Unlike Penrhyn and Dinorwig, Nantlle slate was worked by numerous owners under several landlords who lacked both a private port and control of the ground between them and the sea. Despite this disadvantage, by 1828, with the help of outside investors, they had the Nantlle Railway up and running, connecting the valley to Caernarfon.

Of much greater significance was the Ffestiniog Railway, which was opened eight years later. Like the Nantlle line, the Ffestiniog Railway was an independent public railway, but unlike the three foot six gauge of the Nantlle, the Ffestiniog Railway was the two foot 'quarry gauge' of the Penrhyn and Dinorwig railways, and again unlike the Nantlle, which operated as a turnpike road charging users tolls for running private wagons or carriages, the Ffestiniog Railway ran scheduled trains.

The station at Diffwys, Ffestiniog Railway, 1886

The Nantlle line had a fall of some three hundred feet in nine miles, less than half that of the Penrhyn and the Dinorwig in a lesser mileage, so it was spared the delays and bother of the three gravity inclines that beset those lines. Although it had to cope with a drop of well over six hundred feet, the Ffestiniog Railway extended for fourteen miles, so a sinuous route was laid out, which, after the appropriate tunnels had been cut, gave a gradient that enabled continuous gravity running of loaded trains, and permitted easy back-haulage of empties by horse.

The Ffestiniog Railway was emulated some years later by the continuous gradient Corris, Machynlleth and River Dovey Tramway, and by the more modest three-incline Croesor Tramway, which served to connect Cwm Croesor with Porthmadog.

There was a sixth line, the Gorseddau Tramway, which was a private line to Porthmadog constructed almost to main-line standards. Ironically it was laid to a gauge of three foot since quarry-gauge trucks would be unable to cope with the vast tonnages that the Gorseddau quarry was expected to produce. In the event, a strong lad with a handcart could almost have coped.

In 1863 there was an innovation that was almost as important as the original Penrhyn line of sixty years before – the Ffestiniog Railway was converted to steam.

This was not the first steam quarry railway – that had been the Padarn Railway, which had replaced the Dinorwig Railway twenty years before.

Locomotive Holy War *at Dinorwig, 1956*

Locomotive Marchlyn *at Dinorwig, 1956*

In a sense the Padarn was interim technology; it was four foot gauge, the narrowest gauge for which steam locomotives were available at the time, and was almost gradientless to suit their lack of power. The fall was accommodated by one big incline at Port Dinorwig, down which the quarry-gauge wagons that had been carried on the four foot gauge transporter trucks were lowered. The Padarn was a private freight-only line dedicated to carrying the goods of Dinorwig quarry.

The Ffestiniog Railway was something different. It was of quarry gauge, its locomotives could handle its appreciable gradients and it was a full-scale, if not full-sized public passenger railway. As a freight line it was much more than a conveyor of slate: its capacity for carrying food and other necessities to an elevated and isolated settlement enabled Blaenau Ffestiniog to support a population that would match the quarries' almost unlimited growth. In addition, as a passenger line, it enabled the workforce to be drawn from a wide area.

When the Corris Tramway had opened in 1859, there was no question of it being steam powered – but when the Talyllyn Railway opened in 1866 there was no question of it being anything but steam. The Talyllyn also established a new pattern – it ran not to a port, but to a main line railway as was the case, with a few very minor exceptions, of every subsequent slate railway.

One of the exceptions was the grandly named Gorseddau Junction & Portmadoc Railways, which was an 1875 relay and extension of the old Gorseddau line; as such it ran to Porthmadog docks, ignoring the Cambrian Railways, which had reached Porthmadog a decade before. This new Gorseddau line did have one De Winton 'coffee pot' locomotive but it carried so little material that its destination was almost irrelevant.

However, long before this, in 1852, London & North Western Railway branches to Port Dinorwig and Port Penrhyn had given over half the slate output of northern Wales access to the main line railway network. As rail charges became progressively cheaper, rail dispatch became an increasingly attractive option.

From the late 1860s, the Ffestiniog Railway was able to load onto the Cambrian Railways via the Porthmadog 'Beddgelert' siding, a transfer that became much easier when the vast Minffordd exchange was opened in 1872.

These three railway connections were made to adjacent pre-existing

*Loading empty Graig Ddu trucks onto transporter wagon
at Blaenau Ffestiniog Great Western Railway station*

main lines, but already in 1869 the London & North Western Railway had thrust into the heart of the slate district. This Llanberis Branch enabled a number of private quarries to develop, as the parallel Padarn Railway only carried its own Dinorwig output. However, in following the Seiont valley it was forced to bridge the river nine times in as many miles, making it a costly exercise.

Much more ambitious and even more costly was the London & North Western Railway's foray to Blaenau Ffestiniog. This eleven and a half mile extension of their Conwy Valley branch involved much civil work plus a two-mile tunnel through some of the hardest rock ever bored. Unlike their Llanberis Branch, it had to compete with a very much entrenched Ffestiniog Railway, and it took so long to build that it did not open until 1879, when the slate trade was in deep recession. Despite coastal shipment going out of fashion, the London & North Western Railway compounded its prodigality by building a dedicated dock at Deganwy.

Nevertheless, the spectre of a London & North Western Railway in Blaenau itself caused panic at Paddington, resulting in the magnificent but costly Great Western Railway Blaenau Ffestiniog Branch from Bala being opened in 1882. Although some three miles was built on the track bed of the Ffestiniog & Blaenau Railway (a short-lived feeder of the Ffestiniog Railway) and despite the fact that there were no tunnels, the remaining civil work was extreme. It was even less successful than the London & North Western Railway in poaching traffic from the Ffestiniog Railway.

Hafod y Llan Tramway

Notwithstanding the continuing depression, the London & North Western Railway opened its ambitiously engineered Bethesda Branch in 1884. Lord Penrhyn was in full control of the district and had just rebuilt his own tramway as the steam Penrhyn Railway, so the Bethesda branch's 300-yard tunnel and elegant Ogwen viaduct carried precious little slate traffic.

There were four other standard gauge lines with slate association: the Mawddwy Railway, a private line acting as a Cambrian branch serving the Minllyn quarry in the upper Dyfi valley; the Maenclochog Railway and the Whitland and Cardigan Railway, both Pembrokeshire branches from the Great Western Railway. The latter took twelve years to complete – almost as long as the whole of the rest of the Great Western system. Finally, the Tanat Valley Railway, which was planned in the 1870s to join the Llangynog quarries to the Cambrian Railways, did not open until 1904, by which time there was scarcely a quarry left for it to serve.

In the meantime there had been narrow gauge activity. The clanking old Penrhyn Railroad, struggling at three times its design capacity, was transformed into the state-of-the art steam Penrhyn Railway in 1876 as already mentioned. Three years later the rather ugly duckling Corris, Machynlleth and River Dovey Tramway had become the sleek swan of the steam-powered Corris Railway.

Over in Denbighshire, the tradition of bringing the 'horse to water' was kept alive as late as 1873 by the Glyn Valley Tramway. In its case the water was the Montgomeryshire Canal. The line was later converted to a sort of steam street tramway, which terminated at Chirk Great Western Railway station. It was able to survive to serve the comparatively small Cambrian and Wynne quarries into the mid-1930s, since it also carried big tonnages of stone.

The final great slate rail development was the North Wales Narrow Gauge Railway. Completed in 1881, it ran from a village to a hamlet: from an exchange with the London & North Western Railway at Dinas to the windswept wastes of Rhyd-ddu.

Had it run to Caernarfon as was originally planned, and had it opened ten years earlier, it might just have been a success. As it was, both the North Wales Narrow Gauge and its successor the Welsh Highland Railway were economic disasters.

Nevertheless it must be remembered that the North Wales Narrow Gauge Railway, and particularly its Bryngwyn Branch, enabled the Tryfan quarries to develop and prosper through the hardest times.

Slate Railways in Wales

Significant narrow gauge lines

From		To
1801	Penrhyn	1961
1825	Dinorwig/Padarn	1962
1828	Nantlle	1964
1836	Ffestiniog	-
1856	Gorseddau	c. 1890
1859	Corris	1948
1864	Croesor	1930
1866	Talyllyn	-
1873	Glyn Valley	1935
1877	NW Narrow Gauge	1922
1923	Welsh Highland	-

Some minor slate lines

1850	Abereiddi	c. 1890
1850	Cwmorthin	1939
1850s	Carnarvonshire Rly	c. 1915
1856	Oernant	c. 1900
1858	Arthog	1868?

1859	Frongoch	1884
1859	Ratgoed	1940
1861	Cedryn	1880
1863	Rhiw-bach	1953
1868	Ffestiniog & Blaenau	1862
1868	South Snowdon	1880s
1868	John Robinson	c. 1875
1868	Hendre Ddu	1939
1868	Cwm Ebol	c. 1900
1870?	Deeside	1947

Standard gauge of importance to slate

1852	P Dinorwig London & North Western Railway	1961
1852	P Penrhyn London & North Western Railway	1963
1867	Mawddwy	1950
1869	Llanberis London & North Western Railway	1964
1873	Whitland & Cardigan	1963
1876	Maenclochog	1965
1879	Blaenau London & North Western Railway	–
1882	Blaenau GWR	1961
1884	Bethesda London & North Western Railway	1953
1904	Tanat Valley	1960

Runaway on No. 2 incline Rhiw-bach Tramway, Cwm Penmachno

11
Gilding the lily

Well before the middle of the nineteenth century, slate was becoming a victim of its own success, particularly as far as slab product was concerned. It came to be regarded as a commonplace material, associated with dreary utilitarian products. Understandably, people did not want items in their homes that were reminiscent of a gentlemen's convenience or a pigsty, and many people therefore disguised their chimney pieces and other slate fixtures with paint..

In order for slate to broaden its appeal and to move up-market, it needed to shake off its humble and utilitarian image by looking like something quite different, and this led to the enamelling process.

Enamelling involved quite simply painting slate artefacts and stoving them to give a permanent and durable finish, but it was not so easy to do.

There was no single inventor of slate enamelling. Several individuals developed different processes independently but the great pioneer was George Eugene Magnus, a writing slate manufacturer of Pimlico, and owner of the Valentia quarry in the west of Ireland. His primary aim was

78 (above) Hosking and Miller's works was at the corner of Cambrian Street and Brewer Street

to imitate marble. 'Magnus Ware' was the result. Magnus Ware was claimed to be more durable than marble, and soon advertisements were proclaiming: 'Marbles, Porphyries and other costly materials are faithfully and beautifully imitated at a fraction of the cost of the articles represented.'

Despite its being unashamedly called 'Mock Marble', panels, pilasters, wall linings and even staircases were found in the grandest houses in Britain and overseas. Allegedly Napoleon III and several Indian potentates were customers.

Magnus' chimneypieces, stove fronts, pedestals, console tables, knick-knacks and whatnots also graced more modest homes, and pot-stands supported aspidistras in countless best-room windows in the serried terraces of industrial towns.

Branching out into a variety of finishes, his success spurred by winning a medal at the Great Exhibition of 1851, there seemed no end to the variety of uses he found for enamelled slate. Tables and other furniture had an immediate appeal in termite-infested climates. In the tropics even slate chairs were popular. It is said that Magnus' seating cooled the Caliph's concubines in the Seraglio at Constantinople. The extent to which Magnus Ware was a 'must have' among the fashion-conscious gentry is indicated by the proprietors of both the Penrhyn and Dinorwig quarries embellishing their respective residences with it, despite the fact that it was made from competitors' slate (their own slate was unsuitable for enamelling).

The initial coating was fairly easy, and consisted of brushing on tar varnish or commonplace pigments in a fairly rough manner. However the subsequent heat treatment was critical.

An order for Enamelled Slate

Pieces had to be dried at 60°-70°F in a drying room prior to painting, possibly for several weeks in the case of thicker slabs. They were then put in the oven and gradually raised to 220°F for some eighteen hours. Afterwards they were allowed to cool to around 120°F before being removed from the oven.

73

Even an incautious momentary opening of a tiny inspection hatch in the oven could result in disastrous cracking.

Then came the tricky bit – putting in the marbling, wood-effect or other finish. This was done by dipping the piece in water in which were stirred immiscible oily pigments, which by various secret sleights-of-hand with bits of stick, rags and sponges, produced the desired result. This was followed by re-stoving.

Not all slate could withstand the thermal shock of the process, but Ordovician slate from the Narrow Vein at Aberllefenni proved ideal. Magnus mainly used this type of slate, opening a dedicated manufactory nearby, which was served by a spur from the Corris railway.

Interestingly, when Inigo Jones' factory at Groeslon changed over to enamelling – it had been established to make writing slates from Nantlle material – they had to seek slate elsewhere, buying up quarries such as Cae Defaid near Dolgellau and Cymerau near Corris to secure supplies. In addition they signed contracts with several quarries such as Gartheiniog and Talymerin in the upper Dyfi area.

Although Magnus remained the dominant manufacturer, many others

Spraying electrical panels prior to stoving at Braich Goch

got in on the act, and towards the end of the nineteenth century there were numerous enamelling establishments. These were of three types:

1. On site as part of a quarry. Hafodlas near Betws-y-coed; Braich Goch at Corris; Rhiw'r Gwreiddyn nearby at Ceinws; Gartheiniog in the adjacent Angell valley, and Dolbadau in Pembrokeshire all had ovens on site. The Aberglaslyn Slate Quarries Enamel Co. was also formed in 1886 at Cwm Caeth quarry, near Beddgelert, although there is no evidence of any production.

2. Off-site but adjacent to quarrying areas. These were normally operated by independent owners. Matthews Mill, founded by Magnus at Aberllefenni was the most notable example, and Inigo Jones at Groeslon was the most successful. The Towyn (later Maglona) Company operated at the Bodtalog Mill, Tywyn, before taking over Rhiw'r Gwreiddyn quarry. For a time they also used the oven at Machynlleth. This was originally built by Ratgoed quarry near Aberllefenni, and was sited partly to save carrying coal and partly for labour availability and, indeed, to enable them to employ women. Later the Cambrian Slate Company, operating in conjunction with Decorated Fireplace & Materials of London, enamelled chimneypieces of Llwyngwern slate at their Machynlleth works.

Enamelling also took place at several works at Aberystwyth, such as Hoskins and Miller and Peter Jones. They used material from Corris, Llwyngwern and several small quarries on either side of the Dyfi estuary, and Glandyfi quarry was bought to safeguard supplies.

working, &c. in scagliola.

47 BUCKLEY, G. Bayswater, Prod.—Column and two slabs, painted in imitation of Sienna marble.

50 MAGNUS, G. E. Pimlico, Inv.—Manufactures in slate: Enamelled slate; representing various marbles inlaid after Florentine mosaic, &c.

51 NICOL & ALLEN, 57 Upper Marylebone St. Des. and Painters.—Imitations of marbles; design for a table-top, imitation of inlaid marbles.

52 LAMBERT, C. Abbey, Ireland, Prop.—Dark green Connemara marble tables and Serpentine tables from Bally-nahinch.

An entry from Catalogue of Great Exhibtion, 1851

75

At the slate ports, merchants such as Nicholas & Owen at Caernarfon and H. Williams at Bangor had enamelling ovens. In the early twentieth century some enamelling was done at Pentrefelin mill near Llangollen using material brought down the Oernant Tramway from quarries on the Horseshoe Pass.

3. Outside area. Enamelling was done in a number of big cities and ports, usually by manufacturing merchants, such as Sessions in south Wales and Gloucester, or both the Bow Slate Company and Langer, Powell & Magnus in London.

In addition, several Welsh quarries without enamelling facilities had arrangements to have the work done for them. Rosebush in Pembrokeshire, for instance, had a tie-up with Langer, Powell & Magnus, although no record has been found of them actually selling any enamelled items.

With the rejection of Victorian knick-knackery in the early twentieth century, the enamelled market narrowed. Domestic uses concentrated on chimneypieces, usually coated black and often decorated with gold lining and paintings of a very high standard.

In accordance with the craze at that time for 'graining', imitation wood was also popular.

Fortunately as the demand for household items ebbed, it was replaced by the need for items for electrical purposes.

As a stable, non-conducting material, enamelled slate was ideal for switchboards, and a big trade for black enamelled slabs developed for power stations, substations, factories, electric railways and tramways. It was widely used on board ships, and the 'Queens' and other ocean liners had control panels of Braich

76

Goch material. For a time enamelled slate was also used to mount domestic fuse-boxes and main switches.

For electrical work, the face and four sides were coated and stoved. After cooling, the treated surfaces were buffed to a high polish, whilst the back was painted but neither stoved nor polished.

This market continued into the 1970s, by which time spraying had replaced the traditional dip, splash and dab of the process.

During the 1920s, people moving into the new suburbias were demanding that their semi-detached 'villas' be clearly distinguishable from the old drab industrial terraces. Coloured tiles on the roofs could do this, but the acme of fashion was the green slate, which came mainly from north-west England.

To meet this competition, several of the largest quarries got together to establish the Colloidal Slate Company at Llandudno Junction, which was accessible by rail from both north Caernarfonshire and Blaenau Ffestiniog. Almost any colour could be produced by a relatively simple dipping process. The product sold at about 15% more than the natural Welsh material, but was still almost 25% less than 'Lakeland Green'.

Despite being dearer than tile, it enjoyed early success, but when the 'Westmoreland Green' fell from favour, business slumped. Oakeley, one of the original sponsors, bought out and transferred it to Blaenau but the works closed during the Second World War.

12
Slate art

The instinct to create depictions is so strong and slate is so easily marked by a piece of metal or a hard stone, that the creation of images on slate must have very ancient origins.

Modern slate art can be said to have begun in the Middle Ages when the scratched initials and date on rough-hewn grave markers were augmented by outlines and simple designs, such as the classic sunburst or haloed head.

It was in the nineteenth century that monuments moved from the simple rectangular or round-headed upright shape to become a blaze of facets and fretting. Some monuments were complicated assemblies, cemented and dowelled together. In areas that were not served by railways, and where the local slate was poor, it was often the custom to insert an inscription panel of slate from northern Wales into an assemblage of local material. Sometimes these fabrications were modular, which allowed for a separate but contiguous memorial for several members of the family or, poignantly, for several children dying in infancy, possibly in the same epidemic.

'Hare Over a Blue Moon.' Bas-relief in slate by Meic Watts.
By the kind permission of Mrs Ann Cole.

As decoration became more complex, the deeply incised reliefs and even three-dimensional embellishments more than justified monumental masons calling themselves 'sculptors'. They would have their own trademark designs, and their individual lettering style also became an art form in itself.

Many of these sculptors became highly regarded, and they reaped rewards far greater than any other journeymen, often living in fine style. Whilst in these days of reconstituted 'stone' and computer-generated, router-cut lettering, producers of grave markers are not so well rewarded, the lettering of slate still produces its calligraphic superstars such as John Williams, Ieuan Rees or the late Jonah Jones.

Independent of such professionals, slate workers using the skills and tools of their trade beautified and personalised their homes by incising, inscribing and carving parts of the structure, such as fireplaces, lintels, sills and gateposts. Besides displaying the accomplishments of the craftsman many also showed a highly developed artistic sense.

'Genesis.' Bas-relief by John Clea.
By kind permission of the
Cwmaman Institute.

This instinct for the image was manifest in the commercial adornment of many slate artefacts. Items as diverse as reusable coffins and animal feed-boxes were often elaborately inscribed and incised.

Painting using slate as a substrate, whether for its nature, its permanence or its texture, is an old art form. Since as early as the eighteenth century artists such as Richard Wilson or Alfred Worthington have found slate to be a more stable and permanent base for oil paint than more conventional materials. Today artists such as the miniaturist Ken Taylor continue the slate-painting tradition.

A number of artists such as Sara Humphreys are finding that slate can be an appropriate material for

'Eye Witness.'
Bas-relief Ivor Richards

pendants, cuff links, bracelets, necklaces and other jewellery items. Indeed there are many people who feel strongly that slate is itself a 'precious stone' and regard its more mundane use as profligacy.

Slate is not often used for three-dimensional art, particularly for figurative work, but sculptors such as Barbara Hepworth have produced major abstract items in slate.

It is in relief carving that the suitability and versatility of slate really comes into its own. Drawing on the techniques of the old 'monumental sculptors', forms and representations not only exploit the basic nature of the material but also its texture and colour.

A number of eminent artists such as Reg Beach, Ivor Richards, Diana Hoare and John Cleal have excelled in this medium.

Banding and other inclusions can enhance the beauty of artwork, and differing colours can be used in juxtaposition to create effects that artists such as William Rice employ to advantage.

Besides these uses, slate is increasingly being employed in a new form in building in Wales. Its incorporation into the elevations and facades of the Assembly building, the Millennium Centre and the National Maritime and Industrial Museum not only enhances these structures but also makes them an unequivocal proclamation of Welsh identity.

Going beyond the visual and the tactile, Will Menter has added the aural, with his creation of percussive musical instruments in slate.

Slate plaques, Clean Slate Design

13
Slate of the future

The 1969 closure of Dinorwig did not see the end of the depression. Penyrorsedd closed in 1977 leaving the Nantlle valley almost a slate-free zone, when once it had supported a couple of score of workings.

The 1980s saw yet another false dawn. The Williams family whose slate associations span half a dozen generations, having wrested Bwlch y Slaters (the famous Manod picture store quarry) from a tenacious government, developed it, reopened Oakeley and Penyrorsedd quarries, and planned a re-development of Rhosydd.

An outside firm also re-activated Croes y Dwy Afon and enlarged the late Robin Williams' small underground working at Cwmorthin.

However, the facts are that Continental producers working on green field sites unencumbered by old workings, out-of-date structures and debris, can undercut the prices of Welsh quarries. Even in instances where sentiment and social responsibility might take precedence over price, it is illegal for clients to specify 'Welsh', or to draw up an artificially tight technical specification that could favour the local product. The best that can be done is to demand conformance to a very generously defined British Standard, to whose requirements all but the worst of the imported products conform.

Clock by William Rice

Fortunately, overseas buyers are free of such constraints and in many parts of the world the terms 'Welsh' and 'Best' are regarded as synonymous. As a result, Penrhyn quarry prospers, and although other components of the 1980s revival languish, Oakeley and Bwlch y Slaters continue (although sadly with all production centralised at Penrhyn, with whom they now share common ownership). Llechwedd continues, and great determination and bold investment has revived Berwyn quarry near Llangollen to meet a niche market. At Twll Llwyd in Nantlle, the Humphreys brothers carry on applying more than two centuries of expertise. Several very small-scale operations also continue.

Admittedly the output of the Welsh slate industry is now a fraction of its late nineteenth century total, but it is far from being a sentimental clinging to a bygone way of life. It is run by businessmen who respect the past, but look to the future. It is staffed by men and women well able to get the best from the latest micro-chipped machinery. The once museum-like mills and workshops are now showplaces for the latest technology.

The present Welsh slate industry has found a niche to match competition from EU producers, but increasingly the Continental producers will be undercut in turn by low-wage and less regulated developing countries. The present vulnerability of slate quarrying was sadly illustrated by the closure in 2004 of Aberllefenni quarry after more than five hundred years of continuous operation. However, to counterbalance this somewhat, there has been the small-scale re-activation of Cefn quarry at Cilgerran in Pembrokeshire, Braich Ddu at Trawsfynnydd and Alexandra at Rhosgadfan

There is also a bright future for Welsh slate in other directions. The slate gravestone is not a thing of the past, but is very much present in the yards of specialist monumental masons who maintain much of the old sculptors' flair. In the architectural field, firms such as Inigo Jones of Groeslon, Cerrig of Pwllheli, Snowdonia Slate of Blaenau and Clean Slate Design of Trawsfynydd successfully apply generations of slate-working

Table by Clean Slate Design

experience, transforming such mundane objects as the scullery slab into the high-fashion worktop.

Traditionalists may scoff at house-names and knick-knacks, but wine coasters, for instance, retail at twenty times the per-ton price of Best roofing slate. Indeed this trade is merely continuing the constant striving for added value that was typified by products such as Kellow's Patent Ridging.

Small speciality items are labour intensive, which has a social payoff and preserves skills that laser-controlled saws and mechanical handling are killing off in ordinary slate working. In addition, unlike conventional slate working, which has become increasingly capital-intensive and volume-dependent, the making of such items can be profitable on a modest scale with a minimum of investment.

The artistic use of slate calls for skills vastly different from those required for splitting a large block, but nevertheless requires a similar sympathy for and understanding of the rock, which again maintains an ancient skill passed from generation to generation. Even artists lacking this dynastic advantage find that by living and working with it they acquire a similar empathy with the material.

It can therefore be said that the Welsh slate industry is certainly not dying but is undergoing a metamorphosis. This augurs well for the survival of the unique social and cultural fabric of places such as Bethesda or Blaenau Ffestiniog. Admittedly the culture of the Caban no longer exists, if indeed it ever did quite to the extent that historians would have us believe. Nor does the industry have poets of the stature of Eifion Wyn (a clerk to the Croesor quarry), hymn writers like William Owen (a Bethesda quarryman), or prose writers to match Kate Roberts (daughter of an Alexandra quarryman), nor bibliophiles such as Bob Owen (another Croesor clerk), all of them literary giants of the nineteenth and twentieth centuries. Yet who is to say that their peers may not appear at some time in the twenty-first?

Nevertheless, like everywhere else, the visual image is displacing the written word, and scions of slate working dynasties are already nationally prominent in drama, film and television.

It is in music that the old traditions are most tenacious. Brass bands and choirs are fewer and are no longer chapel-driven or quarry-based, but both are still central to the old slate communities. The Deiniolen Band, for instance, which is headquartered in an old writing-slate factory, is the centre-piece of village life. The Moelwyn Male Voice Choir probably has a stronger following in Blaenau Ffestiniog than even the rugby team. The magnificent Faenol Festival held in the grounds of the erstwhile Dinorwig quarry owner's house has obvious slate associations, while that centre of musical and artistic excellence, Y Tabernacl at Machynlleth, draws on a

Llechwedd quarry. Mill in centre of picture now forms part of quarry tours.

cultural tradition forged in the slate workings of southern Meirionnydd.

Music has also moved with the times and the slate regions are in the forefront of developments in modern music. Pesda Roc places Bethseda firmly in the national scene, leading Wales if not the UK in the production of recordings, its only rival being Blaenau Ffestiniog.

Meanwhile, the exploitation of the great mountains of waste is becoming an industry of increasing importance. Although not using the old skills, it is developing new ones and is contributing to the vibrancy of the communities.

Devising uses for slate waste has exercised great minds for years. There was at one time great excitement that the French were converting slate waste to a saleable product – but quite how could not be discovered owing to the then ongoing war with Napoleon. In fact over the years a number of quarries have converted waste to powder and sold it for a wide variety of purposes – as an abrasive, as a basis for cosmetics and as a filler for plastics manufacture. More recently, powdered slate has been used with fibreglass to make artificial slates, with a dedicated plant at Oakeley quarry for example. Unfortunately the cost of crushing is not cheap and generally such uses demand fresh waste that has not been contaminated by prolonged exposure. A more promising outlet for slate waste is bulk-fill. Only a fraction of the several hundreds of millions of tons of slate waste generated by the industry is economically recoverable, but the fiscal regime is making such activity increasingly attractive. The availability of portable crushing plants means that comparatively small and relatively inaccessible tips can now be economically worked, providing the potential for a widely spread industry.

A happy spin-off of the Dinorwig closure was the creation of the Welsh Slate Museum, largely thanks to the efforts of the late Mr D. Morgan Rees of the National Museum of Wales. This move, coupled with the resourcefulness of Mr Hefin Davies in setting up Quarry Tours at Llechwedd quarry, Blaenau Ffestiniog, not only ensured the preservation of much machinery and the nurturing of old skills, but generated public awareness of them.

This paved the way for other museum and visitor-centre initiatives such as Inigo Jones workshops and Llanfair quarry. This awareness has not been confined to the slate industry, and has spurred the establishment of several textile and mining creations. It has also developed an interest in old skills and past activities and created recognition of the need to conserve the physical remains of them – hence for instance the work done by the Snowdonia National Park in stabilising the unique Cwm Ystradllyn slate mill.

Some quarry sites

Cwm Ystradllyn, the mill for Gorseddau quarry – 'The Slate Cathedral'

Drumhouse, Main Exit incline, Llechwedd quarry

Abercwmeiddaw	SH746093
Abereiddi	SM705315
Aberllefenni	SH768103
Alexandra (Cors y Bryniau)	SH518562
Arthog	SH650151
Braich	SH510552
Braich Goch	SH748074
Bryneglwys	SH695954
Cae Defaid	SH784233
Cilgwyn	SH500540
Conglog	SH668467
Croesor	SH657457
Cymerau	SH779116
Cwm Caeth	SH605466
Cwm Maengwynedd	SJ075326
Dinorwig	SH595603
Dolbadau	SN198209
Dorothea	SH500532
Gartheiniog	SH822117
Glandyfi	SN698961
Glanrafon	SH581540
Goleuwern	SH621122
Graig Ddu	SH724454
Hafodlas	SH779562
Llwyngwern	SH757045
Maenofferen	SH715467
Moel Tryfan	SH515559
Penmachno	SH751470
Prince of Wales	SH549498
Rhiw'r Gwreiddyn	SH760054
Rhos	SH729564
Rhosydd	SH664461
Rosebush	SN079300
South Snowdon	SH613524
Talymieryn	SH825119
Treflan	SH539584
Votty & Bowydd	SH708462

Slate works

Bodtalog	SN598994
Crawia	SH536643
Glandinorwig	SH572632
Newborough	SH699456
Pentrefelin	SJ218436

Abandoned villages

Rhiw-bach	SH742462
Treforus	SH560454

Quarries now extracting slate

Alexandra	SH519562
Berwyn	SJ 185463
Braich Ddu	SH718384
Cefn	SN204428
Llechwedd	SH670087
Manod	SH732455
Oakeley	SH690466
Penrhyn	SH620650
Twll Llwyd	SH490518

(Tip workings are excluded, but some very small quarries only nominally active are included.)

FRON HAUL QUARRYMEN'S TERRACE

This row of houses come originally from Tanygrisiau, Blaenau Ffestiniog – they were dismantled in 1998 and re-erected at the Welsh Slate Museum, Llanberis. There are four houses in the terrace – No. 4 has been designated as an interactive area for educational use. In No. 3, the house has been renovated in the style of golden era of Welsh Slate, 1861; No. 2 is a re-creation of a home of a quarryman on strike – the three-year Penrhyn strike, 1901 and at No. 1 we can see the end of an era – 1969, the year Dinorwig quarry was closed.

WELSH SLATE MUSEUM

Y Gilfach Ddu, Parc Padarn, Llanberis, Gwynedd LL55 4TY.
Tel: 01286 870630 Fax: 01286 871906
e-mail: slate@nmgw.co.uk
website: www.nmgw.ac.uk

The Welsh Slate Museum is located in the Gilfach Ddu workshops of the old Dinorwig quarry on the shores of Llyn Padarn. The museum is open throughout the year, free admission. Amongst the attractions and facilities are a short 3D film on the history and heritage of the Welsh quarrying society, an opportunity to see slate dressing by local craftsmen, the largest water-wheel on mainland Britain, Fron Haul quarrymen's houses, carpenter and blacksmith workshops, manager's house, the incline (working daily between 2-3 pm, weather and staff permitting), café with home-cooking and a gift shop.

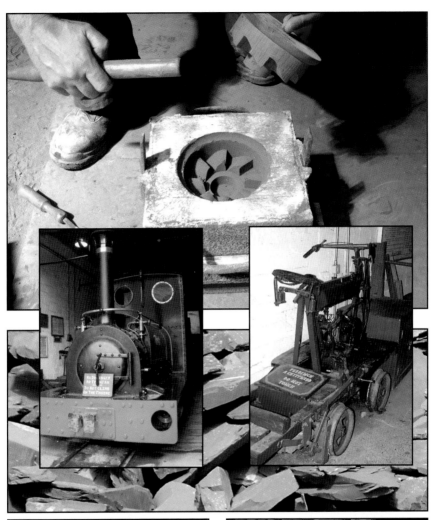

LLECHWEDD SLATE CAVERNS

Blaenau Ffestiniog, Gwynedd LL41 3NB.
Tel: 01766 830306 / Fax: 01766 831260
e-mail: info@llechwedd-slate-caverns.co.uk
website: www.llechwedd-slate-caverns.co.uk

This unique location offers two different types of underground rides. The Miner's Tramway is a guided tour through an 1846 network of awe-inspiring man-made caverns, supplemented with tableaux and demonstrations of ancient mining skills. The Deep Mine is the steepest passenger railway in the British Isles. On reaching the bottom, a 25-minute walk takes visitors through 10 *son et lumière* sequences which unfold the social life of a Victorian slate mining community. Back on the surface, a quarryman's village has been created including workshops, tavern, smithy and there is a restaurant and shop at the Visitor Centre.

Open all year; winner of all top tourism awards.

INIGO JONES

Groeslon, Caernarfon, Gwynedd LL54 7UE.
Tel: 01286 830242 / Fax: 01286 831247
e-mail: slate@inigojones.co.uk   website: www.inigojones.co.uk

Inigo Jones Slate Works was founded in 1861 in what had been the old timber mill of the Glynllifon estate. Initially it made school writing slates, later diversifying into slate enamelling. The business was developed substantially in the last quarter of the twentieth century and in 2001 a new shop, gallery and café was opened on the site.

Today the self-guided tour starts with an informative film in the new video room. It is possible to wander through the workshops and view the machines, accompanied by personal taped commentary. The visitor centre houses a range of original top quality slateware produced by Inigo Jones along with other Welsh crafts, heritage books and prints.

LLANFAIR SLATE CAVERNS
Llanfair, Harlech, Gwynedd.
Tel: 01766 780247
e-mail: owen@llanfairslate.fsnet.co.uk
website: www.llanfairslatecaverns.co.uk

The entry to this old but important slate mine is through the main tunnel and into the lofty cathedral cavern. These were all man-made over 100 years ago with only a candle for lighting. The slate in this mine is among the oldest in the world and was exported to towns in Ireland and England from the Artro estuary below. There is a gift shop and café at the site; open from Easter to mid-October.

FFESTINIOG RAILWAY

Gorsaf yr Harbwr, Porthmadog, Gwynedd LL49 9NF.
Tel: 01766 516073
e-mail: info@festrail.co.uk   website: www. festrail.co.uk

Take a 13-mile ride on a railway steeped in industrial history. For 140 years steam-hauled trains have carried slate from the caverns of Blaenau Ffestiniog to the harbour of Porthmadog, from where they were exported to every corner of the globe.

Open daily, mid March to early November; limited winter opening.

LLANBERIS LAKE RAILWAY

Llanberis, Gwynedd.
Tel / Fax: 01286 870549
e-mail: lake-railway.co.uk
website: www.lake-railway.co.uk

A delightful lakeside trip on a historic narrow gauge train offering magnificent views over Llyn Padarn towards Snowdon's craggy peak. A new extension reached Llanberis in 2003 and from the main station near the Welsh Slate Museum, visitors can follow the track that carried slate from the quarry towards the quay at Felinheli on this 5-mile return journey.

TAL-Y-LLYN RAILWAY

Tywyn, Gwynedd.
Tel: 01654 710472 / Fax: 01654 711755
e-mail: enquiries@talyllyn.co.uk   website: www.talyllyn.co.uk

From Tywyn a coal fired narrow gauge steam train takes you seven miles into the Snowdonia National Park, as far as the old quarry of Bryneglwys. This was the first railway in the world to be reopened by volunteers in 1956. There is a narrow gauge railway museum at the station at Tywyn.

WELSH HIGHLAND RAILWAY (Caernarfon)

Ffordd y Santes Helen, Caernarfon, Gwynedd.
Tel: 01286 677018 or 01766 516000
e-mail: info@festrail.co.uk   website: www.festrail.co.uk

A journey along the old quarry line through the heart of Snowdonia. The line is being re-built at present and will eventually reach from Caernarfon to Porthmadog.

WELSH HIGHLAND RAILWAY (Porthmadog)

Ffordd Tremadog, Porthmadog, Gwynedd LL49 9DY.
Tel: 01766 513402
e-mail: webmaster@whr.co.uk   website: www.whr.co.uk

This narrow gauge train trip includes a visit to the sheds with a chance to climb on the engines and see how they work. Travel in old-fashioned coaches on a short journey to Pen-y-Mount station.

CORRIS RAILWAY AND MUSEUM

Iard yr Orsaf, Corris, Machynlleth, Powys SY20 9HS.
Tel: 01654 761303
e-mail: enquiries@corris.co.uk   website: www.corris.co.uk

The original tramroad dates back to 1859 when slates were carried down from Corris Uchaf and Aberllefenni to the quay on the Dyfi river. It was closed in 1948 but steam locomotives ran again in 2005. There is a small museum on site.

PENRHYN CASTLE

Llandygái, Bangor, Gwynedd LL57 4HN.
Tel: 01248 353084 / 371337   Fax: 01248 371281
e-mail: penrhyncastle@nationaltrust.org.uk
website: www.nationaltrust.org.uk

This was the family seat of the owners of Chwarel y Penrhyn – the slate quarry visible 5 miles up the Ogwen valley at Bethesda. The family created its wealth on the backs of West Indian slaves and Welsh quarrymen and there are a number of relevant pictures and items in this massive fantasy castle which is now in the care of the National Trust. The stable block houses an industrial railway museum – the Penrhyn quarry line was the first industrial railway in the world.

CERRIG

Glandon Industrial Estate, Pwllheli,
Gwynedd LL53 5YT.
Tel: 01758 612645   Fax: 01758 612410
e-mail: info@cerrig-granite.com

A family company which manufactures high standard Welsh slate worktops, countertops, plaques, window sills, table tops, fireplaces and memorials in slate as well as in granite, marble and fine stone from every corner of the world.

ELECTRIC MOUNTAIN AND DINORWIG POWER STATION
Llanberis
Tel: 01286 870636 / Fax: 01286 873002
e-mail: info@electricmountain.co.uk
website: www.electricmountain.co.uk

A lakeside centre (with films, interactive displays, art galleries and a café/bistro) is the starting point of a guided tour to Dinorwig Power Station in a huge cavern inside the slate mountain of Elidir Fawr. Discover how water generates instant electricity for the national grid of Wales and England.

MARICRAFT SLATE WORLD

Units 1 & 2, Stryd Fawr, Blaenau Ffestiniog,
Gwynedd LL41 3ES.
Tel: 01766 831028 / Fax: 01766 831339
e-mail: len@slatecraft.co.uk   website: www.maricraft.co.uk

Maricraft produces goods using Blaenau Ffestiniog's finest slate. As well as the usual famous slate gifts – table-mats, clocks, fans, etc. – the company also produces a wide range of personally manufactured goods. There is a great demand for house names (deep carved letters, coloured to the buyer's specifications), pet memorials, company and publicity plaques and prize trophies. Maricraft offers a 5-day postal service. They also supply floor tiles with a natural surface.

LLECHEN LAS

Alan and Ianto, Welsh Slate Crafts, Wrysgan Fawr, Tanygrisiau, Blaenau
Ffestiniog, Gwynedd LL41 3SB.
Tel: 01766 831460

After 36 years' experience as a quarryman in the Blaenau Ffestiniog area, Alan turned to create a variety of slate craft in his workshop at Tanygrisiau. He works garden furniture and flower pots from the local blue slate, also traditional door-weights, coasters, paper holders, shepherds crooks and lovespoons.

BERWYN SLATE QUARRY Ltd.
Bwlch yr Oernant, Llangollen, Sir Ddinbych LL20 8DP.
Tel: 01978 861897 / Fax: 01978 869292
e-mail: sales@berwynslate.com   website: www.berwynslate.com

This quarry was established about 1700 on a slate vein 1360 feet above sea level near the Horseshoe Pass (Bwlch yr Oernant) in the hills between Llangollen and Rhuthun. The quarry saw heavy investment at the site in 1991 when it was taken over by Bickfords of Swansea. With special cutting and polishing machinery, the quarry can supply a wide range of tiles, pavers, fireplaces and worktops as well as landscaping material and sills and steps.

THE SLATE SIGN COMPANY
9 Cowbridge Road, Pontyclun, Morgannwg CF72 9EA.
Tel: 01443 225224 / Fax: 01443 228354
website: www.slatesign.co.uk

Producers of house signs, awards and plaques from 100% Welsh slate.

National Park Award
Gwobr Parc Cenedlaethol

THE SLATE WORKSHOP
(Richard a Fran Boultbee)
Melin Pont Hywel, Llangolman, Clunderwen, Sir Benfro SA66 7XJ.
Tel / Fax: 01994 419543
e-mail: dothebiz@slate-workshop.co.uk
website: www.slate-workshop.co.uk

The Slate Workshop design and make unique high quality items from Welsh slate in a renovated 18th century corn mill. As well as housenames and numbers, commemorative and business plaques, memorials and sundials, Richard also produces wonderful curving sculpture, clocks, barometers, lamp-bases, cheeseboards, bookends, vases and tableware. The company offers a postal service.

WILLIAM RICE
Fine craftsman from Blaenau Ffestiniog; exhibits and sells through galleries and shops.

William Rice is from a family of slatemen and lives and works in Blaenau Ffestiniog. He has combined the old craft with his technical expertise and has been turning slate to an exceptional high standard since 1968. He uses slate from different quarries to create interesting colour combinations in his work.

103

CLEAN SLATE DESIGN Cyf.

Craig y Tân, Trawsfynydd,
Gwynedd.
Tel: 01766 540885
website: www.cleanslatedesign.co.uk

Producing high quality garden furniture/landscaping using modern designs.

SNOWDONIA NATURAL SLATE PRODUCTS

Benar View, Blaenau Ffestiniog, Gwynedd.
Tel: 01766 832570
Mobile: 07813016615
e.mail: info@snowdonianaturalslateproducts.co.uk
website: www.snowdonianaturalslateproducts.co.uk

Manufacturers of quality Welsh slate products from local quarries and using local craftsmen. Their range of slate products includes crafts, headstones and memorials, flooring and tiles, walling, slate sign engraving, fire places, hearths and garden landscaping. Computer aided design and sandblasted engraving enables this company to apply your personalization to the slate product.

THE SCIENCE OF SPORT

Squash

THE SCIENCE OF SPORT

Squash

Stafford Murray, with Mike Hughes, Nic James and Goran Vučković

Forewords by Jonah Barrington
and Peter Nicol MBE

THE CROWOOD PRESS

First published in 2016 by
The Crowood Press Ltd
Ramsbury, Marlborough
Wiltshire SN8 2HR

www.crowood.com

British Library Cataloguing-in-Publication Data
A catalogue record for this book is available from the British Library.

ISBN 978 1 78500 179 6

Acknowledgements
Stafford and the editing team would sincerely like to thank the following people: all the chapter
authors who have given their time, effort and expertise to help make this book the first to pull
together the various disciplines of sports science deployed in squash; the expert coaches that
have willingly shared their incredible knowledge and insight, bringing this book to life from a
pedagogical aspect and helping us all to look at sports science in a different way; the fantastic
players that gave their valuable time to be interviewed, adding a player-focused dimension to
the book that is unique within sports science texts; Peter Nicol MBE and Jonah Barrington for
giving up their time and offering their kind and insightful words within the forewords; and Steve
Cubbins and Tommy Berden for their help and work on the pictures. Steve Cubbins (SquashSite)
provided all the photographs with the exception of Fig. 10.34 (Sarah Murray).

Stafford would personally like to thank his wife Sarah, son Bowdon and mum Lynda for being
so helpful and patient with him during the pulling together of this book; he promises not to do
another one anytime soon! He would also like to express his heartfelt gratitude to his Mum,
Brother, Nan and Grandad for giving him the inspiration and capability to complete this project.

Typeset by Servis Filmsetting Ltd, Stockport, Cheshire

Printed and bound in India by Replika Press Pvt Ltd

CONTENTS

About the Editors 6

About the Authors 8

About the Players and Coaches 11

Forewords by Jonah Barrington and Peter Nicol MBE 16

Preface 19

1 The Evolution of Sport Science in Squash *Edward M. Winter* 20

2 Physiological Underpinnings of Training and Match Play in Squash
Edward M. Winter and Mark Campbell 27

3 Strength and Conditioning in Squash *Keith Barker and Mark Campbell* 39

4 Physiotherapy in Squash *Jade Leeder, Ian Horsley and Jonathan Leeder* 72

5 Performance Nutrition: Applying the Science
Chris Rosimus and Stephanie Shreeve 88

6 Effective Mental Training for Performance *Kirsten Barnes* 110

7 The Psychology of Match Play *Simon Hartley* 133

8 The Science and Art of Coaching
Danny Massaro (with David Pearson) 147

9 Skill Acquisition in Squash *Oliver Logan and Nic James* 172

10 Current Applications of Performance Analysis Techniques in Squash
Mike Hughes, Julia Wells, Stafford Murray, Mandie De Beer and Michael T. Hughes 186

11 What Learning Can we Take from this Book?
Mike Hughes and Stafford Murray 234

Index 239

ABOUT THE EDITORS

Stafford Murray (Editor-in-Chief) is a Performance Lead at the English Institute of Sport helping to coordinate the sports science delivery to five key Great Britain Olympic and Paralympic Sports. For thirteen years prior to this he was Head of Performance Analysis, Skill Acquisition and Biomechanics again at the English Institute of Sport. As a sports science practitioner he has worked as a consultant with over fifteen international and professional sports teams (including the Lawn Tennis Association, English Cricket Board, South African Cricket, McLaren F1, and Welsh Rugby) and to date has presented at forty-one international conferences (sixteen world congresses). He has published over thirty papers, (as well as seven book chapters) on both the technical and tactical analysis of squash. From 1998 to 2013 he was the head Performance Analyst for the England Squash Team, working with multiple World Individual and Teams Champions during his tenure. Between 2007 and 2010 he was the England Squash senior team manager culminating in being team leader at the Commonwealth Games Team in Delhi 2010, where England topped the squash medal table for the first time in the CWG history. He has post-graduate qualifications in Research Methods and Sports Performance Analysis/Coaching Science. As a junior squash player he was British No.1 and an England International.

Mike (M.D.) Hughes (Associate Editor) is Emeritus Professor of Sport and Exercise Science at Cardiff Metropolitan University, and a Visiting Professor at Middlesex University; Nottingham Trent University; OvG, Magdeburg, Germany; Zagreb, Croatia; WHU, Hungary; University of California, Berkeley, USA; UPM, Malaysia; Edith Cowan University, Perth, Australia and the Institute of Technology Carlow, Eire. He was founder and is now President of ISPAS (International Society of Performance Analysis of Sport). As a squash coach he has produced players that have reached a World Top 30 ranking and successfully coached the British Universities Team to win the World Student Games in 2000 and 2002.

Nic James (Assistant Editor) is Professor of Sport and Exercise Science at Middlesex University, and is a Visiting Professor at the University of Zagreb, Croatia. He is Chair of the International Society of Performance Analysis of Sport, a Member of the Coordination Council for the International Network of Sport and Health Science and a Fellow of the Higher Education Academy. He has represented Wales at senior level and was one of the national junior coaches for over ten years.

Goran Vučković (Assistant Editor) is an associate professor in the faculty of Sport at the University of Ljubljana, Slovenia. He is a member of the basketball and racket sports department and works with students on different study programmes such as sport coaching and physical education. As an athlete he was national champion (former Yugoslavia) in high jump, played professional basketball in the Slovenian Premier League and was national squash champion in 1995, 1998 and 1999. He is consultant coach and scientist for the junior national female basketball team and coaches the top Slovenian squash players. His research work is focused on performance analysis and motion analysis of athletes in different sports, with a special interest in racket and team sports.

'Sports science has undoubtedly played a huge part in the development of all successful athletes and I attribute much of my success to the advances made in this area. Squash is one of the most physically demanding sports with all players looking for marginal gains. Stafford and his colleagues have been at the forefront of this development and they certainly played a major role in my success.'

Lee Beachill, Former World Number 1 and 2 x Commonwealth Gold Medallist

ABOUT THE AUTHORS

Edward M. Winter is Professor of the Physiology of Exercise at Sheffield Hallam University. He trained in Physical Education at Loughborough and took his BEd, MSc and PhD from that University. In 2011 he became one of only five sport and exercise scientists in the United Kingdom who hold a DSc, awarded to him by the University of Bedfordshire for his contributions to the study of the physiology of exercise. He has taught, researched and provided consultancy in exercise physiology for forty-one years. In 1985 he co-authored the British Association of Sport and Exercise Sciences' criteria for the accreditation of physiology laboratories and personnel (and those criteria remain in use). In 2013 he led the Association's successful application for admission to the Science Council. On behalf of the Council, by dint of its accreditation scheme, BASES is allowed to award Chartered Scientist status to accredited members and Edward was one of the first recipients.

Mark Campbell works for the English Institute of Sport and is the Lead Strength and Conditioning coach for the Sheffield region. He delivers strength and conditioning service to the GB Boxing squad and in his capacity working as a multisport practitioner has delivered the physical preparation programmes for Nick Matthew and James Willstrop for a number of years as well as working with many other national- and international-level squash players. Before coming to the UK in 2007 he worked in professional rugby union in New Zealand with the Highlanders super rugby team based in Dunedin. He attended Otago University in Dunedin, gaining a Bachelor's and Master's degree in Physical Education.

Keith Barker is a Senior Strength and Conditioning Coach with the English Institute of Sport, a National Lead Strength and Conditioning Coach for England Squash, and a UK Strength and Conditioning Association Accredited Coach, Tutor and Assessor. With a background in physical education and sport and exercise science, he has built an extensive track record of leading and delivering effective strength and conditioning programmes for elite athletes. Prior to leading the successful England Squash Strength and Conditioning programme, he worked as a Head S and C coach in professional rugby union and rugby league.

Jade Leeder is Lead Physiotherapist to England Squash and has worked with the team since 2009. She is employed by the English Institute of Sport, and has attended multiple major championships including the

2014 Commonwealth Games. She has an MSc in sports injury rehabilitation from the University of Salford, and has published research on functional movement screening. She has specialist expertise in the hip and lumbar spine areas, alongside squash-specific rehabilitation strategies. She was an integral member of the team who were able to fast track the rehabilitation of Nick Matthew from a career-threatening knee injury, to win gold and silver medals at the Commonwealth Games in 2014.

Ian Horsley is the Lead Physiotherapist and Technical Lead for the North West for the English Institute of Sport, the clinical director of Back in Action Rehabilitation in Wakefield, West Yorkshire, and an associate lecturer at Salford University. He has been a physiotherapist for over twenty years. He worked for England Rugby Union for fourteen years with various teams, and spent the last six years working with the Elite Playing squad as physiotherapist to England 'A'. He has just concluded his PhD around the issue of shoulder injuries in professional rugby, has published articles on the subject of musculoskeletal injury management, and contributed chapters to books on sports injury management. He worked as part of the HQ medical team for Team England at the 2010 and 2014 Commonwealth Games and was a member of the Team GB HQ medical team at the 2012 Olympic Games.

Jonathan Leeder is a Performance Lead with the EIS in Sportcity working with England Squash. He completed his Masters in Exercise Physiology in 2007 before joining the EIS where he started working for the British Cycling Team as a physiologist. At the 2012 London Olympics, he was Lead Physiologist to the British Cycling Team, and Head of the physiology department in Manchester. During this time, he completed his PhD at Northumbria University with a focus on optimizing recovery

strategies for elite athletes. He is experienced in developing optimal recovery protocols for athletes both in training and competition and provided support to England Squash at the 2014 Commonwealth Games.

Chris Rosimus is a registered sports and exercise nutritionist, providing performance nutrition support to elite, professional and recreational athletes. He joined the English Institute of Sport in 2011 to work as Performance Nutritionist for the England Cricket team. He also provides nutrition support to England Squash alongside a lecturing position on sports nutrition with Manchester Metropolitan University. Prior to joining the EIS he was a performance nutrition intern at IMG Academies in Florida and worked as a nutritionist in Abu Dhabi with Manchester United soccer schools. He has a football coaching background and holds UEFA qualifications.

Stephanie Shreeve completed her BSc in Sport and Exercise Science with Human Nutrition and her MSc in Sports Nutrition at Chester University. She then took up a community nutrition role with the NHS, before joining the English Institute of Sport in May 2012 as Sport Nutritionist, where she works with British Para-Swimming and England Netball.

Kirsten Barnes has a BA in Human Performance from the University of Victoria in Canada and completed a PhD in sport psychology at the University of Bristol in 1998. She competed for Canada in rowing in the 1988 and 1992 Olympic Games, and she is a double Olympic gold medallist from the 1992 Games and World Champion in 1991 at the Rowing World Championships in both the 4− and 8+. She worked with England Squash from 1998 to 2004 and provided support to Commonwealth Games England in 2002, 2006 and 2010. She lives in Canada and is the Lead for Mental

Performance at the Canadian Sport Institute Pacific. She works with several National Team programmes preparing for International competition and the Olympic Games.

Simon Hartley is the founder and director of Be World Class coaching academy. For twenty years he has been working in elite and professional sport as a sport psychology consultant and performance coach. He has worked with coaches helping Olympians, world-class athletes and International teams to success. His expertise lies in helping organizations, teams and individuals to consistently engineer peak performance and become world class in sport.

Danny Massaro has been a Lecturer of Sports Coaching for eighteen years, and at the University of Central Lancashire for the last eight years where he has lectured on Master's Modules in Coaching Philosophy, Coaching Processes and Performance Psychology. He teaches on the Elite Coaching Practice Level 4 Course that runs in conjunction with UK Sport and the University of Central Lancashire, and whose participants are professional coaches employed by National Governing Bodies. He has coached and mentored his wife, Laura Massaro, since she turned professional in 2002. In 2013 Laura became World Champion, and the only British woman to hold both the World Open and coveted British Open titles. As a player Danny was twice runner-up in the National age-group Championships.

Oliver Logan has worked for the English Institute of Sport since 2006, and is currently Head of Performance for Archery GB and Biomechanics Technical Lead at the EIS. He worked for four years as Technical Lead for Skill Acquisition with a number of sports across the institute. He has an MSC in Sports Biomechanics from Liverpool JMU and a BSc

in Physics with Materials Science from Queens University Belfast, and is currently working towards a PhD in Biomechanics and Motor Learning of Explosive Lifting.

Julia Wells is Senior Performance Analyst and Technical Lead at the English Institute of Sport, having started out with Cardiff Metropolitan's Centre for Performance Analysis team providing services to many international-level athletes. She joined the English Institute of Sport in 2004 as a regional lead performance analyst and since then has worked with GB Canoeing's Canoe Slalom Olympic Programme, attending both Beijing 2008 and London 2012 Olympic Games.

Mandie De Beer is a sports Performance Analyst and consultant project manager. She was lead performance analyst for England Squash for four years culminating at the successful Glasgow Commonwealth Games in 2014. During this period she also helped project manage the Performance Analysis team within Team GB House during the London 2012 Olympic Games. She holds a BSc in Sports Science and an MSc in Sports Performance Analysis.

Michael T. Hughes has worked in elite level sport for the last ten years, with outstanding teams including the British and Irish Lions, England Rugby, British Cycling and England Squash. Since starting with the RFU in 2008, he has been responsible for designing and implementing all data collection and processing protocols from the senior team, throughout the Performance Pathway, to the Academy teams. He was a Senior Performance Analyst on the British Lions Tour in 2013 when the Lions won a test series for the first time in sixteen years and for the first time in Australia in twenty-four years, and was a part of the England management team at the 2011 Rugby World Cup.

ABOUT THE PLAYERS AND COACHES

THE PLAYERS

Nick Matthew OBE is a three-times World Squash Champion and treble Commonwealth Games gold medallist. He has enjoyed a prolific career since turning pro in 1998, achieving a string of historic breakthroughs which have led the Yorkshireman to become one of England's most successful squash players of all-time. In June 2010, he topped the world rankings for the first time and in December became the first Englishman in the premier event's thirty-five-year history to win the PSA World Championship. In November 2011, he successfully defended his world crown in Rotterdam, becoming the first player for fifteen years to retain the title. His record-making run continued on home soil in 2012: in May,

at the O2 Arena in London, he became the first Englishman ever to win the British Open title for a third time. In 2014 he was named the official flag bearer for Team England at the Commonwealth Games opening ceremony. The Games proved to be a triumph, with Nick taking gold in singles before teaming up with Adrian Grant to bring England a silver medal in doubles. He is managed by international-SPORTgroup™.

Laura Massaro is one of the most decorated female English squash players of all time. Her achievements to date are: double silver medalist at the Commonwealth Games in Glasgow 2014, World Champion 2013, British Open Champion 2013, Windy City Open Champion 2014, KL Open Champion 2013, US Open

champion 2011, two-times World player of the year, 2010 Commonwealth Games silver medalist in Delhi, 2014 two-times Commonwealth silver medalist in Glasgow and three-times British Closed Champion. When Laura won the British Open in 2013 she was the first English woman to do so for twenty-two years. In 2014 she successfully made the final shortlist at the Sunday Times and Sky Sports Personality of the Year – the sole squash player to achieve this feat. Laura is still constantly challenging the World No.1 ranking and in May 2015 once again defeated long-term World No. 1 Nicol David to reach the final of the British Open in Hull.

James Willstrop crowned a sensational junior squash career in 2002 when he claimed his third consecutive British Junior Under-19 National Championship title, to establish himself as England's most successful junior player of all time. He went on to be one of the youngest players ever to play for the senior England team, at both the European and World Team Squash Championships in 2003. In 2004 and 2005 he won multiple world tour events and this success led to him

leaping six places to World No. 2 in the world squash rankings. He headed up the England team that won 2005 World Team Championships in Pakistan. He is two-times British National Champion and two-times Commonwealth silver medallist, and in January 2010, he won his first Tournament of Champions title in New York, defeating World No. 1 Ramy Ashour. He ended his 2011 season by winning fifteen matches in a row en route to winning the Hong Kong Open, the Kuwait Open, and The Punj Lloyd 2011 PSA Masters. This string of results helped James achieve his lifetime goal of becoming World No. 1 in 2012. He is trained by his father, Malcolm Willstrop, at Pontefract Squash Club in West Yorkshire.

Jenny Duncalf is a former World No. 2 female squash player and has represented England at the Commonwealth Games. She has been a professional player for fifteen years. As a junior player, she won the British and European Championship titles. She won the Senior European Individual Championship title in 2006 and 2007, and the British National Championship title in 2007 and 2009. She was also a member of the England team that won the World Team Squash Championships in 2006. In 2008, she finished runner-up at the British Open and ended the 2009 season winning three titles in a row: the SohoSquare Open, the US Open and the prestigious Qatar

Classic. In October 2010 she reached the women's singles final of the Commonwealth Games in Delhi bringing home the silver medal. She was an integral part of the England Team that topped the squash table at the 2014 Glasgow Commonwealth Games, winning a silver medal in the ladies doubles.

Alison Waters is one of the most capped England Internationals in history. As a junior she won all British Junior age categories and was part of the winning England team in the world junior team championships in 2001, reaching a career-high world ranking of No.3 in 2010. Then in late 2011 she had a major Achilles injury. However, this did not stop her determination and eventual progression. She came back in stronger than ever in 2012 to win five World Tour Titles and sweep up the prestigious 'Comeback Player of the Year' title awarded by her world governing body. She had been a member of the winning England team at the world team championships in 2006 and was so again in 2014. She competed in three Commonwealth Games, hauling both bronze and silver medals in Glasgow 2014. She is a multiple British National Squash Champion, successfully defending the title in 2014 to win it for the fourth time.

ABOUT THE COACHES

David Pearson is one of the most successful squash coaches in the history of the sport. On an individual level he has coached multiple world champions, including Peter Nicol MBE and Cassie Jackman MBE. During his unprecedented tenure as England National coach he guided his country to seven world senior team titles, fourteen Commonwealth Games medals, sixteen straight European team championships and countless World and European junior team titles. This success earned him the Mussabini Medal for outstanding contribution to sport in the UK in 2002. As a player he was known as one of the finest touch players on the circuit and this high level of skill helped gain him over forty England Senior Caps. He is now a self-employed consultant working with, amongst others around the world, recent World Champions Nick Matthew and Laura Massaro. He was seminal in the integration of sports science into the England Squash programme in the late 1990s and without doubt this visionary approach has shaped the way that players train and practise in squash all around the world today.

Malcolm Willstrop is renowned the world over for producing outstanding players who not only play the game well but also play the game with the right ethics and attitude. Based out of Pontefract Squash Club in Yorkshire, his coaching philosophies are clearly successful, producing world senior number ones (including Lee Beachill and James Willstrop), a number of individuals reaching the top ten in the world rankings, and countless British Junior Champions. He is currently coaching two of the world's top ten senior male players. His passion and knowledge for the sport is second to none and without doubt the world of squash would not be in such a good place without his invaluable input.

Paul Carter spent seven years as a professional player on the world circuit during the heyday of squash when Jahangir Khan was dominating the world game. Paul reached the world top sixteen and won many titles, including the 1998 British Senior Men's Championships, the 1986/87 British Doubles Championships and the 1998 British Over-35 Championships. He is a proud England International player and represented his country on twenty-four occasions, being a member of the winning England Team at the 1988–1991 European Team Championships. His successful playing career was followed by an even

more exemplary coaching career. As assistant England Coach from 1999 to 2010 he helped take the England Squad to successes at four world team championships, two Commonwealth Games, and eleven European Senior Team Championships. He was head coach for the England Junior Team that won the world championships in 1998 and has produced five players that have achieved world top ten rankings (including Peter Barker and Alison Waters). He is currently a high performance coach for England Squash looking after a selection of the elite players and is responsible for the overseeing and strategy of the coach education system nationwide.

David Campion has been a member of the coaching staff at England Squash for seventeen years, working his way up from one of the junior programme coaches to assistant senior national coach. As a gifted player he was thought by many to be a

possible world leader in the sport – he was a member of the England Junior Team that won the World Championships in 1990. However, injuries stopped him short in his playing career, and coaching quickly became his passion. During his early coaching career he dedicated his time to coaching juniors and he has successfully taken eleven England junior teams to World and European titles. He has worked with many players who have achieved a world top ten ranking (including Adrian Grant and his half-brother James Willstrop). Recently he was the assistant England Coach at the 2014 Commonwealth Games in Glasgow (where England brought home an historic nine medals) and coached the England Women's team to success in the 2014 World Championships. He is married to England International squash player Sarah Kippax.

FOREWORDS

Jonah Barrington

I do feel especially privileged to have been asked to provide a foreword for this remarkable book. Having spent most of my playing career on the fringes of emerging sports science and medical support systems, I must say how fortunate are today's gladiators that so much varied expertise is now readily available. This book encompasses all that is currently relevant to our wonderful game and so much of it pertains also to those other most

testing sports. It sets out, with forensic analyses and fascinating case studies, from a litany of highly regarded experts, to give the most excellent must-have guide for the players, coaches and of course academics, and reaches into the very core of squash.

The minds behind this book come with exemplary credentials. I first met Stafford Murray when he was a very young teenager, a hugely hard-working youngster with significant talent, beating the best of his peers at squash and with a manifest eagerness to 'go places'. I am not in the slightest bit surprised that he has put his own particular stamp on the world of sports science. Again, and so importantly, we have here a man passionately imbedded in our own sport and with the overview that the coach must always remain at the heart of the player's development.

I first met Professor Mike Hughes at Liverpool Polytechnic (now John Moores University) more than twenty years ago and quickly understood that a pioneering process (notational analysis, now Performance Analysis) was being excitingly developed by this urgent, inspiring mind. The sphere of technology is quite properly a potent underwriting aspect of most sports and we must remember that this man was a trailblazer in an environment hugely set in its ways and very resistant to change. Mike is unquestionably the world's leading sports performance analyst, and with his own squash background as a county standard player, national standard coach and world leading academic, he is the ideal person to gather a team together here with Stafford Murray to display the knowledge of so many specialists within our amazing game.

This irresistible, irrepressible collaboration has given us a tome that will, I believe, set the standard for those aficionados researching the mysteries of squash and indeed other marvellous sporting pursuits.

Jonah Barrington, six times British Open Squash Champion (1967–1973) and author of international best-selling book Murder in the Squash Court: The Only Way to Win

Peter Nicol MBE

I started my career with very old school techniques in all areas of training and preparation. When I began to work with Stafford Murray and his team, this changed dramatically. From training more intelligently to analysing my opponents, the use of science to reach the best possible results changed my career as a player. The first results that had a meaningful effect on my game – which, being a selfish professional athlete, was all I cared about – came from analysing matches and physical testing during matchplay. Making a direct (and immediate) difference to how I performed was the best way to get my buy-in to using sports science more.

This change came about when I was in New York for the Tournament of Champions in January of 2002 along with Stafford, Phil Newton (physiotherapist) and David Pearson (coach). The first round was relatively easy, but straight after the match I fell ill and went straight to bed. Luckily I had a two-day period before my next match, which is unusual for squash events, so I was able to rest up and try to recover.

We realized as a group that I was never going to get through the event playing my usual physical style and had to adapt if I wanted to progress. Sitting down (that's all I was able to do!) with Stafford and David, we trawled through footage and statistics from my next opponent to find areas I could exploit whilst also limiting my physical output. I would have to play shorter, more aggressive squash, but rather than just doing it in the style I would usually prefer, we came up with a structured game plan that took advantage of my opponent's weaknesses. Sounds very simple but I was way out of my comfort zone playing this style and had no idea if I could perform this way at the level needed to win.

The second round ended up being a comfortable win, as did the quarter-final. I was still sleeping most of the time, not playing, and eating lightly so I felt tired and weak. My semi-final match was going to be the biggest test, coming up against David Palmer, the three-times World Champion. Stafford came to me with the simplest of plans, having analysed David's previous games that week: counter drop him in the front right corner as much as possible. This seemed risky as David was known for hitting short and then stepping up the court, taking the ball earlier and earlier. My first reaction was that I would be playing into his hands, giving David free balls to hit at the front and making me run lengths of the court – which would not have been many in my state! However, early on in the match the tactic caught David by surprise and I either replayed outright winners or he gave me easy balls to kill. Once he understood my tactic, David would move up the court anticipating the counter drop but he still struggled to achieve any kind of success. The plan worked perfectly and I walked off the court 3–0 winner, exhausted but delighted to be in the final. I went on to win that final and played the only perfect event in my career, winning all my matches 3–0.

Lying in bed after that first match, I would have been surprised to make it to the court for my second round but instead, with the knowledge that analysis of my opponents gave me, I was able to slowly recover physically through the week whilst playing some of the best squash in my career. I still shake my head thinking about that event and how we all got through it together.

As my career started to slow down and I went from a goal of World No.1 to winning specific events, my training also adapted to take that into account. I could no longer, mentally and emotionally, train continuously and prepare in the way I had done throughout my twenties. One day at a training camp in Manchester, we took my blood and monitored my heart rate during a match that was prolonged to make it incredibly physically challenging. The results showed that a well-structured circuit almost exactly replicated a squash match, just with a higher top-line heart rate and lactic acid reading.

From that point onwards I used specific circuits to prepare me for events, as it gave

me the confidence knowing it was replicating game play and also was a manageable (mentally!) time of flat-out physical effort. Understanding this allowed me to reduce time spent training and playing so that I was content on court and not resenting spending so much time training. I know this may sound childish but that was how I felt after so many years working towards a singular goal without any real break or rest. This small change was instrumental in getting me back to No.1 in the world rankings and able to go on to win double gold in my last event, the Melbourne Commonwealth Games 2006, as I would not have been able to train as before, and I would have retired sooner.

There are so many more examples of how sports science helped me throughout my career, but I wanted to share here a couple that were obviously practical. The only reason for a player to use sports science is to benefit practically from using those techniques. After all, I was a professional squash player and the way to judge success was by how often I won! I now use these techniques to help me as a coach and I believe understanding these methods would help any player interested in improving themselves, or as a coach, to help their players. My biggest hurdle was keeping an open mind – if you are able to accept using science and therefore implementing change, anything is possible!

Peter Nicol MBE, three times Commonwealth Gold Medallist, Former World No. 1 and World Champion

PREFACE

Academic research and athlete testimonials suggest that squash is one of the most physically demanding, mentally draining, and tactically challenging sports in the world. In order to succeed in this sport players must have extreme levels of fitness, optimal and specific strength, relentless psychological toughness, intelligent tactical prowess, and sublime technical proficiency, to mention a few!

This books aims to explore how science has impacted and subsequently improved elite squash, along the way giving examples and case studies from some of the best players and coaches in the world of squash.

The book aims to:

■ Provide an overview of how sports science is currently used in elite squash and, where appropriate, offer sports science methodologies that could be deployed by the reader;
■ Demonstrate how sports science techniques and interventions have impacted on both coaches and players at the elite end of the sport;

■ Offer quotes from world-leading players and coaches, along with case studies, to bring the outlined scientific theories to life and to give examples of the positive (and sometimes negative!) implementation of sports science.

With contributions from some of the finest academics and applied practitioners in the world of squash, this book covers the following sports science disciplines:

■ Physiology
■ Strength and conditioning
■ Physiotherapy and rehabilitation
■ Performance nutrition
■ Psychology
■ Coaching science
■ Skill acquisition
■ Performance analysis.

Never before in the history of squash has this type of book been pulled together – a must-read for all that have any kind of interest in either science or squash.

CHAPTER I

THE EVOLUTION OF SPORT SCIENCE IN SQUASH

Edward M. Winter, Sheffield Hallam University

WHAT THE PLAYERS THINK

Nick Matthew OBE

There is no doubt that sports science enabled me and my coach to completely change my technique when I was nineteen. Without this I would not have become world No.1. Over the years the work I have done with sports science – in particular Performance Analysis, Psychology and Strength and Conditioning have given me a platform to deliver my technique and tactics properly. Sports science has enabled me to tick every box – it made me a more professional athlete from a young age and helped me get the extra I per cent out of my body. Without the education in sports science I received in my teens I would not have been able to achieve my goals.

James Willstrop

Squash is a brutal game and creates massive impacts on the body. Sports science has enabled me to deal with those better and essentially have a longer career. Squash is so unique and specific it is vital that sports scientists have a knowledge of the sport to be most valuable in their support.

Laura Massaro

Sports science taught me how to plan my training and enables me to peak at the right time. It has made me realize it's not just about playing squash, you have to have the whole package physically and mentally. A good sports scientist needs to be comfortable being questioned by the athlete and be able to demonstrate the value of the session to the player. The partnership should be a two-way conversation. I am now at a stage where I would not be comfortable just being told what to do – but when I was eighteen I would have. A good sports scientist will always take into consideration the age and maturity of the player and tweak the session accordingly.

Alison Waters

Without sports science you would just be guessing what is the best training and practice for you to do. During my career sports science has guided me down the right path.

Jenny Duncalf

Sports science makes me feel more professional and confident that I have covered all bases in my preparation.

Fig. 1.1 The sweat on Nick Matthew's shirt demonstrates the physical demands squash can put on players' bodies.

Fig. 1.2 Jenny Duncalf shows the range of movements you need to play squash.

WHAT THE COACHES THINK

David Pearson

The very best players in the world are willing to make changes, even when they are at the top – ironically that's what makes them the best! Sports science gives players confidence in their ability and makes them feel like every base is covered in their preparation – whether it works or not is another thing, but it creates confidence. Some players go head over heels for sports science and forget about coaching and playing – it has to be a blend. A lot of players these days forget the art of the sport and rely too much on the support services, but this never works – at the end of the day it's a sport.

Sports science should be driven by the coach and athlete. One of the main benefits of applying science to a player's programmes is the reduction of injuries – this will allow better and longer training, coaching and playing, inducing longevity of careers. For sports science to be fully successful the scientist should work not only with the national coach, they should also be working with the player's individual coach. The most important, and often the hardest, part of a scientist's role is to create a good relationship and trust with the coach.

The danger is that sometimes scientists think they are more important than they are. They have a key role but they need to be constantly aware of where that role starts and finishes. There is a danger that players can rely too much on science and become very strong mentally and physically – but forget the art of the sport! Players and scientists need to be acutely aware of this.

Paul Carter

Sports science questioned and changed some of my preconceived ideas about squash and how we best prepare for it. It challenges traditional thinking within the sport and can completely change how you coach the sport. Sports science enables you to back up your opinion with evidence when presenting information to your players, but it always needs to be contextualized, individualized and delivered within the right environment.

Malcolm Willstrop

All sports have benefitted from and need sports science, and squash is no exception. Improved standards of fitness and technique have made it necessary, when the body is subject to greater demands. Coaches should use sports science in a balanced and considered way as part of the whole, not as the be-all and end-all.

David Campion

Sports science has had a massive impact in our sport; it has created more rounded and smarter athletes in squash. Sports science should be guided by the squash coach to ensure the on-court needs of the player are being covered by the science interventions.

Fig. 1.3 Sports science has helped Alison Waters to acquire the level of physical fitness needed to compete at the top end of the game.

INTRODUCTION

Scientific and medical support for sport in particular and exercise in general is not new; it has a history of at least two millennia. Hippocrates (460–370 BC) advised athletes who were competing in the ancient Olympic Games on training, nutrition and other aspects of preparation. Galen (129–216 AD) was appointed by the Roman Emperor Marcus Aurelius to tend to the medical and surgical needs of gladiators. Moreover, some 3,000 years earlier, Egyptian physicians had been interested in the exercise capabilities of humans because of occupational demands such as those required to build the pyramids.

The polymaths Leonardo da Vinci (1452–1519) and Galileo Galilei (1564–1642) were interested in the exercise capabilities of humans and in particular, how the body's structure and composition influenced those capabilities.

Leap forwards two or three centuries and we see in 1896 the resurrection of the Olympic Games, and concerted academic and practical interest in athletes was rekindled. In 1926 for example, Archibald Vivian Hill CH OBE FRS was awarded the Nobel Prize for Physiology or Medicine for his work on muscle. Much of this work was based on investigations of athletes.

In the 1930s, German coach Dr Woldemar Gerschler and cardiologist Dr Herbert Reindel developed the form of training known as interval training. Such training required an exercise challenge that raised heart rate to approximately 180 beats per minute. Challenges were approximately 30–60 seconds duration and were alternated with rest intervals that were sufficient to lower the rate to 120 or so. Hence, multiple high-intensity challenges could be performed that aggregated to high-volume training. One of the first notable successes of this form of training was German middle-distance runner Rudolf Harbig, who broke the world record for 800m in 1939 with a time of 1min. 46.6sec.

In the late 1960s, interest in the role of carbohydrates to sustain endurance performance in sport was developed by Bengt Saltin. Similarly, for scientific and commercial reasons, interests in the fluid requirements for sportspeople gathered pace. These developments are especially relevant for squash, which is characterized by its intermittent, high-intensity nature and the ways in which it challenges thermoregulation in players.

SCIENTIFIC SUPPORT FOR SQUASH

It is against this background that scientific and medical support for squash can be considered. In the context of competitive sport in general, squash was invented comparatively recently, in 1830 or so. Since then the game has developed into a global sport but has still to attain the accolade that many consider to be entirely worthy: inclusion as an Olympic sport.

It was not until the late 1960s that formal scientific support for squash emerged. In England physiologist Professor N.C. Craig Sharp adapted the principles and practices of interval training to squash. Working with player Jonah Barrington and his coach 'Bomber' Harris, Sharp devised 'ghosting' routines in which phantom shots were played as a coach called out, at random, court positions to which the player had to run. It was not long before this development demonstrated its effectiveness. Barrington's improvement and prodigious achievements were in large part the result of his remarkable fitness that 'ghosting' had developed.

From his characteristic philanthropy, Professor Sharp assessed the physiological characteristics of players in his laboratories at Birmingham University. This 'testing'

along with its link to 'ghosting' confirmed the establishment of formal scientific support for squash in England. For some twenty years, Professor Sharp continued this support.

Financial Support

From traditions in physical education, undergraduate programmes in sport and exercise science in the United Kingdom began in 1976.

In 1988, a major advance occurred in state-funded scientific support for sport. The English Sports Council introduced the Sport Science Education Programme in which national governing bodies combined with institutes of higher education. PhD bursaries were provided for students to pursue doctoral-standard work on sport-related issues. The total annual fund was £400,000. This combination of academic and applied approaches was designed to support national teams and contribute to the development both of coaching and talent identification schemes.

In 1992, at least in part to counter the prominence of Pakistani, Egyptian and Australian players, the Squash Rackets Association bid successfully for such a studentship. Professor Sharp handed his programme to Dr (later Professor) Edward Winter at Bedford College of Higher Education, with Damon Brown as the student. Professor Sharp had provided an excellent legacy: a twenty-year base on which to build.

Development of the Programme

The programme developed physiological testing into laboratory- and field-based procedures. Moreover, mental skills support was introduced using the expertise of Dr Kirsten Barnes (see Chapter 6), and the physiological support extended to advice on nutrition for training and competition. Moreover, match analysis systems were being developed by Professor Mike Hughes and Stafford Murray (*see* Chapter 10).

Another major development was the expansion of medical support for players. This included physiotherapy that was designed to provide immediate access for the treatment of injury but of more importance, to reduce the incidence of injury in national squads. It was an exciting time for scientific and medical support in squash because such support was firmly engrained in national and junior squads as well as coaching programmes.

Importantly, Ed Winter and Damon Brown worked closely with then England national coaches Paul Wright and Alex Cowie. Formal involvement in the Squash Rackets Association (SRA) coaching award scheme occurred to underscore the importance of sport science's contribution. Senior squads were supported but greater emphasis was placed on junior squads because it was juniors who were to be the spark that ignited future success.

The backing of journalists was also important. *The Times'* Colin McQuillan was prominent in broadcasting the benefits of the support programme via the SRA's and wider publications. Most squash-related publications now have regular columns not just on coaching-type hints and tips but for science-related topics such as match-analysis, physiology, biomechanics, medicine and physiotherapy.

Damon Brown worked tirelessly with squads and individuals and the already impressive successes enjoyed by England teams at European and World level began to be accompanied by individual successes.

Further Funding

As regards funding, a major development occurred in UK sport in 1997: the launch of the National Lottery. This scheme was designed to provide financial support over and above that provided by the state to support sport and the arts plus other good causes. 1998 saw the unveiling of World Class Performance Plans under the aegis of UK Sport. The newly appointed Performance Director for squash was Matt Hammond and he successfully navigated the SRA's plan through to acceptance. In 2001 the Association was re-launched as England Squash. Financial upheavals had seen the departure of Paul Wright and Alex Cowie, who were replaced by David Pearson, whose world-class coaching skills oversaw continuation of the upward trajectory. In 2003, responsibility for scientific and medical support for squash fell into the domain of the English Institute for Sport where it has remained.

The design, implementation and evaluation of laboratory and field-based assessments indicated the ingenuity and productivity of scientific staff in the UK. Dossiers on the match-play characteristics of all top players produced by analysts such as Stafford Murray and Mike Hughes enabled players to improve technique and tactical play and plan strategies to deal effectively with opponents. Ever-improving standards of play were at least in part a result of these developments. In addition, it was recognized that without such support, players were disadvantaged when they competed against those who were so supported.

THE IMPACT ON SQUASH IN ENGLAND

Since these assessments England Squash has seen remarkable success with senior men and women winning individual and world team championship titles as well as similar success at Commonwealth Games.

Over the last thirty years or so, there have

been major changes that have markedly influenced match play: the design and construction of rackets from wood to composites that increased the speed of balls; the use of rubbers designed to reduce the bounce and speed of balls; materials used to increase the quality and durability of squash courts, and for international-standard squash in particular, reduction in the height of the front-wall's tin from 48.3cm (19in) to 43.2cm (17in) and 'slower' televisual all-glass courts.

As standards of play increased, changes in scoring systems attempted to reduce lengths of matches and increase attacking play from conventional point-only-when-serving, to point-a-rally with variations in first-to-fifteen now first-to-eleven for international match play. These structural changes were mapped by the analysts (Hughes, 1995; Hughes and Knight, 2004; Hughes, Watts, White and Hughes, 2008). Simultaneously, attempts by administrators to reduce stoppages in play because of 'lets' became increasingly robust. Players occupy the same playing space so collisions and obstructions are inevitable. However, the onus is clearly on players to make every effort to play the ball and then clear to allow their opponent(s) to do likewise.

Of note is the buoyancy and increased interest in the UK of masters' squash both for men and women. Five-year age groups begin at thirty-five and go all the way to over seventy for men and even over eighty in some tournaments. Similar five-year divisions apply for women. Age might have a slowing effect but it is difficult to see that in the best age-group players whose abilities are remarkable. These abilities are an indication of the application of training principles that enable older players to continue and enjoy their squash. What changes little is the competitiveness of age-group players.

Already high standards of match play show little if any sign of doing anything other than continuing to improve. Moreover, the number of players of such standard also continues to increase. Conversely, margins that define success reduce. These reductions highlight the need for strategic, detailed and sustained scientific support to gain a competitive edge. The battle remains primarily between players but in support, the team of coaching scientific and medical staff is vital, perhaps even decisive.

REFERENCES

www.worldsquash.org/ws/wp-content/uploads/
2012/04/120425_History-of-Squash.pdf

Fig. 1.4 James Willstrop has utilized all aspects of sports science to help make him one of the best players in the world.

CHAPTER 2

PHYSIOLOGICAL UNDERPINNINGS OF TRAINING AND MATCH PLAY IN SQUASH

Edward M. Winter and Mark Campbell, Sheffield Hallam University, and English Institute of Sport

Fig. 2.1 Nick Matthew's facial expression and body position show just how physically demanding squash can be.

WHAT THE PLAYERS THINK

Nick Matthew OBE

My dad was a sports teacher so at an early age we were doing our sessions with a purpose – not just random training. Before lottery funding me and my dad paid for a VO2 max test to see if the training I was doing was actually making a difference.

Having physiological support has helped me learn not only about my own body but also exactly what the requirements of the sport are on my body. In the early days just knowing how to hydrate properly and basically what I should and should not eat had a massive impact on my performances.

WHAT THE COACHES THINK

Dave Pearson

The best players in the world take the physiological science and use it to guide their training patterns, but not to the detriment of actually playing the sport. Being fit makes the players feel confident and in turn allows them to deliver the tactics and technique they need. Without being fit a good technique and tactics are useless – it has to be a combination.

Paul Carter

The danger can be that people become good trainers and not good squash players – the sport has to remain the most important focus.

David Campion

Physiology helps us measure whether the training we are doing is replicating the demands of match play. Physiology is one area that I think squash could apply more. We don't really know enough about the actual physical demands of the sport, therefore we have to ask ourselves: is our training and coaching specific enough?

Fig. 2.2 Nick Matthew consistently pushes his body to the limit during tournament match play.

Fig. 2.3 Laura Massaro literally flying in the Cathay Pacific Hong Kong Open.

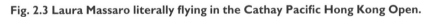

WHAT IS PHYSIOLOGY?

Biology is the study of living and dead things and physiology is a sub-branch of this discipline. Physiology is the study of how living and indeed dead things function. Processes in living things are a principal focus but mechanisms of decay, for example, might also be the focus for some. The physiology of exercise is the study of how the body responds and adapts to exercise.

Responses occur in acute bouts of exercise whereas adaptations occur as a result of training. These adaptations could apply to all levels of the body's organization and structure. This means the whole organism – the whole person – and his or her ability to perform exercise.

Interest could, though, be in adaptations in systems such as the cardiovascular system, musculoskeletal system and endocrine system. Interest might be in how particular organs such as the heart, lungs and kidney adapt to training, or adaptations in tissues such as muscle and bone, or increasingly, adaptations in cellular and sub-cellular mechanisms.

If training is to be effective, it must be evidence-based; that is, there must be a rationale for a training programme and that evidence-base requires knowledge and understanding of underlying physiological mechanisms. Moreover, it is important to understand what is meant by the term 'exercise' or another term that is frequently used 'physical activity'. Only context marks the difference.

The term 'exercise' tends to apply to competitive sport or formal programmes whereas 'physical activity' tends to be used in the context of activities of everyday living. Clearly, the latter could apply to professional sportspeople. However, here, 'exercise' will be used.

EXERCISE DEFINED

Contrary to popular belief, exercise does not necessarily mean that movement has to occur. In competitive sports such as diving and gymnastics for example, competitors lose marks if they are unable to hold static positions. In seemingly dynamic activities such as sliding events in ice sports exemplified by two- and four-person bobsleigh and skeleton bob, participants have to be able to hold streamlined body postures while having to withstand marked external forces. Similarly, in sailing, static activity can be decisive.

In squash, there is clearly dynamic activity and much movement about courts. However, consider drop shots: players might have had to make strenuous efforts to reach a ball at the front of the court and then produce stability in the legs and trunk to allow the racket arm to make the most delicate of shots.

A definition of exercise has to acknowledge that either deliberately or unavoidably, movement does not always occur. Forces either to produce or prevent movement are brought about by muscle. In humans and other mammals there are three types of muscle:

- Skeletal, sometimes known as voluntary or, because of its appearance under a microscope, striated;
- Smooth, sometimes known as involuntary because it is autonomic, that is, it tends not be under conscious control;
- Cardiac, that is, muscle of the heart that has an inherent ability to beat although this ability can be influenced by other factors.

Irrespective of type, when muscle is stimulated it attempts to shorten and hence, exert force. Commonly, though incorrectly, this is referred to as muscle contraction. Some three hundred years ago it was demonstrated that when stimulated and muscle exerts force, it does not reduce in volume (Needham, 1971). 'Contraction' is at least inexact (Rodgers and Cavanagh, 1984). A preferred term is muscle activity.

Such activity can be concentric (when a muscle is successful in its attempt to shorten, exemplified by lifting something); isometric (when a muscle does not change in length, for example when supporting an object or being unable to move an object); and finally, eccentric (when a muscle increases in length when it exerts force such as when one sits down in a controlled way or similarly, lowers a weight).

If required forces are large, requirements will challenge homeostasis, the process that attempts to maintain equilibrium. Activities such as typing, or page-turning while reading are unlikely to perturb homeostasis but an activity like squash will.

Hence, exercise can be defined as: A potential disruption to homeostasis by muscle activity that is either exclusively or in combination, concentric, isometric or eccentric (Winter and Fowler, 2009).

We can now begin to consider factors that influence applications of physiology to squash and importantly, to training and match play.

CONSIDERATIONS

Squash Courts

Over the last three decades or so in particular, there have been marked changes in the design and construction of courts that have included changes to dimensions. Professional players use a tin height of 43.2cm (17in) as opposed to the 48.3cm (19in) regulation height used in all other standards of player. Among other factors, this has increased the need for players to be able to accelerate to the front of the court and once there, still have a variety of shots they could play from the softest of drops to the hardest of drives. Relatedly, the introduction and now mandatory use of ingeniously designed all-glass courts for major tournaments has had major effects: factors such as rebound characteristics off walls and illumination influence patterns of play.

Rackets

As regards equipment, probably most change has occurred in the design and construction of rackets. Some can perhaps remember playing with small-headed fragile wooden rackets that were strung with natural gut. Now of course, rackets have large heads, are made of carbon-related light-weight composites, and there is an array of synthetic strings available. Such changes have improved the durability of rackets and are characterized by less technique-dependent ball speeds of up to 78 $m \cdot s^{-1}$ and greater control for shots that require less speed.

Scoring Systems

Adjustments to scoring systems have also contributed to changes in match play. The fundamental change has been from conventional scoring, in which points could be won only by the server, to point-a-rally scoring whereby either player scores as a rally is won. Conventional scoring plays up to 9 points to win a game although if the score is 8 all, the receiver can decide to play one point for victory or two clear. Point-a-rally was designed to reduce the length of matches. At international standard, games are played to 11 and in district leagues, 15. Some competitions have retained conventional scoring, that is, scoring only on serve to 9 points per game.

Another contribution to attempts to improve the continuity of play has been stricter marking to reduce interruptions to play caused by players asking for 'lets'. As both players in singles – four in doubles – occupy the same playing area, collisions and other instances of interference are probably inevitable. However, players are expected to make every effort to play a ball and similarly, make every effort to allow their opponent free access to play a return. This means that minor contacts should not necessarily be reason to call for a let. This adds to the existing challenges faced by referees and markers.

Improvements in the fidelity of television cameras coupled with the use of coloured all-glass courts and white balls have made squash increasingly televisual.

PHYSICAL CHARACTERISTICS

The need for players to possess athleticism that comprises skill, endurance, speed, agility, guile and tenacity coupled with an appropriate body composition is self-evident. However, there are marked differences in physical characteristics of players both in the men's and women's games that clearly suggest it is optimization of characteristics rather than one alone that is decisive. This challenges talent identification and development programmes.

Accurate distinction between genuinely talented young players and those who have matured early and hence are successful because they are bigger and stronger than their peers bedevils most sports. Diminutive players become discouraged by defeats and similar discouragement can occur in the early maturers when they begin to get beaten by those who now catch them up. Discouragement leads to many discontinuing their involvement. Precise figures are difficult to find but the phenomenon applies to many sports where competition based on chronological age occurs.

What is clear is that the reduced height of the tin has increased the need for players to be able to accelerate to the front of the court to retrieve an opponent's drop shot and similarly, to accelerate to take balls early – usually to volley, but also retrieve from the back of the court. However, all this is repetitive so endurance cannot be neglected. While skill manifest in shot selection and production is vital, before a ball can be hit first it must be reached. Even supreme skill can be negated if a player is weak in other components.

This is perhaps where the coach's input is crucial. As with most if not all sports, he or she has to evaluate a player and then decide whether or not to develop strengths or improve weaknesses. As considered in Chapters 4, 5 and 10 scientific and medical support staff can contribute to the evaluation and indeed formulation of appropriate training programmes but the coach is perhaps second in importance only to the player in question, and in some instances might be the lynch pin.

DEMANDS OF THE GAME

Durations of Play

Squash is what is termed a repeated multiple-sprint activity. Exercise of high, even maximal intensity is interspersed with activities of low intensity, even rest, as occurs in between points and during challenges to officials' decisions as well as formally, the one and a half minutes between games. Durations of matches, games and rallies can vary widely but most matches at least at international standard are usually forty-five minutes or so in duration although players should be prepared for exceptional durations of two hours.

Similarly, durations of games can vary but

are usually in the order of ten minutes or so. Rallies can be as short as one shot if a player faults on service or two shots if his or her opponent hits a winner off the service. Some rallies can be protracted deliberately as a player tries to fatigue his or her opponent. However, this strategy can be risky because high skill is required, loose shots providing the opponent with an opportunity for a 'kill'. Besides, this tactic is unwise against a player who has high endurance levels.

Physiological Demands

Throughout matches players require speed, skill, strength, endurance and agility, yet fatigue to greater or lesser extents eventually occurs and so challenges physiological capabilities. However, mental strength is also challenged. In the face of arduous circumstances, players have to maintain positive approaches and tactical awareness. Ways to do so are covered in Chapter 7.

Physiological demands challenge central systems such as the cardiovascular and cardiopulmonary systems. Heart rates during competition tend to be in excess of 90 per cent of maximum. Physiological and psychological factors contribute to these high rates and disentangling factors is not easy. However, a key physiological requirement is the need to deliver sufficient blood to exercising muscle and so supply substrate, that is, fuel principally in the form of carbohydrate as glucose, and remove metabolites that impair function. In an hour of match play, up to 180–200 grams of glucose might be used from the body's stores of about 350–400 grams.

However, there is a twin challenge: blood is also delivered to the skin in an attempt to lose heat by conduction, convection and radiation to the surroundings as part of thermoregulation. This regulation is severely challenged because play tends to occur on warm courts – at least 20°C – although in competition all-glass courts in warm environments, temperatures can be higher. However, the principal form of heat loss occurs by way of sweating.

Sweat evaporates, that is, it changes from a liquid to a gas and to do so, latent heat is required. This heat is taken from the body's surface, the skin. Blood in the skin is cooled and then returns to the body's core in an attempt to prevent the body rising no more than 2°C or so above the normal 37°C to prevent hyperthermia.

As a result, sweat rates of 1.5 to 2.5 $l \cdot min^{-1}$ occur although precise rates depend on individual characteristics, intensity of play and environmental conditions, principally ambient temperature and humidity. Ways to maintain carbohydrate and hydration are addressed in Chapter 5.

Crucial to all this is the ability to reach the ball because after all, before a ball can be hit, first it must be reached. Once this ability has been lost, no matter how skilful a player might be, he or she could be on the way to a defeat or might already have suffered a defeat.

SPECIFIC PHYSIOLOGICAL FACTORS

Innervation of Muscle

Effective muscle function is crucial to performance in squash and indeed, activities of everyday living. However, it must be acknowledged that there are three types of muscle: skeletal (known sometimes as striated because of its appearance under a microscope), smooth and cardiac. Skeletal muscle is largely but certainly not exclusively under voluntary control. Smooth muscle is largely involuntary and is involved for example in peristalsis, that is, the passage of food through the alimentary canal, and vasoconstriction and dilatation in blood vessels. Cardiac muscle is in the heart and is characterized by its inbuilt rhythmicity. All types of muscle are involved extensively in squash.

Irrespective of type, the function of muscle is to exert force. In skeletal muscle, the motor unit is key. This unit comprises three elements: an innervating neurone, that is, a nerve; a synapse that converts the electrical signal that travels down the neurone to a chemical signal in the form of acetylcholine; and muscle cells (fibres). In large muscles that exert large forces, the number of fibres in the motor unit tends to be hundreds even thousands. Conversely, muscles of fine control such as those in the face and fingers have motor units that terminate in only tens of fibres (Jones et al., 2004).

With skeletal muscle, forces are transmitted via tendons. Tendons are attached to bone, hence, expression of force occurs via the skeleton either as posture or movement. This expression tends to be in the form of torque around a joint. The detailed anatomy of muscle is exquisite, and mechanisms by which proteins such as actin and myosin interact to exert force are still not fully understood. What is clear though, are the roles of high-energy phosphagens, especially adenosine triphosphate (ATP) that are the currency in which energy is provided to allow force production to occur. Nerve impulses in motor neurones are transmitted by the interaction of sodium and potassium ions but not in a single switch-like manner.

Actual force production depends on the number and type of muscle fibres that are recruited. Motor-neurone signals are sent in volleys, and the frequency of the volley influences the type of muscle fibre that is recruited. Type I fibres are predominantly aerobic, that is, they use oxygen and are innervated by low-frequency innervation of some 5–15 Hz. Their twitch characteristics are low so these types of fibre are sometimes called 'slow-twitch'. Type IIx fibres are predominantly anaerobic and are recruited with greater frequencies of 20–30 Hz and more (Jones et al., 2004). These are sometimes known as 'fast-twitch' fibres.

Greater forces are exerted according to the number of motor units recruited (spatial summation) and the frequency of stimulation and hence the type of motor unit that is innervated (temporal summation). Normally, Type I fibres cannot be converted to Type II and vice versa. An exception is if innervation is applied externally at appropriate volley frequencies, then conversion can occur. However, to all intents and purposes, the primary typing is fixed.

What can change is the sub-divisions of Type II fibres. Type IIx fibres can become Type IIa. With endurance training, IIx fibres become increasingly aerobic and hence then possess characteristics both of speed and endurance. These combined qualities are of course highly relevant for squash. Players need to be able to move about the court quickly to retrieve, reach and play individual shots yet have to do so repeatedly for usually forty-five to sixty minutes and, exceptionally, up to some two hours or more.

Cardiopulmonary Function

To sustain exercise, there is interplay between central function, that is the heart and lungs, and peripheral skeletal muscle. Each time the heart beats, it pumps out a quantity of blood. This quantity is called stroke volume. The total volume of blood pumped in a minute is called cardiac output and is expressed in litres per minute. It is calculated as:

Stroke volume $\times$ heart rate

Heart rate at rest is about 70 beats per minute in the untrained but can be bradycardic to as low as 30 beats per minute in endurance athletes. We tend to have about five to six litres of blood in our body, and at rest it takes approximately a minute to circulate that entire volume. Hence, in the untrained individual, cardiac output at rest of five litres per minute means that stroke volume is approximately 70–80 millilitres, whereas in the endurance athlete it is about 120 millilitres.

As exercise increases in intensity, both heart rate and stroke volume increase in an attempt to meet the greater energy demands by pumping more blood and hence oxygen and substrate (fuel) to exercising muscle. Maximum heart rate can be determined directly in laboratory- or field-based testing but as an approximation, it can be determined as 220 minus one's age and is expressed as beats per minute. Maximum cardiac outputs of about 20–25 litres per minute occur in the untrained and up to 40 litres per minute in highly trained endurance athletes (McArdle et al., 2010).

Fick Equation

Crucial to energy release in muscle is the delivery of oxygen. The German-born physiologist and physician Adolf Eugen Fick (1829–1901) developed a relationship that linked oxygen uptake to cardiac output and use of oxygen by skeletal muscle. This relationship is expressed in what has become known as the Fick equation:

Oxygen uptake = cardiac output × arterio-venous oxygen difference

Oxygen uptake is expressed in litres per minute, cardiac output in litres per minute and arterio-venous oxygen difference in millilitres of oxygen per 100 millilitres of blood.

Endurance can be divided into central components that arise from abilities of the cardiovascular and pulmonary systems to deliver blood and hence oxygen and substrate to exercising muscle and remove metabolites, along with peripheral mechanisms that allow muscle to make use of what is delivered and expel what is not required.

From Table 2.1, men and women squash players compare favourably with other endurance performers in their maximal oxygen uptake when values are scaled for differences in body mass using allometry (Winter and Nevill, 2009).

Fatigue

Fatigue, that is, an inability by muscle to maintain required force, occurs in those whose aerobic capability is low or when neuromuscular innervation is compromised. Both probably occur in squash although their contributions vary according to the characteristics of individual players. What is clear is that fatigue that is metabolic in origin occurs when there is insufficient glycogen available in muscle and the liver, or when metabolites accumulate in muscle cells or their immediate environs. Importantly, these metabolites are simply lactic acid or precisely hydrogen protons (H^+) which might simply be a signal for a primary cause perhaps potassium ions (K^+). We simply do not know. Chapter 5 will explore how to maintain carbohydrate concentrations in muscle during competition and training.

TESTS

One of the major developments in sport and in exercise science support for sport in general has been laboratory- and field-based testing (Winter et al., 2008). Such testing is

GROUP	n	O_2max $(ml \cdot kg^{-.67} \cdot min^{-1})$	sd	O_2max $(ml \cdot kg^{-.67} \cdot min^{-1})$	sd
Men					
Badminton players	17	248	28	175	19
Heavyweight rowers	28	310	31	216	21
Lightweight rowers	12	300	15	213	11
Long-distance runners	10	302	18	217	12
Middle-distance runners	18	304	22	217	15
Squash players	7	280	17	198	12
Triathletes	6	282	15	201	11
Total/mean	98	291	30	206	21
Women					
Badminton players	12	192	19	138	14
Heavyweight rowers	16	233	17	165	12
Lightweight rowers	13	232	10	167	7
Long-distance runners	10	232	19	170	14
Middle-distance runners	11	238	19	172	14
Squash players	6	215	13	154	9
Triathletes	8	228	19	163	13
Total/mean	76	225	23	162	17

Table 2.1: Allometric expression of maximum oxygen uptake (O_2max) in elite-standard endurance performers; values are mean, sd. (Source: Nevill et al., 2003)

designed to assess components that contribute to overall performance and so guide training. In addition, testing attempts to identify incipient overtraining.

Training has to be hard to bring about required adaptations. However, when athletes train too hard, they can increase their susceptibility to infections and injury, perform worse and even develop serious metabolic conditions. Identification of markers that indicate incipient overtraining rather than its presence is awaited.

Originally, testing tended to be laboratory-based because of the control that such testing allowed. The influence of contaminating variables could be minimized in, for example, treadmill-running tests to assess maximum oxygen uptake or blood-lactate profiles. Valuable though these procedures are, they lack ecological validity in that their ability to mimic characteristics of match play is at least questionable. As outlined in Chapter 1, both in the UK and elsewhere, there have been strenuous efforts to design court-based tests of endurance, speed and importantly, change-of-direction speed. The validity of tests has been established and so allowed coaches and scientists to evaluate training programmes, readiness for competition, use in talent identification and development programmes and, controversially, in selection.

It is also possible to prepare players for competition in arduous environmental conditions such as high temperature (25°C and above) and in particular, conditions of high humidity (90 per cent[+]). The latter allows determination of sweat rates and hence, fluid replacement strategies for players. Such replacement is considered in detail in Chapter 5.

It is likely that testing will continue to be developed and refined as standards of play in turn continue to rise.

Optimization

The ability to combine physiological, mental-skills, technical and tactical capabilities is a major challenge. The person on whose shoulders this challenge lies is the coach. All support staff can do is attempt to make a coach's decisions evidence-based. While scientific and indeed medical support is important, it should be remembered that it is the coach who is the key person.

SUMMARY

If training programmes are to be effective, they must be based on sound physiological

Fig. 2.4 Nick Matthew acknowledges the crowd after another physically draining match.

rationale. However, programmes have to be designed, implemented and evaluated in conjunction with coaching staff and other members of the scientific support team. That team includes psychologists, nutritionists, performance analysts, physiotherapists, physicians (and perhaps surgeons), strength-and-conditioning staff and, of course, players. All this is for the benefit of those players both now but perhaps more importantly, in the future. Assembling the scientific support team is challenging. Ideally, but not essentially, members should have a knowledge of the game so as to empathize with players. As sport and exercise science is firmly embedded in squash, increasingly players are fully accustomed to such support. It is essential principally for professional-standard players but permeates to all standards and ages. That looks set to continue.

REFERENCES

Jones, D.A., Round, J. and de Haan. (2004). *Skeletal Muscle from Molecules to Movement*. London: Churchill Livingstone.

McArdle, W.D., Katch, F.I. and Katch, V.L. (2010). *Exercise Physiology Nutrition, Energy, and Human Performance* (seventh edn). Baltimore, MD: Lippincott Williams and Wilkins.

Needham, D.M. (1971). *Machina Carnis*. London: Cambridge University Press.

Nevill, A.M., Brown, D., Godfrey, R., Johnson, P.J., Romer, L., Stewart, A.D. and Winter, E.M. (2003). Modeling maximum oxygen uptake of elite endurance athletes. *Medicine and Science in Sports and Exercise*, 35, 488–494.

Rodgers, M.M. and Cavanagh, P.R. (1984). Glossary of biomechanical terms, concepts, and units. *Physical Therapy*, 64, 1886–1902.

Winter, E.M. and Fowler, N. (2009). Exercise defined and quantified according to the Système International d'Unités. *Journal of Sports Sciences*, 27, 447–460.

Winter, E.M., Jones, A.M., Davison, R.C.R., Bromley, P.D. and Mercer, T.H. (2008). *Sport and Exercise Physiology Testing Volume One: Sport Testing*. Abingdon: Routledge.

Winter, E.M. and Nevill, A.M. (2009). Scaling: adjusting for differences in body size. In *Kinanthropometry and Exercise Physiology Laboratory Manual Volume 1: Anthropometry* (eds R. Eston and T. Reilly). Abingdon: Routledge, pp. 300–320.

CHAPTER 3

STRENGTH AND CONDITIONING IN SQUASH

Keith Barker and Mark Campbell,
English Institute of Sport

Fig. 3.1 Jenny Duncalf's position demonstrates why strength and conditioning is so vital in squash.

WHAT THE PLAYERS THINK

Nick Matthew OBE

Physiological support enabled me not only to train hard, but also to train smart. It showed me that the old-school method of doing as many 400 metres as you can on the track and lifting as much weight as possible in the gym is not the best way to get fit for squash.

James Willstrop

Being on the squash court and playing is what we are all about – S and C minimizes your injuries so you can spend more time doing what you love. S and C is the most important aspect of my training regime – it not only increases my squash-specific strength, but it minimizes injuries and allows me to practise and play more consistently. Without S and C input at a young age, my career would be over by now!

Jenny Duncalf

I wish I had paid more notice to S and C when I was a young player. Especially as you get older S and C is absolutely vital to help prevent injuries. You need a good strength base to enhance your explosive movements on the court.

Fig. 3.2 Nick Matthew displays considerable strength to get into this full lunge position.

WHAT THE COACHES THINK

Dave Pearson

The best players in the world take the physiological science and use it to guide their training patterns, but not to the detriment of actually playing the sport. One of the main benefits of applying science to a player's programmes is the reduction of injuries; this will allow better and longer training, coaching and playing – inducing longevity of careers.

As he approached his late twenties Peter Nicol moved to England and changed the way he trained and played. He knew the traditional training methods were becoming too hard on his body, and could end his career early. He looked at the science of training and changed the way he worked – this gave him at least an extra five years on his career.

Paul Carter

Having a good S and C programme will keep players training fresh: it provides a different environment to train in, but it should never replace on-court squash-specific sessions. A good S and C coach must know the minute details of the sport they are working with – a generic programme is not good enough for a sport like squash. S and C sessions should always replicate the demands of the sport.

Malcolm Willstrop

Expert strength and conditioning are absolutely crucial, especially with the physical demands of the modern game. The fitness expert will also educate players how to look after themselves when not supervised, something all players need to learn from a young age.

David Campion

Strength is vital in our sport; you need to be able to control your body weight when playing shots in extreme positions. Squash is a physically brutal game, so a good S and C is vital to make our players robust enough to deal with the extreme movements required to compete at the top level. Physically squash can a very one-sided sport, creating an imbalance of demand on the body. S and C programmes help alleviate this imbalance, thereby avoiding unnecessary injuries. Without strength and conditioning I don't think Laura Massaro would have been world champion. S and C and physio should work very closely together; if you haven't got the strength to support your flexibility or vice-versa that will cause issues physically. S and C is not solely about performance enhancement - one of its main roles is to reduce injury in our players.

Fig. 3.3 Here James Willstrop is in a good strong and balanced position, enabling him to deliver the stroke needed.

DEVELOPMENTS IN SQUASH

Due to changes in the physical demands of world-level squash due to rule, scoring and equipment modifications, the training modalities employed to develop the physical requirements needed to cope with the demands of modern squash competition have evolved considerably over the years. A historical emphasis on aerobic conditioning was very much in response to the style of play of the game of squash with 90- to 120-minute matches played at a steady rhythmical pace requiring high endurance levels of moderate intensity.

The modern game of squash can be classified as an intermittent repeated high-intensity sport characterized by extremely high-intensity bursts of effort to attack the opposition or defend against attacks. Metabolic conditioning activities have had to increase in intensity to help athletes tolerate the demands of the modern game. Various forms of circuit training (including metabolic resistance training) and high-intensity interval training are now a necessity in the conditioning programme of the modern player. Modern squash athletes still require a high level of exercise capacity to recover between bouts of intense work during match play and training as well as tolerating multiple days/weeks of training and competing. This complex mix of training modalities, match practice and tournament play also requires strategically planned training programmes to optimize adaptation and readiness.

Elite-level squash athletes now incorporate significant resistance training and plyometric-type training modalities into their physical preparation. This training focuses on utilizing squatting, lunging, bounding and jumping-type movement patterns to develop both muscular force and impulse application. This along with a greater emphasis on agility has meant that athletes have become faster and more explosive in their movements around the court. This has also created the need for an improvement in movement quality underpinned by strength and mobility characteristics around specific movement patterns.

OBJECTIVE AND APPLICATION

The role of strength and conditioning (S and C) is to provide the player with increased physical potential. It is then up to the player (and squash coach) to make effective use of this increased potential. S and C should therefore not merely simulate competition but should instead overload both energy systems and movement qualities in a specific and general manner. This will enable squash players to better tolerate the intensity, volume and movement demands of their sport-specific training and increase their level of physical performance in both training and competitive match play.

Immediate priorities should be contextualized with a strategic approach to the player's long-term developmental goals. These priorities should be individually determined based on a needs analysis through systematic testing, with improvements in these qualities monitored to ensure appropriate progression is made in relation to key performance determinants.

The congested competition calendar of elite squash players presents significant challenges to the strategic organization of training activities. Distinct development and performance blocks based on individual needs and tournament priorities are required. Typically an eight- to ten-week off-season provides the greatest window of opportunity for significant gains in identified physical qualities prior to the recommencement of competition.

As indicated in Fig. 3.4, effective strength and conditioning training should promote the development of a large exercise capacity that includes both the development of several sport-specific physical qualities alongside general physical qualities that support the squash-specific performance. Exercise capacity in this context can be defined as the capability to perform a high volume of exercise tasks and movements including flexibility and mobility, strength, power, speed, anaerobic and aerobic endurance at an adaptation promoting intensity and volume, consistently throughout training weeks and cycles. As Fig. 3.4 suggests, postural integrity, athletic body composition, stability, and balanced development may be considered as desirable consequences of the skilful development of fundamental physical qualities. Approaches to identifying and developing these fundamental qualities will be addressed in detail within this chapter.

Along with an understanding of training principles and the demands of the sport, successful training for sustained physical development must account for individual differences

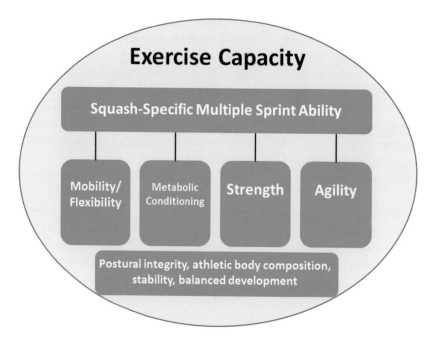

Fig. 3.4 An overview of squash physical qualities.

as all squash players are different and will respond differently to any given training or competition stimulus.

STRATEGIC PLANNING FOR PHYSICAL DEVELOPMENT

Junior players

The primary aim of the long-term physical development of junior squash players must be to establish a broad foundation of movement competence and quality prior to any sustained sport-specific stimulus being imposed. With junior squash players it is recommended that a strong emphasis is placed upon developing dynamic mobility and force, producing capabilities through high-quality strength training. Faigenbaum, Lloyd and Myer (2013) highlight the importance of integrating strength training into junior sports training programmes.

These qualities may then underpin improvements in movement competence and quality during squash performance.

The balanced development of a range of physical qualities rather than an overload of one or two specific aspects must frame the programming of strength and conditioning for junior players. Generic athletic qualities developed through a varied range of training activities will enable the player to develop a range of responses to movement problems on the squash court and help moderate injury risk.

As represented in Fig. 3.5 (Faigenbaum, Lloyd and Myer, 2013), muscular strength and movement proficiency developed through a broad range of activities (integrative neuromuscular training) can provide the prerequisite skills and abilities for later sustained success in squash or other sports. Junior players should learn to manage their centre of mass around base of support and to safely and effectively perform the movements they are required to do on court with increasing

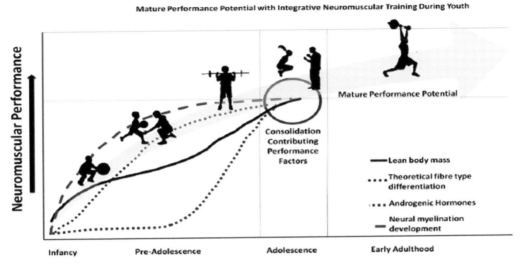

Fig. 3.5. Interactive model for the integration of factors related to the potential for muscle strength adaptations and training-induced performance gains during pre-adolescence.

complexity then intensity. Strength qualities such as unilateral triple flexion/extension, trunk stiffness and rotation/resistance to rotation should also be challenged utilizing increasing complexity with low additional loads. Maintaining healthy postures during training and match-play conditions should be a product of appropriate physical development. The ability to repeat key movements in high-intensity endurance situations should only be challenged progressively once adequate strength and movement quality are consistently demonstrated.

Planning training to optimize performance

Commonly termed as 'periodization', the strategic planning of non-linear training, recovery and competitive performance requires the consideration of many interacting factors. Thorough planning and prescription coupled with a progressive dose-response-led approach is likely to yield the most positive

physical performance from squash players. Fundamental principles of adaptation and performance must be adhered to within the programming of training.

The principle of 'Specific Adaptation to Imposed Demands' (SAID) dictates that the body adapts specifically to imposed stressors on the human system, whether biomechanical or neurological (Berkeley, 1958). Potential adaptation is therefore specific to a particular type of exercise or activity regime. Adaptations may be central or local (peripheral) and repeated specific skills or training may not easily generalize or transfer to other activities.

'Progressive Overload' requires a training programme to provide increasing stresses/challenges to the relevant systems and tissues. This progressive challenge stimulates the natural, adaptive processes of the body, which develops to cope with the new demands placed upon it.

As represented in Fig. 3.6, fundamental to eliciting positive physical adaptation is 'Supercompensation'. This principle describes

45

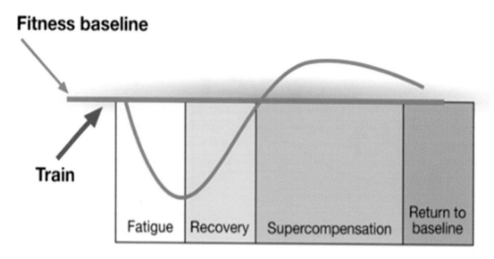

Fig. 3.6 Supercompensation pattern, adapted from Selye (1956). Adolescence, and early adulthood. (Faigenbaum, Lloyd and Myer, 2013)

the process where homeostatic disruption induced by training reduces physical capacity. During recovery, physical capacity increases to baseline, and if appropriate time is allowed, a transient increase in physical state is realized. It is essential to understand that the training undertaken must provide sufficient stimulus to disrupt homeostasis and it must be followed by adequate recovery.

'Detraining/Reversibility' dictates that an individual will revert back to their original level of adaptation if training ceases. The same thing can happen but more gradually if the training programme does not cause adequate stimulation over a period of time. How quickly you lose an adaptation[s] depends on a number of factors but most importantly the level of adaptation present before training was stopped. The higher the adaptation level the faster you tend to lose physical qualities. Upper-end adaptations in elite athletes tend to degrade first, such as explosive strength, repeated speed ability and high-end aerobic power.

Acute training variables such as exercise/activity selection, intensity, volume, density,

frequency and environment should be manipulated by the coach to fit within the principles previously outlined. A broad range of training modes must be employed particularly with developing players in order to facilitate the necessary development of exercise capacity required of an elite senior player.

The nature of the competitive squash calendar presents many challenges to the adherence to the fundamental principles of training, but every effort must be made to do so. Intelligent planning and adaptability to unpredictable competition schedules can facilitate the delivery of meaningful physical performance gains for players.

Competitive tournament involvement may not provide sufficient stimulus to maintain the physical qualities established during developmental training blocks. The knockout format of squash tournament play provides opportunities for players to undertake targeted training once they have been eliminated from the tournament, minimizing detraining. Planning must therefore include several possible training plans to fit around the duration of tournament involvement.

NEEDS ANALYSIS AND MONITORING

As identified by Wilkinson *et al.* (2012), squash-specific multiple sprint ability (SSMSA) is the key physical attribute linked to successful squash performance. The complex mechanical and energetic demands of elite-level squash provide a challenge when prescribing strength and conditioning training. The aim of strength and conditioning training is to elicit a positive physical adaptation that contributes to the individual player's ability to meet the needs of the sport (Girad *et al.*, 2007).

The squash-specific repeated speed test (SSRST) provides the best objective indication of a player's physical preparedness for squash. Improvement of SSMSA performance is underpinned by several physical qualities that will positively affect performance. A lack of requisite levels of development in these underpinning physical qualities will limit the level of SSMSA obtainable. Merely focusing upon SSMSA alone and only training this modality would not optimize this quality due to potential limitations in the contributing physical qualities.

Accurate and thorough assessment guides prescription to where positive impacts in physical performance can be made and allow a profile to be developed that can guide both technical coaches and strength and conditioning coaches in prescribing exercise that will address individual limitations.

This will allow formative, integrated and on-going guidance to exercise prescription that can continue to develop the squash player. This assessment process needs to be consistent and ongoing and informative to the training interventions put in place. When assessing physical qualities it is important to target monitoring of specific physical parameters utilizing objective reliable measures to inform and assess programme outcomes and progression.

Physical qualities that underpin the SSMSA and are important to assess for a squash player include:

- Flexibility and dynamic mobility – the ability to move comfortably through complete sport-specific ranges of motion with ease and fluidity. Structured observation of squatting, split squat and the lateral lunge can form simple markers of improvements in these qualities. Measure is range of movement and postural integrity. A subjective marker to some degree.

- Strength – the underlying force producing capabilities that fundamentally underpin the ability to move fast. Measure is force and can be demonstrated in a number of tasks. An objective measure.

- Speed and agility – both the speed of a player and the ability to decelerate and accelerate using a variety of movements in order to change direction rapidly in a range of tasks. Measure is time and can be demonstrated in a number of tasks. An objective measure.

- Squash-specific speed and agility – how fast the player can move in a squash-specific related agility task. Specific squash movement pattern incorporating lunges and numerous accessory movements related to squash match play. Measure is time. An objective measure.

- Squash-specific repeated speed – an assessment involving the challenge of the metabolic system utilizing high-intensity repeated squash agility movements. An objective measure with fatigue indexes and total repetition time indicating performance.

- Aerobic and anaerobic fitness – assessment of energy system proficiency with the anaerobic system giving an indication of predominantly peripheral factors of energy production, and aerobic assessments giving indications of both central (heart) and peripheral (vascular and cellular) factors. Numerous objective tests can be performed for assessing these two qualities and measures will usually define an amount of work done in a set period or to fatigue.

The Appendix outlines a number of assessments for each of these physical qualities. This table includes assessments that require specialist equipment (Test 1) but also those that offer equivalent measures that will allow a basic assessment of the desired quality without the need for specialist equipment (Test 2).

PHYSICAL QUALITY DEVELOPMENT

Mobility and flexibility for squash

Squash presents a varied range of movement challenges to the athlete, in particular in relation to the large variety of lunging positions that will be encountered during a squash match. The squash athlete needs to be able to achieve challenging dynamic ranges of motion combined with high levels of stability, strength and speed. It is clear that an underlying range of motion properties within the performance of movement patterns needs to be developed to avoid injury and enhance performance. Table 3.1 provides definitions that are important in understanding the development of mobility and flexibility.

Table 3.1. Flexibility and stretching definitions.	
Flexibility	The outcome or property, the increase in range of motion (ROM) of a joint or a related series of joints. Heyward (1984) and Metheny (1952): flexibility is the freedom to move, the capacity of a joint to move fluidly through its full ROM passively.
Mobility	The ability to move actively in an environment and through the full range of motion required with ease and without restriction.
Stretching	The means by which flexibility is enhanced. Stretching is the act of placing a joint in an extreme position, placing a tensile stress on the muscles or fascia that oppose that position.
Active Flexibility	ROM that can be produced under active muscular control for a particular degree of freedom of any joint.
Passive Flexibility	Maximum ROM that can be produced passively by imposition of an external force without causing joint injury.
Active Insufficiency/ Inadequacy	The difference calculated by subtracting active flexibility from passive flexibility.
Passive Insufficiency/ Inadequacy	The difference between passive flexibility and the sport-specific required range of motion.

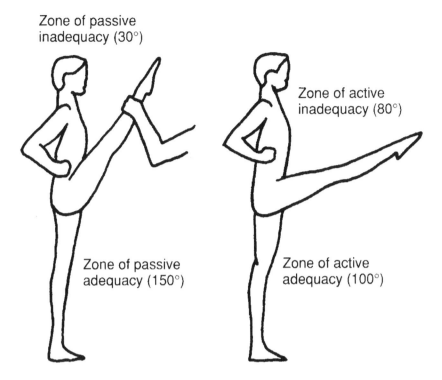

Fig. 3.7 Flexibility zones. (Alter, 1996)

Flexibility and stretching

Stretching and flexibility are not necessarily synonymous. Some flexibility exercises are not stretching exercises although they increase range of movement, as they may focus on modifying neuromuscular processes, in particular the stretch and tendon reflexes. Stretching exercises tend to ignore the neuromuscular processes and tend to concentrate on eliciting structural changes in the soft tissues such as the fascia. Such structural changes improve passive flexibility, which provides a protective reserve if a joint is unexpectedly stressed beyond its normal operational limits. However, it is active flexibility that is most important for sports participants as it correlates highly to sporting performance. Development of active flexibility has a strong transfer to sporting performance particularly when it is developed in conjunction with strength levels within the range of active inadequacy (Siff, M.C., 2003).

Fig. 3.7 illustrates active and passive flexibility, as well as the zones of inadequacy that relate to these flexibility qualities.

Making improvements in range of motion requires an understanding of the main tissues that cause restriction. A sarcomere (contractile muscle tissue) can be stretched to 150 per cent of its resting length (Wang et al., 1991). Obviously, then, the contractile elements (filaments) of the sarcomere cannot be a limiting factor in flexibility when the muscle is relaxed. The most important component of muscle relating to flexibility is the connective tissue (fascia) that envelops and surrounds the muscle at its various levels of organization (muscle fibre, bundle and whole muscle) (Alter M.J. 1988).

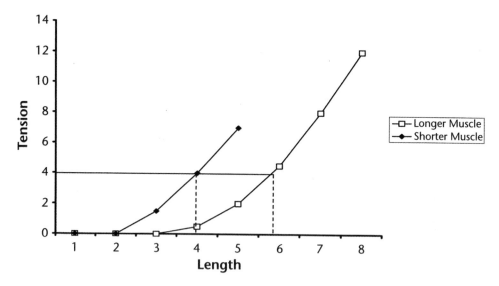

Fig. 3.8 Model of shifting length/tension curve. (Weppler and Magnusson, 2010)

An area's resistance to stretch originates in the meshwork of these connective tissues; as you stretch, your connective tissues become tauter. Two types of connective tissue (CT) can significantly affect an athlete's range of motion: collagenous CT and elastic CT. The relative contributions of the soft tissues to joint stiffness (Johns, R.J. and Wright, V., 1962) are as follows:

■ Muscles and their fascial sheaths: 41 per cent
■ Structures of the joint capsule, including ligaments: 35 per cent
■ Skin: 11 per cent
■ Tendons and their sheaths: 10 per cent
■ Joint structure, age and sex are all factors that affect ROM and cannot be altered.

These observations negate the need to consider the long-held practice of stating what muscles are being stretched as the fascia is the main restrictor of range of motion and as the fascia is an intertwined linking of meshwork that will have areas of restriction that are not necessarily directly aligned with muscle origins and insertions. Therefore it is important to pay attention to patterns of tension in the body (predominantly held in the fascia) in order to free up restrictions and improve movement qualities and ability.

Improvements in passive range of motion involve permanent changes in the tissues limiting this range. This improvement involves increasing the length of the different soft tissues comprising the muscle complex, especially the collagenous tissues such as the fascia. Plastic changes in tissue length can only be confirmed when there is a decrease in tension at the same angle, or greater angle (range of motion) achieved with the same tension (resulting in shift to the right of length/tension curve, as shown in Fig. 3.8).

Other adaptations proposed to occur in response to chronic lengthening forces include:

■ Change in structural tissue properties – increased number of sarcomeres in series, viscoelastic deformation (Marshall, 2011). Essentially the body produces more muscle fibres along a longitudinal axis, which produces less tension for the same length.

- Modifying the neuromuscular processes that control tensions and length on tissues in the muscle complex. Sensory change: increase length or decrease resistance due to improved tolerance to stretch, not length in tissues (Magnusson and Aagaard, 1996); the stretch feels easier for any given range of motion.
- Lengthening and strengthening other soft tissues, especially those of the joint capsule and the ligaments. Restructuring the articulating surfaces of the joints, a process mediated by many years of regular heavy loading in specific patterns.

Benefits of stretching

Importantly the majority of the research into the development of flexibility does not suggest strong acute benefits of stretching, with many of the positive benefits of stretching being seen following long-term chronic practice of stretching regimes. The acute effects of stretch training are transient, peaking immediately post – with total loss within twenty-four to seventy-two hours. Therefore it is important to consistently perform mobility/flexibility training five to seven times/week that consistently exposes structures to lengthening tensile forces, in order to elicit plastic changes in restricting structures such as the fascia.

This enhancement of range of motion can also be utilized prior to competition or training to target tight structures that may inhibit full range motion. Following pre-training static stretching the performance of a thorough dynamic warm-up routine will ensure that this range can then be utilized by the neuromuscular system to promote ease of movement.

There are a multitude of proposed benefits of performing stretching regularly including (Alter, M.J, 1998):

- Increase the useful range of motion.
- Reduction in the incidence of injury; healthy, flexible tissue is less susceptible to damage.
- Decrease the severity of injury.
- Delay in the onset of muscular fatigue.
- Prevention and alleviation of muscle soreness after exercise.
- Increase in the level of skill and muscular efficiency.
- Prolonging sporting life.
- Development of required range of motion to allow optimal movements and positions.
- Improved mobility enables movement efficiency thereby reducing injury risk due to overloading overused and inappropriate tissues.
- Reduction of imbalances.
- In combination with full range strength development injury risk may be reduced when an individual is in extreme ranges of motion.

Areas of the body affected

In developing flexibility and mobility that is useful for squash it is important to consider the main areas of the body that will need to be focused on. The ankle needs to maintain range to ensure that it can act as a force absorber for the large impacts that occur in lunging and thereby reduce loading up the chain allowing efficient force acceptance and transfer. The thoracic spine will allow rotation of the upper body to deliver range of movement that will increase the ability for force to be utilized in the squash swing to generate speed in striking the squash ball. Most importantly hip range of motion will play a vital part in the allowing the fast efficient twisting and lunging movements through extreme ranges that are common in the playing of squash. The movements in Figs 3.9, 3.10 and 3.11 offer an assessment of the ability of an athlete to move optimally through ranges in these joints that relate to squash movement. They can be used to assess a squash player's dynamic mobility and potentially identify areas that they need to work on to help improve this quality.

In considering how to approach the development of flexibility and mobility it is important to identify for the individual the sport-specific shapes that offer challenges to ease of movement. As mentioned the dynamic lunge that is employed frequently in the sport of squash will be the main challenge to mobility and flexibility. As can be seen in Fig. 3.12, there are a wide range of lunge positions that can be attained in the competitive squash environment. Individuals may have different areas of restriction preventing them from attaining optimal lunging positions and it is important to assess the cause of these restric-

tions and focus on releasing these, particularly if they prevent ease of movement. Utilization of myofascial release techniques (through self-administered or specialist massage treatment) or movements or stretches that positively influence an individual's ability to achieve enhanced ranges of motion can be applied in a variety of combinations to elicit changes.

If there are potential isolated regional specific restrictions in range of motion then it may be necessary to isolate and target these first via static flexibility or soft tissue work to improve passive range of motion before or in combination with dynamic range of motion development. This change in range of movement (via a number of methods) about a joint can then be utilized in dynamic specific and general global full range joint movements to develop strength in the newly increased range of motion.

Figs 3.9, 3.10 and 3.11 Squash player demonstrating optimal end of range positions for the overhead squat, lateral lunge/squat and split squat.

Fig. 3.12 Lunge positions.

Athletes should focus on developing both range of movement and strength in and through these sport-specific shapes. This will increase active range of movement available in performing movements through extreme ranges of motion. The aims of mobility training for the squash player should be to attain optimal ROM in key movements and positions.

In considering flexibility and mobility strategies to allow the optimal development of these characteristics in relation to squash a multi-layered situational approach to utilizing different techniques may prove useful. In increasing passive range of motion, static stretching techniques that focus on eliciting changes in restrictive fascial structures should be performed gently, often and for extended periods of time per exercise (45 seconds up to two minutes). Non-engagement of the sympathetic nervous system during these methods is important to allow relaxation of muscles to effectively place tension on the fascial system. These types of passive methods of flexibility enhancement are best performed once warmed up so post training or competition is ideal.

From static flexibility work to ROM

However, gaining an extended ROM without associated strength and stability may increase injury risk. Direct transfer from static flexibility work to ROM in sports performance cannot be assumed, and the performance of creative dynamic flexibility and mobility sequences utilizing exercises requiring associated speed, strength and stability in a variety of related movement patterns and also during exhaustive conditions will help to increase

Table 3.2 Flexibility techniques, outcome, focus and application.

Technique	Intended Outcome	Tissue Type	Dosage
Static Short static holds Passive stretching	Acute passive range of motion increase	Neural output reduction	3–5 sets 5–10 exercises 15–30secs per stretch @ 60–70% intensity
Static Long static holds Passive stretching	Chronic passive range of motion increase	Fascial plastic change in restricting structures (predominantly fascia)	10–20 exercises 60sec holds per stretch @ 50–60% intensity
Static Eccentric conditioning and static hold	Chronic range of motion increase Strength in outer ranges of targeted movement	Fascial plastic changes Increase outer range strength/reduce active insufficiency	4–6 movement patterns with restrictive end ranges of motion 1–2 sets 2 x 30sec eccentric with 30sec holds
Static Fascial release techniques – massage, foam rolling	Release of fascial restrictions including scar tissue	Fascial tension reduction	Foam roller: 20–30min progressing through various areas/ structures Massage: 30–90min of various release techniques by massage specialist
Static Concurrent stretch and vibration	Fascial lengthening Improvement in range through interruption of pain restrictions	Fascial plastic changes Interruption of pain inhibitory neural feedback to allow greater range for chronic changes	6–10 exercises 1min on 1min off Frequency of vibration below 30Hz
Static Microstretching	Reduction in tension signalling Agonist tension release and range of motion increase	Musculotendinous pain reduction, tension reduction	4–6 stretches 1min each 3 sets Fully supported 1min holds of 30–40% effort
Static PNF (CR/CRAC)	Reduction of inhibitory neural reflexes to allow increased stretch of fascia	Fascial Interruption of neural feedback to allow greater range for chronic changes	2–3 x 90sec with 3 x 6–10sec antagonist contractions CRAC + 6–10sec agonist contractions

Technique	Intended Outcome	Tissue Type	Dosage
Dynamic Nerve stretch/Flossing	Reduce neural tension through movement	Neural release reducing inhibitory muscular tension associated with neural tension	2–3 exercises 6–10 repetitions of slow movement repetitions through nerve tensioning or flossing patterns 1–2 sets
Dynamic Ballistic resisted	Acute enhancement of antagonist strength	Muscular strengthening of antagonistic muscle groups producing improvements in active insufficiency	4–6 exercises 6–10 repetitions 1–2 sets
Dynamic Active isolated stretching	Reduction of inhibitory neural reflexes to allow increased stretch of fascia through reciprocal inhibition	Fascial Improvements in active insufficiency	8–12 exercises 6–10 repetitions 1–2 sets Active movement with passive end-range enhancement via straps or partner
Dynamic Sport-specific movement patterns	Increase active range of motion and strength through range	Neural/fascial changes due to repetition of pattern	Performance of repetitions or time periods of exercise at set tempos, varying in position and challenge

usable active range and promote ease of movement in all situations during squash match play. These types of exercises require voluntary muscular actions in key movements and positions, involving the coordination of the fully available ROM and variety of contraction speeds around several joints promoting the essential development of balanced strength and stability between agonist and antagonist muscles through a dynamic range.

Table 3.3 lists suggested options as to the frequency of prescription that is required to deliver a marked change in permanent flexibility characteristics through the application of static stretching.

Table 3.3 Static stretching prescription guideline, with options to elicit plastic change in physical structures.

Static Stretching Prescription Formats	
10min (minimum every day)	20min (1 x per week)
50sec on/10sec off	90sec on/15sec off
30min (2 x per month)	40min (1 x per month)
2min on/15sec off	3min on/15sec off

METABOLIC CONDITIONING

Optimizing game-related endurance for squash requires the development of both muscular (strength) endurance and energy system output. As described by Gastin (2001), energy production relies on three inter-related processes:

- ATP – PCr system: the splitting of stored phosphagens (adenosine triphosphate [ATP] and phosphocreatine [PCr]).
- Anaerobic glycolytic system: the break-down of carbohydrate in the absence of oxygen.
- Oxidative (aerobic) system: the combustion of carbohydrates and fats in the presence of oxygen.

As with any other training activities, it is essential that metabolic conditioning sessions are well matched to the individual player's physical state, training age, training phase and developmental needs. Within a comprehensive training programme the player should employ a blend of conditioning activities including squash-specific and non-specific protocol in order to enable intensity to be effectively manipulated and a high volume of training completed.

Trends in a range of sports including squash have led to the popular use of 'specific game-related' interval training where competition time-motion data is utilized to create simulated match-play intervals of exercise and recovery. Used intelligently around competitive match-play events this method can form part of an appropriate conditioning regime. The limitations of solely adopting this approach to conditioning for squash lie mainly in the varied demands of match play that partially utilize energy systems throughout without purely challenging energy production.

If the training goal is to elicit positive changes in energy system output then match play and simulated match play must be supplemented with additional 'metabolic conditioning' activities to allow the targeting of energy systems that may not be achieved in squash-specific training situations.

As the intensity of exercise efforts within an interval training session are key to stimulating positive adaptations it is necessary to monitor intensity via a simply applied non-invasive method. Heart Rate (HR) monitoring can be an effective tool for quantifying prolonged sub-maximal exercise intensities but is of limited value during maximal or very high-intensity short-duration (sprint) exercises intervals. If using heart rate as a guide, it is essential that an individual peak heart rate value is used to calculate any percentages of max heart rate (HRmax) as generic estimates of HRmax are likely to be inaccurate for the individual player. In the context of 'all-out' or very high-intensity exercise intervals, rating of perceived exertion (RPE) may be effective for intensity prescription. Following a period of familiarization, players are normally able to use RPE as a meaningful method of describing exercise intensity with reasonable consistency regarding how strenuous the exercise feels (Borg, 1998).

In some specific circumstances it may be appropriate for players to undertake long-duration moderate-intensity (60–75 per cent HRmax) continuous exercise sessions but these instances would be limited and expectations regarding any positive changes in fitness qualities would be low. It may well be the case that this type of 'aerobic base' activity already forms an integral part of a player's squash training sessions. Far more significantly, players should aim to challenge energy system production in a targeted manner with the aim of either increasing peak output or extending the duration of effective energy output. As a consequence the individual should then be able to either endure moderate – high intensities of squash activity for longer durations, be able to exercise at elevated intensities, or recover more rapidly between high-intensity bouts of exercise. High-intensity interval training is therefore a valuable component of the squash player's training schedule.

Exercise modality

The exercise modality chosen for metabolic conditioning sessions should enable the development of energy systems in relation to neuromuscular fatigue and cardiopulmonary stress. The most direct correspondence from conditioning training to squash performance would be achieved through the use of squash-type movements – enabling both central cardiopulmonary and local neuromuscular adaptations. Commonly utilized sport-specific conditioning modalities include:

- Ghosting – rehearsal of sequences of footwork, lunge patterns and shot play to various areas of the court with recoveries to the centre of the court.
- Pressure feeding – coach-fed drills that challenge the movements and shot play of the player. Pressure feeding may be effectively alternated with ghosting patterns.
- Conditioned match play – the player competes to win points against an opponent under predetermined conditions. Example conditions include confined target areas for shots or continuous play where the coach uses multiple balls to eliminate breaks in play due to errors.

Non-specific conditioning modalities such as running, metabolic resistance training, circuit training, static cycling and row ergometer may be most appropriate in specific instances. Although these modalities have less neuromuscular and kinematic correspondence to squash performance than squash-specific movements, they can be extremely valuable to provide variety, easily manipulated intensity and reduced impact forces.

Operational framework for sessions

An operational framework for the prescription of metabolic conditioning sessions with four distinct themes is outlined below and in Table 3.4.

- Maximal-Intensity (Sprint) Intervals: 'All-out' intensity intervals of short duration (5–45 seconds) designed to provide an intense neuromuscular stimulus and provoke high levels of lactate production. Inter-interval recoveries should provide sufficient opportunity to replenish energy stores and readiness prior to the commencement of subsequent efforts (2–4 minutes). Modality may be specific (ghosting or feeding) or non-specific running, cycling, ergometer row or metabolic resistance training (MRT).
- High-Intensity Aerobic Intervals: 'All-out' intensity intervals of short to moderate duration (10–60 seconds). Short, often negative (recovery duration is shorter than exercises duration) recovery intervals facilitate only partial recovery. Effort level should be 'all-out' but fatigue will limit actual exercise intensity. The degree of inter-interval recovery is facilitated by an effective aerobic system. Modality may be specific (ghosting or feeding) or non-specific running, cycling, ergometer row or MRT.
- Aerobic Intervals: moderately high to high-intensity sustained exercise intervals of 2–5 minutes duration. Exercise intensity

Table 3.4 Framework for metabolic conditioning sessions.

	Training Modality	Exercise Duration and Intensity	Inter-Interval Recoveries	Example Session Outline
Maximal-Intensity (Sprint) Intervals	Ghosting, feeding, run, bike, row or MRT	5–45secs All-out	Positive recoveries 2–4mins	Outdoor Running: 6 x 45secs all-out sprint intervals. 4min passive inter-interval recovery (adapted from Mujika, 2007)
High-Intensity Aerobic Intervals	Ghosting, feeding, run, bike, row or MRT	10–60secs All-out.	Negative recoveries 10–45secs	Ghosting: (work–rest in secs) 60–30 x 6, 3min recovery, 45–15 x 8, 3min recovery, 20–10 x 8. All-out maximal-intensity intervals with active recoveries
Aerobic Intervals	Run, bike, row or circuit	2–5 mins 85–90% HRmax	Negative recoveries time or HR prescribed e.g. return to 70% HRmax.	Treadmill Running: 6 x 4min intervals @≈90%HRmax. 90secs active inter-interval recovery (adapted from Mujika, 2007)
Game-Simulated Protocol	Ghosting, feeding, run, bike, row or MRT	Varied 10 – 120secs Moderate–very high Intensities	Negative recoveries 10 – 20secs. 2 Mins inter-sets	Ghosting: (work-rest in secs) ([100–20, 40–20, 20–10, 20–10, 100–20] x 3, 2min recovery) repeat whole sequence x 3–5. High intensity intervals (RPE 8/10) with passive recoveries

may be monitored using HR with >90 per cent HRmax being deemed to constitute high intensity. Inter-interval recoveries should be negative and may either follow prescribed timings or be dictated by HR recovery rate with the subsequent exercise interval commencing once HR has moved towards homeostatic levels by a pre-determined value, such as 70 per cent HRmax. Non-specific modalities such as running, cycling, rowing or circuit training should be utilized.

■ Game-Simulated Protocol: interval or fartlek style protocol utilizing match-play time-motion data. Varied short to long exercise intervals (10–120 seconds) of moderate to very high intensities. Exercise modality may be specific (ghosting or feeding) or non-specific running, cycling, ergometer row or MRT.

STRENGTHENING WORK

Successful squash performance requires the skilful manipulation of momentum through

Table 3.5 Classification of strength exercises.

Force Production	Squash Specific	Muscular Conditioning
Maximal Strength	*Strength*	− Loaded Calf Raise (Extended Knee)
− Back Squat	− Rear Foot Elevated Split Squat	− Loaded Calf Raise (Flexed Knee)
− Split Squat	− Rear Foot Elevated Split Deadlift	− Front Loaded Step Up
− Dead Lift	− Single Leg Stiff-legged Deadlift	− Lateral Step Up
− Stiff-legged Deadlift	− Extended Forward Lunge	− Lateral Plank Leg Raise
− Sumo Deadlift	− Dynamic Lateral Lunge	− Single Leg Hip Thrust
− Trap Bar Deadlift	− Lunge and Press	− Lateral Sled Pull
− Step Up	− Reverse Lunge	− Roll Out
	− Single Leg Pistol Squat	− Hanging Leg Raise
Explosive Strength	− Dumbbell Sumo Squat off Blocks	− V − Up
− Snatch and Derivatives		− Pull Up Variations
− Clean and Derivatives	*Speed − Strength*	− Dumbbell Single Arm Row
− Split or Push Jerk	− Touchdown Explosive Hop	− Swing Gym Row
− Med Ball Chimney Throw	− Bound to Rebound	− Heavy Prowler Push
− Overhead Med Ball Throw	− Med Ball Lateral / 45 degree Step and Throw	− Kettlebell Swing
− Box Jumps	− Rear Foot Elevated Explosive Hop	− Nordic Hamstring Lower
− Drop Jumps	− Overhead Split Squat Changeover	− Glute − Hamstring Raise

repeated application of impulse within the ground contact time available (Rodgers and Cavanagh, 1984). Rapid force generation, application and manipulation characteristics are therefore key qualities that squash players should aim to optimize (Naoki, Kazunori and Newton, 2013). The development of strength qualities that are applicable to squash performance should therefore be a significant element of the physical preparation for squash. Rather than merely overloading squash-like movements with additional loads, strength training should instead aim to provide the player with increased potential to apply impulse within their movements on court to effectively manipulate their momentum and direction. Due to the potential risks associated with incorrect exercise execution, any strength training undertaken should be done so under the supervision of a suitably accredited strength and conditioning coach.

Considerations in designing a strengthening programme

Maturation, movement competence, training age and phase of training should all be considered when selecting strengthening exercises to support and develop an individual's squash performance. Strengthening work should prioritize functional loading, to ensure that physiological capacity is developed in synergy with motor competence, to support technical performance (Turner and Barker, 2014). This requires strength training prescription comprising predominantly complex multi-joint exercises.

The forces involved in the frequent lunging and bounding movements that players are required to perform during match play demand the ability to suppress impact loading forces following coordination of high initial impact force (Cronin, McNair and Marshall, 2003). Performance enhancement therefore necessitates coaching that emphasizes motor control as the player learns to exert and absorb greater force. Exercise progression must be underpinned by safe and effective movement competence with the ability to perform controlled strengthening exercises with excellent technique being a prerequisite prior to undertaking more specific higher velocity exercises.

Junior players or those with a low training age must learn to perfect the coordination of strength and movement to control the impact landings experienced during explosive lunging movements. The programming of high-force or high-velocity exercises must therefore be supported by a range of reduced force exercises that enable the synchronized development of movement competence. Rather than having a strength or power emphasis, these 'assistance' exercises provide the athlete with either a stability or range of motion challenge to elicit a positive impact on the overall performance of explosive squash movements (Turner and Barker, 2014).

As indicated by the examples in Table 3.5, the prescription of strengthening exercises for squash players can be guided by the classification of exercises according to the physical qualities they are able to develop.

MAXIMAL STRENGTH
EXERCISES
Multi-joint strength exercises that utilize a stable bilateral base allow the individual to maximize the force that they can exert. To optimize adaptation these high-force–low-velocity movements should be performed with the intent to move explosively against a relatively heavy external resistance. Improving the ability to express a high level of force in squatting and lunging patterns relative to body mass should be one priority of strength training for squash. A stable bilateral base facilitates high force production capabilities requiring high nervous system (neural) drive (Aagaard, 2003 and Fimland et al., 2009). The prescription of strength training for squash players should include a small number of these high-force exercises that the individual can perform competently and progressively load.

EXPLOSIVE STRENGTH
Relatively high-velocity complex multi-joint exercises such as Olympic lifts (and their derivatives), medicine ball throws and explosive jumping and bounding exercises should be prescribed to enable the player to express force as rapidly as possible. Rate of Force Development (RFD) and specifically the impulse produced during each ground contact on court are integral to effective squash performance. High-velocity triple flexion and extension (ankle, knee and hip joints) exercises can improve the individual's ability to effectively express impulse within the time

frames available on court. This RFD attribute cannot be optimized using purely maximal strength movements (Tillin and Folland, 2014; Oliveira *et al.*, 2013 and Stone, Plisk and Collins, 2007).

SQUASH-SPECIFIC STRENGTH

Resistance and explosive exercises that more closely correspond to the precise kinematics of squash movements may be utilized within a strength programme in a progressively loaded regime to develop the ability to perform critical squash movements. The unilateral or split-stance nature of these exercises dictates that forces are reduced when compared to maximal strength exercises. In addition to force production, this classification of exercises may challenge hip and trunk flexion or range of motion in extended split-stance and unilateral positions. Dynamic multi-planar bounds or medicine ball throws and extended dynamic forward lunges (with extended front knee and heel strike on contact) are examples of specific modifications to traditional strength exercise techniques. These 'specific' exercises should constitute a minor portion of the overall strengthening programme and should only be prescribed following sustained maximal strength and explosive strength training.

MUSCULAR CONDITIONING (STRENGTH ENDURANCE)

Assistance exercises that target either muscle groups that are placed under high levels of stress during squash match play or maintenance of postural integrity should supplement the strength programme. Rather than increasing force production, these exercises should be prescribed with the aim of developing qualities such as trunk 'pillar' force transmission or fatigue resistance, for example in the calf-achilles complex. The desired outcome of this classification of exercises is that tissues

Table 3.6 Example under 13s strength session; external resistance such as barbell dumbbells or sand bag may be included and progressed as competence allows.

Exercises	Sets	Reps
Hop and Hold (10/leg)	2	20
*Overhead Squat	2	12
*Split Squat (10/leg)	2	20
*Arabesque (10/leg)	2	20
Horizontal Pull Up	2	8

Table 3.7 Example under 17s strength session.

Exercises	Sets	Reps
Hang Clean	3	5
Back Squat	3	8
Dynamic Forward Lunge (6/leg)	3	12
Stiff-Legged Deadlift	3	12
Lateral Step Up (5/leg)	3	10
Lateral Pull Down	3	10

become better conditioned to cope with the prolonged repeated bouts of high-impact movements required during training and match play.

Tables 3.6 and 3.7 provide sample strength training sessions that could be utilized with junior squash players. The exercises, sets and reps are all merely indicative of what could be prescribed. Needs-based prescription must be well matched to the individual player's current physical state.

SPEED AND AGILITY

Speed and agility are precious physical qualities on the squash court, with those athletes able to display these traits at a high level in combination with strong technical racquet skills having a decided advantage. Agility has been defined as a rapid whole-body movement with change of velocity or direction in response to a stimulus (Sheppard, J.M. and Young, W.B., 2006).

Wilkinson et al. (2012) found that high-intensity variable-direction exercise capabilities are important for success in elite squash. In data collected over six years through the English Institute of Sport on elite squash players ranging across junior, development and elite squads, on-court change-of-direction speed was an underpinning physical quality predicting squash match performance, rated through international squash rankings or coaches' subjective ratings. It is therefore important to develop the strength, explosive muscular qualities and technical movement proficiency required to perform these movement-specific skills with high levels of speed. It must also be remembered that the development of strength through both full and extreme ranges of motion in squash-specific movement patterns (lunge, split squat, side lunge) is vitally important in the development of squash-specific speed and agility as it is fundamental force production that allows the expression of muscular impulse (impulse being the amount of force that can be delivered in a set time and impacts on changing momentum of the body).

Agility performance in squash involves both short and long stretch shortening cycle (SSSC and LSSC respectively) muscular actions.

These are predominantly displayed when moving off the T with a split step (SSSC) or moving into and out of the lunge (LSSC) while striking the ball. There are also various accessory movements that are utilized in transitions between shots back to the T and then moving in response to the opponent on the court and the shot played that also require speed of movement.

Both SSSC and LSSC movements are underpinned heavily by strength characteristics and the development of high levels of strength in relation to the athlete's bodyweight needs to be a focus to help in the achievement of high levels of speed and agility in both SSSC and LSSC. Also important to consider in relation to speed and agility is the need for the athlete to be able to deliver high levels of rate of force development (impulse) to move out of lunge-type movements quickly and efficiently.

In order to change direction fast the ability to rapidly absorb large forces through eccentric muscular actions in order to decelerate into movements during the process of reaching and striking the ball is paramount. Without requisite strength levels this ability to decelerate fast and with control will severely limit a squash player's movement speed on court.

A review of the research literature (Brughelli, M. et al., 2008) investigating the methods of training that were most effective for producing improvements in change-of-direction (COD) ability showed a number of training modalities were effective in improving COD ability. Training methods that improved specific COD ability included sport-specific COD training, jump squat training, unilateral and bilateral horizontal jump training. Sport-specific speed and agility training has its effectiveness based in movement familiarity; squash players are likely to display high levels of speed and muscular force moving in a way they are most accustomed, hence this type of training offers a potent stimulus for improving these qualities. Bilateral and unilateral vertical and horizontal jump training deliver non-specific technically simple movement task(s) that squash players can deliver maximum intent to in the development of intramuscular rate of force production capabilities. These non-specific movements can be performed in a relatively high volume to elicit positive training adaptations.

Both testing and training speed and agility in squash is best performed in a specific manner due to the very unique movement patterns of the sport. It is important that general strength and rate of force development qualities are improved but that work is also done utilizing these qualities during specific movement patterns that will transfer well to the court. The ability to produce and apply impulse to improve agility is best developed in specific movement patterns mimicking the sport to allow improvements in these qualities and to allow optimal transfer onto the squash court. Drills, exercises and training should be structured in particular to target the variation in lunge patterns that a squash athlete can face a multitude of times during a match.

In order for the body to adapt in a positive way (become faster) to improve speed and agility the training stimulus must be applied to target this adaptation. The movement must therefore be of a high enough speed for the body to adapt positively (get faster). This adaptive stimulus for improving speed and agility is by definition an excitatory one in which any level of significant fatigue will lessen the effectiveness of the response and adaptation as this will slow down the movements being performed and therefore they will not be of a high enough stimulus to elicit a positive response (why would the body need to get faster if it is moving slower in training). Therefore correct prescription of speed and agility training involves the optimal number of maximal explosive, fast repetitions performed with maximal intent and complete rest to help target the development of the specific physical and movement qualities required done as fast as possible. Tables 3.8, 3.9 and 3.10 provide examples of workouts (specific and general movement patterns) with appropriate work rest guidelines that would target the development of speed and agility qualities.

The movement patterns utilized in developing speed and agility capabilities for squash can and should have a high level of variation from a movement, neuromuscular and sensory input as this will lead to positive adaptations

Table 3.8 Squash-specific movement pattern speed and agility workout.

Exercise	Sets	Reps	Rest Period	Intensity
Lunge changeovers + court shuttle	2–4	5 el + 1 shuttle	60–90sec	
One turn court shuttles	2–4	1	60–90sec	
Three turn court shuttle	2–4	1	60–90sec	MAXIMAL
Side to side ghosting	2–4	4–6 shots	60–90sec	
Four corner ghosting	2–4	1	60–90sec	

Table 3.9. Explosive jump example for improving explosive force production characteristics.

Exercise	Sets	Reps	Rest between reps	Rest between sets	Intensity
Split Squat Jumps	2	3–8 el	1min	2min	
Standing Long Jump	2	3			
Tuck Jumps/Hurdle Jumps	2	8–12			MAXIMAL
Hopping for distance	2	3–5 el			
Jump Squats	2	3–6			

Table 3.10 Example of a speed and agility workout utilizing non-squash-specific movement patterns.

Exercise	Sets	Reps	Rest between reps	Rest between sets	Intensity
T agility test	2	2–3	1min	2min	
505 Agility	2	2–3			
10–30m Sprints	2	3–4			
Side to Side shuffles (varied short distances)	2	3–4			MAXIMAL
Back Pedal (varied short distances)	2	3–4			

that transfer to the multitude of situations that a squash player will face in a match. It is important that the application of fundamental movement mechanics is delivered in collaboration with squash coaches and ideally it is the squash coach that should be leading and defining the movement focus for the individual athlete in any squash-specific speed and agility session.

SUMMARY

Key messages

Training activities for the physical development of squash players should be prescribed using an objective needs-based approach rather than following traditional accepted practice. Prescription should be guided by fundamental principles and the programme should be monitored and modified according to the individual's response to the training stimulus imposed.

A long-term developmental view should be taken with the progression of loading and intensity built upon a foundation of movement competence. Developing all-round athletic potential rather than just adopting a narrow sport-specific focus best supports sustainable improvements in squash performance. There are many essential physical qualities that affect squash performance and any significant deficiencies will limit the player's potential.

Future directions

The evolution of strength and conditioning support for squash continues. Potential areas for further development of practice entail:

- A range of interventions targeting the progressive development of movement competence, strength and mobility of junior players should be applied broadly across the junior squash population.
- Improvement in time-motion, metabolic and kinematic competition data should be used to further inform more individualized prescription of training activities.
- Bespoke individualized recovery protocols have previously been implemented by several players at major events, but the application of optimal recovery activities during tournament competition is currently underdeveloped for many players.

REFERENCES

Aagaard, P. (2003). Training-Induced Changes in Neural Function. *Exercise Sport Science Review*, 31(2), 61–67.

Fig. 3.13 Nick Matthew demonstrates great physical tenacity to get back what appears to be a winning drop shot from his opponent.

PLAYER TESTIMONIALS

Nick Matthew OBE

The modern game of squash is incredibly dynamic and challenges the body in an all-round way, unlike many other sports. You need to train to become powerful yet nimble, quick but with great stamina, and strong yet incredibly flexible. Strength and conditioning training helps you to become robust enough to perform day-in day-out at a high level whilst helping to avoid injury. I view my physical training as the key that unlocks the door to improvements in the tactical, technical and mental areas of the game. Training should be smart, not just hard, and tailored to the specific needs of the athlete and the sport.

James Willstrop

At the time of writing, at thirty-one years old, I have just had fairly significant hip surgery, which I hope might give me a few more years playing a sport somewhat unkind for joints. I have played International squash for fifteen years and it has taken a considerable toll on my body. I know I would not have lasted as long as I have without following a committed strength and conditioning programme throughout my career.

As a sixteen-year-old I was lucky enough to fall into the age of Lottery Funding and so I benefitted from the work of Damon Leedale Brown, who was squash's first strength and conditioning coach. I then worked solidly with Mark Campbell, who has run my programme in Sheffield for the last seven years, and with Keith Barker, the current lead for squash. Every session has been designed to strengthen the body and equip it to make the continuous jarring, multidirectional movements required of squash. The sessions I do in the gym, together with the work I do with my physio, give me mobility and strength, which not only aid my performance but keep the body injury-free.

While I know I'm not young to be having hip surgery, I'm convinced the help I have received over the years and the correct training I have done gives me a chance to have another go at reaching the top levels once more. I would guess that without this sound training, my body simply wouldn't have the wherewithal to go again. If I do ever manage to play at the highest level again then all that work will have made a huge difference. In the past squash careers have been cut short much earlier by such injuries and I'm thankful I had the input that made me realize I needed to train correctly, at the right time. Strength and conditioning has been an absolutely vital part of my squash career.

Alter, M.J. (1988). *Science of Stretching*, 2nd edn. Champaign, IL: Human Kinetics.

Borg, G. (1998). *Borg's Perceived Exertion and Pain Scales*. Champaign, IL.: Human Kinetics.

Bucheit, M. and Laursen, P. (2013). High-Intensity Interval Training, Solutions to the Programming Puzzle. *Sports Medicine*, 43, 313–338.

Bucheit, M. and Laursen, P. (2013). High-Intensity Interval Training, Solutions to the Programming Puzzle. *Sports Medicine*, 43(7), 927.

Brughelli, M., Cronin, J., Levin, G. and Chaouachi, A. (2008). Understanding Change of Direction Ability in Sport: A Review of Resistance Training Studies. *Sports Medicine*, 38(12), 1045–1063.

Cronin, J., McNair, P. and Marshall, R. (2003). Lunge Performance and its Determinants. *Journal of Sports Science*, 21, 49–57.

Eubank, C. and Messenger, N. (2000). Dynamic Moves and Stepping Patterns Typical to the Game of Squash. *Journal of Sports Science*, 18, 471–472.

Faigenbaum, A., Farrell. A. and Fabiano, M., Radler, T., Naclerio, F., Ratamess, N.A., Kang, J. and Myer, G.D. (2011). Effects of Integrative Neuromuscular Training on Fitness Performance in Children. *Pediatric Exercise Science,* 23(4), 573–584.

Faigenbaum, A., Lloyd, R. and Myer, G. (2013). Youth Resistance Training: Past Practices, New Perspectives, and Future Directions. *Pediatric Exercise Science,* 25, 591–604.

Fimland, M., Helgerud, J., Gruber, M., Leivseth, G. and Hoff, J. (2009). Functional Maximal Strength Training Induces Neural Transfer to Single-Joint Tasks. *European Journal of Applied Physiology,* 107(1), 21.

Gastin, P. (2001). Energy System Interaction and Relative Contribution during Maximal Exercise. *Sports Medicine,* 31(10), 725–41.

Girard, O., Chevalier, R., Habrad, M., Sciberras, P., Hot, P and Millet, G.P. (2010). Game Analysis and Energy Requirements of Elite Squash. *Journal of Strength and Conditioning Research,* 31, 909–914.

Heyward V.H. (1984) Designs for fitness: A guide to Physical Fitness Appraisal and Exercise Prescription, Burgess, Minneapolis, MN.

Jeffreys, I. (2011). A Task Based Approach to Developing Context-Specific Agility. *Strength and Conditioning Journal,* 33, 52–60.

Johns, R.J. and Wright, V. (1962). Relative Importance of Various Tissues in Joint Stiffness. *Journal of Applied Physiology,* 17(5), 824–828.

Magnusson, S.P., Simonsen, E.B., Aagaard, P., Sorenson, H. and Kjaer, M. (1996). A Mechanism for Altered Flexibility in Human Skeletal Muscle. *Journal of Physiology,* 497(1), 291–298.

Marshall, P.W.M., Cashman, A., Cheema, B.S. (2011). A randomized controlled trial for the effect of passive stretching on measures of hamstring extensibility, passive stiffness, strength, and stretch tolerance. *Journal of Science and Medicine in Sport,* 14(6), 535.

Methany, E. (1952). *Body Dynamics,* New York, NY: McGraw-Hill.

Meylan, C.M.P., Nosaka, K., Green. J. and Cronin, J.B. (2010). Temporal and Kinetic Analysis of Unilateral Jumping in the Vertical, Horizontal and the Lateral Directions. *Journal of Sports Science,* 28, 545–554.

Moreside, J. and McGill, S. (2013). Improvements In Hip Flexibility Do Not Transfer To Mobility In Functional Movement Patterns. *Journal of Strength and Conditioning Research,* 27, 2635–2734.

Mujika, I., Santisteban, J., Angulo, P. and Padilla, S. (2007). Individualized Aerobic-Power Training in an Underperforming Youth Elite Association Football Player. *International Journal of Sports Physiology and Performance,* 2, 332–335.

Naoki, K., Kazunori, N and Newton, R. (2013). Relationships between Ground Reaction Impulse and Sprint Acceleration Performance in Team Sport Athletes. *Journal of Strength and Conditioning Research,* 27, 568–573.

Rodgers, M and Cavanagh, P. (1984). Glossary of Biomechanical Terms, Concepts and Units. *Physical Therapy,* 64, (12), 1886–1891.

Oliveira, F., Oliveira, A., Rizatto, G. and Denadai, B. (2013) Resistance Training for Explosive and Maximal Strength: Effects on Early and Late Rate of Force Development. *Journal of Sports Science and Medicine,* 12, 402–408.

Sarshin, A., Mohammadi, S., Shahrabad, H.B.P and Sedighi, M. (2011). The Effects of Functional Fatigue on Dynamic Postural Control of Badminton Players. *Biology of Exercise,* 7, 25–43.

Sheppard, J.M and Young, W.B. (2006). Agility Literature Review: Classifications, Training and Testing. *Journal of Sports Science,* 24, 919–932.

Siff, M.C. (2003). *Supertraining (6th edn),* Denver, CO: Supertraining Institute.

Stone, M., Plisk, S. and Collins, D. (2007). Training Principles: Evaluation of Modes and Methods of Resistance Training – a Coaching Perspective. *Sports Biomechanics,* 1(1), 79–103.

Tillin, N. and Folland, J. (2014). Maximal and explosive strength training elicit distinct neuromuscular adaptations, specific to the training stimulus. *European Journal of Applied Physiology,* 114(2), 365–375.

Turner, G. and Barker, K. (2014). Exercise Selection to Develop Optimal Explosive Lunge Movements for World-Standard Squash. *Strength and Conditioning Journal,* 33, 36–42.

Wang, K., McCarter, R., Wright, J., Beverly, J. and Ramirez-Mitchell, R. (1991). Regulation of Skeletal Muscle Stiffness and Elasticity by Titin Isoforms: A Test of the Segmental Extension Model of Resting Tension. *Proceedings of the National Academy of Science (USA),* 88(16), 7101–7105.

Weppler, C. H and Magnusson, S.P. (2010). Increasing Muscle Extensibility: A Matter of Increasing Length or Modifying Sensation. *Physical Therapy,* 90(3), 438–449.

Wilkinson, M., Cooke, M., Murray, S., Thompson, G. and Gibson, A.S., Winter, E.M. (2012). Physiological Correlates of Multiple-Sprint Ability and Performance in International Standard Squash Players. *Journal of Strength and Conditioning Research,* 26, 540–547.

Wilkinson, M., McCord, A. and Winter, E. (2010). Validity of a Squash-Specific Test of Multiple Sprint Ability. *Journal of Strength and Conditioning Research,* 24, 3381–3386.

APPENDIX

Physical Assessment Tests

Test 1 in this appendix refers to those used regularly by Strength and Conditioning coaches; some require specialist equipment and some require specialist understanding and training to reliably assess and implement.

Test 2 are assessments of the equivalent physical qualities as Test 1 but without the requirement of specialist equipment (may also be used by Strength and Conditioning coaches).

These can be used to help monitor and guide coaches and athletes in understanding what physical qualities need to be developed to ensure all-round physical preparedness for squash play.

Table 3.A1 Squash-specific multiple sprint ability			
	Name of Test	Description	Frequency
TEST 1	Squash-Specific Multiple Sprint Test (SSMST) (Wilkinson. M., McCord, A. and Winter E., 2010)	Requires electronic timing gates. 10 x 2 laps of squash-specific circuit with 20 seconds rest between repetitions giving fatigue index and total time measure	3–4 times per year
TEST 2	Squash Court Multiple Sprint test (SCMST) (movement design can be individualized as long as consistent)	Multiple repetition timed movement sequences that can be timed using a stop watch giving a fatigue index and total time measure	3–4 times per year
SQUASH-SPECIFIC SPRINT ABILITY			
	Name of Test	Description	Frequency
TEST 1	Squash-Specific Sprint Test (Wilkinson, M., McCord, A. and Winter, E., 2010)	Requires electronic timing gates. 1 lap of squash-specific circuit giving time measure	3–4 times per year before performance of SSMST
TEST 2	Squash Court Sprint test (movement design can be individualized as long as consistent and should form a part of SCMST)	Single repetition timed movement sequence that can be timed using a stop watch giving a time measure	3–4 times per year before performance of SCMST

MOBILITY/FLEXIBILITY

	Name of Test	Description	Frequency
TEST 1	Functional Movement Screen (FMS©)	Movement screening that assesses basic movement qualities to clear for exercise	3–4 times per year until symmetrical and appropriate score is achieved consistently
TEST 2	Sport-specific movement observation	Regular recorded observation of: Overhead Squat Split squat Lateral Squat/Lunge movements	4–6 times per year until high-level position is achieved consistently

SPEED AND AGILITY

	Name of Test	Description	Frequency
TEST 1	Sprint test (10–30min)(Straight line) (Gives an indication of physical ability to apply force rapidly indicator of basic physical trait)	Straight line sprinting speed giving a time measure (NB: full recovery needed for maximal performance and valid measure of targeted physical quality)	2–3 times per year
TEST 2	505 Agility Illinois Agility test Shuttle test (various distances) Court shuttle tests (various distances)	Numerous short change-of-direction tasks that give a time measure and assess ability to decelerate and accelerate body in set patterns (NB: full recovery needed for maximal performance and valid measure of targeted physical quality)	2–3 times per year

STRENGTH

	Name of Test	Description	Frequency
TEST 1	Isometric Pull	Static full body strength measure using force plate and giving force in Newtons.	4–6 times per year
TEST 2	Exercise based strength testing for eg: Squats Deadlifts Bench Press Chinups	Weight lifted in chosen strength exercises measure is load lifted and can give actual or predicted 1RM	4–6 times per year or regularly as part of normal strength training

IMPULSE/EXPLOSIVE STRENGTH

	Name of Test	Description	Frequency
TEST 1	Countermovement Jump (CMJ) Drop Jump (DJ)	Both long and short SSC impulse tests measuring ability to generate force rapidly. Measures are height (CMJ and DJ) and reactive strength index (DJ). Measured using electronic jump mats with timing switches	4–6 times per year
TEST 2	Jump and Reach Standing Long Jump	Both long SSC impulse tests. Measures are height (Jump and reach, cm) and distance achieved (Standing long jump, cm). Measured using tape measure	Up to 2–3 times weekly if appropriate for training phase

AEROBIC CAPACITY

	Name of Test	Description	Frequency
TEST 1	Beep Test Yo-Yo Test	Both progressive runs to fatigue involving changes of direction	4–6 times per year or until acceptable level is achieved
TEST 2	12 minute Cooper run test 3km run test 12 minute bike test	Distance attained and time attained tests	3–4 times per year or until acceptable level is achieved

MUSCULAR CONDITIONING TESTS

	Name of Test	Description	Frequency
TEST	Press Ups Inverted Row Single Leg Hip Lifts Prone Hold Supine Hold Side Plank Max Calf Raise	Repetitions to failure or time to failure of muscular endurance tasks. Physical quality underpins basic strength, metabolic and speed tasks	3–4 times per year

CHAPTER 4

PHYSIOTHERAPY IN SQUASH

Jade Leeder, Ian Horsley and Jonathan Leeder, English Institute of Sport

Fig. 4.1 The extreme demands on the body and the physical nature of squash make injuries almost inevitable in all players' careers.

WHAT THE PLAYERS THINK

Nick Matthew OBE

Prehab is absolutely vital and every player has a different routine or preference – the key is to find your preference and keeping that pattern or habit going.

When you are injured if you only focus on the long-term goal it can feel so distant that it can turn into a negative. You need to set daily goals to keep the momentum of your motivation. Sometimes you have to make big sacrifices, and it doesn't matter how long the rehab takes – you have to complete your rehab and be certain to get it right and make sure it never happens again in your career.

Having tournament support is vital, especially if the physio knows you and your little pre-match routines. During tournament I like to see Jade (England Squash Team Physio) after the morning practice and get a stretch so my hips are flexible but not too loose – Jade helps me get the perfect balance between the two. A good physio is someone that knows your routine and knows what you need to play your best. During competition it's all about performance.

James Willstrop

Prehab is very important to me, it helps me avoid injuries and helps fire and strengthen the key muscles I use during the match. Prehab never stops, I use it every day of the year. That body maintenance is absolutely vital; prehab has saved me from countless injuries and pulled muscles that would have stopped me training and playing. I probably average 40–60 minutes of prehab a day. But if you do 15 minutes every day, that soon adds up over the year (over 100 hours).

Rehab can be frustrating and at times boring but I am very confident of what it does and the benefit so I make sure I am very thorough when doing this – I know this is going to help me.

Where possible I would always have a physio travelling with me – it's huge to us as players. Depending on my physical state at times it could be more important taking a physio than a coach.

Laura Massaro

No one can guarantee being injury-free in squash, but good prehab is essential because it gives you confidence that you are doing everything you can to stay away from injuries.

No one can deny rehab is boring, but you need to keep focused on the goal of getting back to playing the sport you love.

Physio cover at every tournament would be ideal for me. But there is also a danger that you can rely on the physio too much – you always have bizarre niggles and that's life – sometimes you have to just man-up and get on with it!

Jenny Duncalf

If I've done a good period of prehab I feel more secure with my body when going on court and it takes the worry of getting injured away. The benefits of prehab are massive, but it can be tedious. You have to remember boredom is only short-term and the benefits from doing rehab properly are very much long-term.

If you don't commit fully to the rehab programme it may take twice as long and you could be susceptible to the injury recurring and affecting your career. Being an athlete is a job, and nobody loves every aspect of their job!

In tournament physio is great for aligning and getting the most out of your body between matches.

WHAT THE COACHES THINK

Dave Pearson

It's absolutely essential all players do prehab – it reduces injuries and prevents recurring problems enabling players to train properly. All top players take their prehab extremely seriously and do it all the time. Nick could not have won the CWG 2014 gold without the expertise Jade gave him. As with all sports scientists the player needs to implicitly trust the physio. First and foremost the physio needs to be a good practitioner, but just as important is to gain the trust of the player. A good physio does not get jealous when others treat their players – it's about the player not the practitioner.

When long-term injury takes place the athlete must listen to the physio and be prepared to do exactly what it takes day after day – regardless of how boring it is!

This is one of, if not the most valuable science support for the players; time after time this has enabled players to win tournaments that would normally not have been possible. Top players need this support at tournaments – and whether it is placebo or not it doesn't really matter – it works 100 per cent!

Paul Carter

There are no dangers with prehab: you can't do enough of this stuff! Prehab should be an everyday activity for players that want to be successful.

The key to getting through long periods of rehab is to have short-term goals and keep your mindset in the moment.

Having a physio travelling with you to an event is probably more important than having your coach there. Even if the effect that tournament physio treatment has on the players is placebo that doesn't matter – it is still extremely positive. Obviously apart from the players, for me physio would be first on the travelling team sheet.

Malcolm Willstrop

Boredom depends on the mentality of the player. Some will find plenty to do besides the required rehabilitation work: others may struggle. Certainly it is not a problem for James (Willstrop – Malcolm's son) and he has been productively employed in lots of worthwhile areas during his injury.

Physio support at events and at all times is another crucial requirement. Players need pre- and post-match assistance as well as when problems occur during matches. A squash player has to play five or six matches in as many days to win an event, and there is no way, bearing in mind the intensity of the sport, that they can survive without physio support.

David Campion

A comprehensive combined S and C and prehab programme undoubtedly prolongs a player's career. During tournaments prehab is the best way to fire up the muscle groups you need and create strength maintenance without causing fatigue.

Any top athlete has an all-consuming desire to play the sport they love; they will treat rehab with the respect it deserves, as without doing it properly recovery will not be possible. A long period of rehab can be a very positive thing; it gives the player time to reflect on what they need to do next and how they can change the way they work to do it better.

You could argue that for the elder mature players tournament support from a physio is probably more important than having a coach there.

Fig. 4.2 Early in his career Nick Matthew used intensive physiotherapy interventions (prehab and rehab) to successfully overcome lower back issues.

Fig. 4.3 Nick Matthew has had to overcome many injuries – more so than many of his adversaries – to become one of the most successful squash players in the history of the game.

INTRODUCTION

Physiotherapists are an integral component of the multi-disciplinary team providing support to squash players. This chapter will discuss the main roles of the physiotherapist working with elite squash players: epidemiology of injury; screening and prehabilitation; competition support; and rehabilitation of common injuries. This chapter will discuss the science behind these four areas, as well as use case-study examples.

EPIDEMIOLOGY OF INJURIES

Squash is a high-intensity, intermittent sport, causing players to make rapid movements around the court (which has an area of $62.5m^2$) to play a ball that can travel up to 230km/h (Montpetit, 1990). To enable the players to engage in a rally, participants require a large range of joint motion and velocity of limb action (Finch and Eime, 2001).

Despite the growing popularity of squash internationally, there has only been a limited amount of musculoskeletal injury-related research (Macfarlane and Shanks, 1998). The general incidence of squash injuries has been reported as being approximately 45 per cent (Berson et al., 1981), with most injuries being of a musculoskeletal nature, the majority occurring to the lower limb (ankle and knee) (Finch and Eime, 2001), and upper limb injuries occurring to the shoulder (Benson et al., 1981; Cullen and Silko, 1994) and elbow (Chard and Lachmann, 1987), as well as lumbar spine (Macfarlane and Shanks, 1998). Contributing factors to squash injury have been reported as: the physical demands of the sport; the speed, size and physical characteristics of the ball; the confined area of the court and the close proximity of players to one another

when making a shot; the court surfaces; lack of sufficient warm-up and the level of competitive play (Montpetit, 1990; van Dijk, 1994; Locke et al., 1997; Clavisi and Finch, 1999; Myer et al., 2007; Pforringer, 1980).

Other reported injuries within squash are head, face and eye injuries, where one study reported an incidence for eye injuries of 64/100,000 participants, compared with 28 eye injuries/100,000 in participants of badminton and tennis (Fong, 1994). These injuries were the result of impacts to the eye, from either the racket or the ball.

Five years of anecdotal evidence from injury surveillance at England Squash suggests the predominant lower limb injury is hip joint pathology, predominantly damage to the articular cartilage and labrum – a ring of fibrocartilage that deepens the hip socket. The labrum has a vital role within the hip joint by providing stability 21 per cent (Tan et al., 2001), dispersing force across joint by increasing the surface area by 28 per cent, maintaining the intra-capsular pressure by creating a seal that helps to keep the synovial fluid within joint, decreasing joint surface loading. The labrum is highly susceptible to high direct loads and therefore at high risk of injury. The common causes of labrum pathology are either from direct trauma or repetitive micro trauma. The recurrent twisting and turning within squash coupled with the extremes of range of motion place the labrum under extreme forces and therefore it commonly becomes damaged.

SCREENING AND PREHABILITATION

In recent years, elite sports participation has seen a huge increase in training and competition demands corresponding with a large increase in injury rates (Hawkins and

CASE STUDY 1: LUMBAR SPINE STRESS FRACTURE

Lumbar spine (LSP) stress fractures are not uncommon in female athletes (Micheli and Curtis, 2006), although they have not previously been reported in the squash population. The repetitive nature of the sport places excess stress through the lumbar spine due to repeated flexion and rotation under high loads and forces. Athletes can be subjected to forces up to eight times their body weight.

The Player

This case study concerns a female, professional squash athlete (age twenty-three years, mass 80.1kg, ht 1.83m, world rank 17) diagnosed by CT scan with bilateral lamina stress fractures of the L5.

Presenting Features

Due to the increased playing schedule and higher training loads the athlete's total court time had significantly increased over a six-month period of time as she transitioned onto the Women's World Tour. Her rising ranking led to more time on court in competition as she progressed further into events.

The level of intensity and the quality of play will also have altered in conjunction with the added match play. However monitoring training load within squash remains poorly researched and understood. Gross training load may be estimated using training diaries and total court time but little is understood as to directly monitoring the load the body is subjected to during various training sessions.

Over a period of two weeks, the athlete began to complain of some LSP stiffness, which was generalized to the lower area of her back. Initially, it was aggravated by prolonged periods of sitting and felt tight after match play. There were no neurological symptoms reported. Her

initial examination showed some muscle restrictions and tightness as well as some muscular recruitment problems within her gluteal. She had no focal joint tenderness and her range of motion was within her normal limits. She was still able to train and play with no discomfort on court and was due to play two world tour events in America over a period of two weeks.

Diagnosis

On her return, following a long flight, her symptoms worsened and she began to complain of pain when sleeping and generalized discomfort throughout the day. Her examination had altered significantly. Her range of motion was significantly reduced and produced pain particularly when extending backwards. Due to the changes in both symptoms and physical findings, she was sent for an MRI scan of her spine. The results showed that she had a bilateral stress fracture to her L5 lamina, the arms of the vertebrae.

Rehabilitation

Following diagnosis of this injury, the athlete was unable to tolerate axial loading for a prolonged period of time (approximately twelve weeks). The aim of the rehabilitation and reconditioning programme was to return the athlete quickly and safely to readiness for the specific high-force loading required by the training and competition involved in elite level squash. This specific type of injury is a risk within a squash population due to the nature of the sport and therefore careful monitoring of LSP movements is essential to detect problems before they occur (see screening section).

During the rehabilitation phase, it is common for athlete's muscles to atrophy because of the reduced high-force stimuli. A novel form of training was implemented to

(continued)

(continued)

alleviate muscle atrophy and avoid further delay to her return to play.

It is imperative to maintain lower limb strength within a squash player to help dissipate the forces throughout the whole body. To achieve this, a blood flow restriction resistance exercise programme was implemented. Recent evidence has shown low load resistance exercise with blood flow occlusion can induce the same magnitude of strength gain compared to traditional higher load training (Takarada et al., 2002). This involves using strength training exercises such as leg extensions whilst occluding blood flow to the target muscles using a cuff, in this case the quadriceps.

Institutional risk assessment was conducted and informed consent gained prior to the intervention. Pre- and post-intervention gluteal, mid-thigh and calf girth measurements along with sum of eight skinfolds were taken by a certified anthropometrist, adhering to International Society for the Advancement of Kinanthropometry guidelines.

The blood flow restriction intervention involved the athlete completing ten sessions over a period of twelve days (2 × 5 successive days separated by two rest days). Each session contained four sets of seated bilateral knee extension to failure with the athlete completing 20–25 repetitions per set. Inter-set passive recovery duration was forty-five seconds. The athlete wore occlusion cuffs at the proximal thigh on each leg. Meaningful increases in girth measurements were evident post-training, whilst the sum of eight skinfolds remained constant (−1mm).

The results of this training showed significant improvement in leg girth whilst the athlete was unable to complete traditional high-load resistance training and therefore could be considered as part of future rehabilitation interventions within squash.

Fuller, 1999). The economic costs of injury have prompted research to begin to identify mechanisms and risk factors within athletic populations (Minick et al., 2010). The interest in this area has also led to an increase in the implementation of screening tools to attempt to identify those athletes at greater risk of injury.

The aetiology of injury is thought to be due to an interaction of both intrinsic, that is, age and previous injury, and extrinsic factors such as biomechanics, flexibility and strength (Plisky et al., 2006). Within these, neuromuscular control has been identified as a vital area often overlooked by common screening methods (Hewett et al., 2005). Normal movement requires the interaction of both muscle contractility and neuromuscular information to allow joint mobility, strength and stability of actions throughout the kinetic chain. Neuro-muscular control may be affected by previous injury throughout the whole body as restrictions to range of movement or alterations to proprioceptive input may result in developed compensation strategies or altered mechanics (Minick et al., 2010; Nadler et al., 2002). It has been suggested that this is a major risk factor for injury (Hewett et al., 2010).

Early identification

Early identification and prevention of injury is becoming common practice within sports and teams. Previously, screening has focused on isolated assessment methods such as flexibility, strength, joint range of movement (Butler et al., 2010). However, this isolated approach fails to encompass the entire kinetic chain. More recently tests encompassing a more global approach to screening have been introduced; one such test is the Star Excursion Balance Test (SEBT), which has been shown to be a reliable tool at predicting increased lower limb injury risk (Herrington *et al.*, 2009). However, much of the research uses athletes with pre-existing pathology leaving the sensitivity of the tests questionable. More complex assessment methods have used a 3D kinematic assessment to analyse movement patterns, specifically joint angles related to increased injury threat. Plisky *et al.* (2006) proposed that a more global approach may improve the efficacy in identifying those at risk of injury, as focusing on isolated areas may overlook problems that have arisen elsewhere in the chain either due to injury or compensation strategies.

Prehabilitation is now a commonly accepted part of elite sports training. It involves sports-specific exercises encompassing both strength and endurance to target the specific muscles, joints and systems that are predisposed to higher risk of injury due to the nature of both the individual and sports. The aim is to identify areas that may be at risk and prevent an injury from occurring. It is a more proactive approach to injury prevention.

Within squash, this requires an in-depth knowledge of the sport and its physical demands coupled with the common sites for injury. By using screening tools, each individual's areas of weakness can be identified and then both generic and individual prehabilitation programmes can be implemented.

Analysis

The first stage is to understand the sport's demands. It is imperative to look at the range of motion that each joint is required to move through and common movement patterns.

Within squash, the lunge is the principal movement; therefore the screening tests must incorporate this for analysis. By understanding the requirements of this fundamental movement, exercises can be specifically directed to reflect this and be integrated into any return-to-play programme, ensuring the body can tolerate the physical demands safely and efficiently.

Currently, when analysing athletes it is thought that using functional, whole body movement patterns are preferable. By using whole body patterns, it allows the whole kinetic chain system to be assessed and is more reflective of the movements used within sport, as rarely is a muscle used in isolation. In addition, they should also mimic the movement patterns used frequently in the sport. Specifically within squash, the lunge is both multi-directional and under a varying range of movements and speeds. This must also be accounted for in any screening programme. By analysing a fundamental movement pattern, it will then be possible to use more specific tests to highlight any potentially problematic areas. For example: analysis of a straight line lunge may show a difference between the right and left leg in how far the knee travels forward. Further tests such as a range of motion test may then be used to analyse the hip, knee and ankle joints, which will help to identify where the restriction may occur. For example, a modified Thomas test will be used to assess hip and knee mobility and range of movement, a knee-to-wall test may assess ankle and calf range and length.

Specific movement tests may also be implemented such as a single leg squat. These tests can be videoed and scored and therefore used for comparative purposes either after injury or after interventions are put in place. The single leg squat is an excellent test as it challenges the multiple systems such as mobility, proprioception and strength. It allows assessment of pelvic alignment, hip, knee and ankles, all of which may commonly be affected within squash. Another useful test within squash-specific screening may be a single leg bridge, which analyses pelvic stability, glute activation and hamstring strength. These tests can also be incorporated into rehab programmes if required as they are core movement patterns.

Common injuries can be identified formally by using injury audits, but within squash there is little supporting evidence for prevalent injury patterns. It seems that injuries are predominantly occurring in the lower limb and spine, particularly relating to pelvic alignment, lumbar spine issues, ankle instability/sprains and hip impingement.

The individual screening of an athlete is vital to gain an understanding of any restrictions, imbalances or weakness that then may predispose that athlete to injury. The exercises can be strength, endurance, proprioceptive or flexibility. Analysis of all the information can then lead to the formation of prehab exercises. Within squash there may be some generic based exercises to target common problems such as ankle stability exercise/balances, glut activation and lumbar spine/hip dissociation.

Education plays a pivotal role in prehab, particularly with younger athletes. It is important to help athletes recognize the difference between soreness induced from training and more serious pain that may lead to injury if not addressed. An awareness of biomechanics and exercise technique helps to ensure excellent form and maximal effectiveness of exercises. Teaching athletes a battery of common exercises to use in training enables them to use these exercises in competition scenarios where they are responsible for their own maintenance and preparatory work. This is common when travelling and playing overseas where physiotherapy intervention may not be

available. To retain good technique in these exercises over a season, physiotherapists commonly add these exercises into warm-ups and cool-downs.

Nick Matthew OBE
You shouldn't just go to the physio when you are injured – it is just as important to work with your physio to improve things, not just putting out fires on a purely reactive level.

COMPETITION SUPPORT

There are a number of elements that a physiotherapist is required to address during a competition period: the treatment of acute injuries, general physical maintenance and recovery assistance. The main aim at a tournament is to maintain the players in optimal physical condition to limit any possible injuries. The rigours of the game can mean players are subjected to five or six continuous days of match play with matches lasting anything from thirty minutes to over two hours.

The focus is predominantly on maintaining flexibility in the major joints such as hips, lumbar spine and ankles. This may involve mobilizing the joints themselves or using soft tissue techniques to release any tight areas. Both active and passive stretching are included in a player's routine, either pre-match warm-up where more active techniques are used to lengthen the muscles or post-match involving more static stretching. This is normally specific to the needs of each individual player. It is not uncommon for players to have periods of anxiety or stress during competitions, and a physio must therefore be prepared to have an understanding of the individual's psychology and have a certain degree of emotional intelligence to respond appropriately to each athlete.

Nick Matthew OBE
A good physio is someone that knows your routine and knows what you need to play your best. During competition it's all about performance.

General maintenance is another key element of tournament support. Athletes may well be returning from injuries or working on current physical aspects that are still requiring manual treatment. It is usual that any common areas are assessed to detect any small alteration that could lead to injuries. Ordinarily this includes lumbar spine mobility, hip range of movement, pelvic alignment, ankle mobility and lower limb muscle length. Most physiotherapists work with the players routinely on a day-to-day basis and so have an excellent understanding of the individual's 'norms'. By using repeatable tests such as Thomas test for hip flexor length it is easy to identify any abnormal restrictions.

Nick Matthew OBE
During tournament I like to see Jade after the morning practice and get a stretch so my hips are flexible but not too loose. Jade helps me get the perfect balance between the two.

As with any sporting event or competition, injuries do occur. Within squash the common on-court injuries are ankle sprains, muscle tears and blood injuries. During competition, physiotherapists are present courtside during match play in case such incidents do occur. Predominantly there is a primary assessment of the injury to decide if it requires immediate withdrawal from the competition. All non-serious injuries will be treated courtside as appropriate. The most common is blood injuries due to contact with the floor. These can be dressed and covered before returning to the field of play. More serious injuries that require further assessment or treatment will be done back in the medical area.

Recovery is an important facet of tournament support as there are only twenty-four hours or less in which to return a player to optimal physical condition. The main physiological factors contributing to reduced performance levels in the hours and days after a squash match are twofold: extreme repeated eccentric loading, and metabolic stress of high-intensity repeated sprinting. These two factors together contribute to exercise-induced muscle damage and muscle soreness, which can limit performance for several days. A growing body of evidence suggests that the magnitude of muscle damage and muscle soreness can be alleviated with targeted recovery strategies such as ice baths and compression garments (Leeder et al., 2012; Hill et al., 2014). Soft tissue massage is frequently used to reduce muscle soreness too, with the lower limbs and lumbar spine being targeted specifically. Every squash player should have a tried and tested recovery schedule to aid their recovery, which in squash commonly incorporates an active warm-down, nutritional supplementation, cold water immersion and compression garments.

REHABILITATION

Rehabilitation can be an arduous process for any athlete. It is a very time-consuming process if done properly. The majority of athletes normally find this period of return from injury stressful and worrying and the rehabilitation specialist should take this into

CASE STUDY 2: IN-EVENT CALF INJURY

The Player

A senior player, ranked within the world top 10.

Presenting Features

He was playing in the first round of the world championships. There was an incident as he pushed off to move forward for a ball retrieval and he immediately pulled up grabbing his calf. It was evident that he was unable to continue as he was finding it very difficult to weight-bear. He was assisted from the court and an immediate assessment was completed with some muscle strength tests, palpation and range of movement. It was decided that he would have to concede the match as the injury was too serious to continue.

He was immediately moved to the medical area and a full assessment was carried out in conjunction with the sports medicine physician. In this situation we were able to access an ultrasound machine to have a closer look at the muscle integrity. Initial findings indicated that there was significant damage to the gastrocnemius muscle.

Treatment

The primary treatment was to manage any swelling and to prevent further damage by limiting his weight-bearing. He was placed on a very strict icing schedule using a game ready machine that provides ice and compression simultaneously. Although he was no longer participating in the tournament, he was treated three to four times a day. He was also placed on crutches and immobilized in a walking boot to limit his movement and weight-bearing allowing the injury's site to be offloaded. He was also sent for an MRI scan within twenty-four hours to fully assess the damage.

consideration when planning a rehabilitation programme.

The goal of any rehabilitation programme is always to try and return the player to their previous level of performance. In order for this to happen, you must have an excellent understanding of the sports-specific movements and demands the game places on various systems. Rehabilitation tends to be most successful when a multi-disciplinary approach is taken to ensure that all aspects and areas of the athlete's needs are addressed, particularly during long-term rehabilitation where you may need to maintain strength, body composition or CV fitness whilst addressing another area.

For rehabilitation to be successful, you must firstly diagnose the injury using a subjective overview of the incident (if one occurred) and then a physical examination. Within elite sport, more often than not this will be done in conjunction with sports medicine physicians who also have access to further investigative testing such as ultrasound scans and MRIs. The history and presentation of injuries can provide vital information to help develop an accurate picture of the nature of the injury. Once a diagnosis is established then rehabilitation can commence.

Initial input may be therapeutic and manual techniques, in conjunction with the goals and aims of treatment that have been set out using a detailed problem list. For example, if an athlete is diagnosed with a lateral ankle sprain the initial treatment will focus around managing pain, swelling and restoring range of motion using modalities such as cold therapy, soft tissue massage and joint mobilization.

Exercise prescription and selection is a very important element in rehabilitation. Although each injury may be different, ranging from muscle damage or ligament sprains to joint problems, the basic principles remain the same. Again, a thorough understanding of the demands of the sport is required to help progress in an appropriate fashion throughout the process.

Due to the high forces and loads that the body is subjected to in squash, strength is a highly important factor when undertaking a rehabilitation programme. While local strength may be targeted around the injured structures, a programme of general strength should be implemented; this is normally in conjunction with a strength and conditioning coach. Within rehabilitation for the lower limb, it has been established that an individual's lower limb strength should be the equivalent to 1.5 x body weight in order to reduce injury risk when higher loads are placed through the system. General weighted strength exercises such as squats, lunges and leg press are normally incorporated into any rehabilitation programme where possible. By ensuring the athlete has a good strength foundation, the risk of further injury is then reduced and more squash-specific movements can be introduced when this target has been met. This also serves as a guide for a return to court activities.

Low-load, squash-specific exercises can be introduced alongside a strength block to target the injured areas and to begin to mimic a sports-based motor pattern. Integration of any exercises into common movement patterns will enable the body's proprioceptive system to be challenged in familiar manner. For example: the athlete with a lateral ankle sprain may be able to strength train from an early stage of rehabilitation. Whole kinetic chain movements such as a single direction lunge may be introduced as a squash-specific exercise. Initially, the speed will be low and the forces that the athlete is subjected to will therefore be low.

Gradually, by using frequent monitoring and reviewing the measurable, time-specific goals, there are many variables that can be manipulated to progress through the rehabilitation process. Speed of movement, multi-directional movements, controlled versus uncontrolled movements, can all be increased slowly in order to move towards the end goal of court play. It is very important to only alter one factor at a time in order for any adverse effects to be seen quickly.

The introduction of ghosting movements is a relatively late part of the rehabilitation process. It can be a very useful training exercise to replicate squash movements in a controlled environment. Any specific movements that an athlete may find challenging can be targeted in such drills to help increase confidence before court work is started. For example: an early introduction into a ghosting pattern may be done at almost a walking pace with the aim being to allow the athlete to move through the ranges of movements but at a very low load and speed. Gradually, the speed may be increased with all movements planned out and dictated. As the athlete progresses, the drill may be randomized to represent a court-based situation.

The final part of any rehabilitation process will be the return to court scenarios. Again, all the factors previously discussed such as direction, speed, controlled versus uncontrolled movements, can be gradually introduced and manipulated to allow a progressive return to full play. During this stage, time on court should be carefully monitored to ensure a steady increase in loading rather than a sudden acceleration as this could be highly detrimental

CASE STUDY 3: PRE-EVENT KNEE OPERATION

The Player

An elite, male squash player, world ranked No.3, six weeks out from competing in the Commonwealth Games.

Presenting Features

The athlete had no previous history of knee injuries or any knee pain. During a normal technical court session he reported a sudden onset of right knee pain following an innocuous reach and twist overhead, whilst weight-bearing on the leg. Initially, there was some minor swelling around the infrapatellar fat pad. The initial pain was in the anterio-medial part of the knee. It was aggravated when the knee was in an extended position. On examination, there were no findings that indicated any problems with the cartilage. The initial impression was that the fat pad had been irritated or impinged.

Initial Treatment

As the injury appeared to be relatively minor, a programme of rest, ice, taping to offload the fat pad, and patellar femoral joint mobilization was put in place.

Further Analysis

Five days after the initial injury there was a sudden increase in joint swelling and pain after a running session on an anti-gravity treadmill. He developed anterio-medial joint line tenderness and slight loss of hyperextension with pain. After a review with the medical staff, it was deemed that an MRI scan was necessary.

The MRI scan showed a bucket handle tear of right medial meniscus, a tear to the cartilage on the inside of the knee. There was also some degeneration through meniscal body with moderate joint swelling extending into popliteal muscle belly at the back of the knee.

Surgery and Rehab

Due to the timescale leading up to the CWG, following a review with an orthopaedic surgeon it was decided that the best intervention was to undergo a knee arthroscopy and medial menisectomy, which resulted in removing 50 per cent of the right medial meniscus.

The immediate post-operative aims were to reduce swelling, restore full active range of movement and maintain quadriceps activation and strength using common physiotherapy techniques such as ice, exercises and electrotherapy including a muscle stimulator for the quadriceps.

A progressive reloading programme was written to be introduced at one week post-op. All progressions were monitored closely for adverse reactions using a pain scale, swelling circumference around the knee, joint position sense tests to monitor proprioception and hand-held dynamometry for strength. Any deterioration in these markers would have altered the rate of progression and were taken every morning, evening and following any intervention.

The anti-gravity treadmill was used to promote a normal gait pattern, joint load tolerance and maintain CV fitness in an activity that is aligned to the requirements of squash. Initially, body weight was off-loaded to 60 per cent and the time was kept to a minimum (approximately ten minutes) in order to gauge the reaction. Over the course of four weeks, the body weight was incrementally increased to up to 90 per cent. The total running time was also increased, but this was done on separate occasions from any increases in weight-bearing to prevent overloading the joint.

(continued)

(continued)

In addition, the athlete had a specific CV training programme incorporating non-weight-bearing modalities as well as physiotherapy-specific exercises to prepare them for the sports-specific demand, based on a needs analysis of the sport. All of the rehabilitation exercises were based upon the specific muscles and physical demands of squash. A lunge-based movement pattern was introduced from Week 2, progressing from one direction to a multi-directional pattern before being introduced into squash specific drills such as a lunge and ghost.

It was imperative to gradually increase the amount of load passing through the knee joint to prevent placing too high a demand on the recovering areas. Court-based work was implemented around Week 3 in close liaison with coaching staff. It commenced with static based drills, gradually increasing to slightly more dynamic movement patterns and drills. It is thought that the forces during movements to the front of the court place significantly higher demands through the lower limbs due to the higher angles and speeds at which the athlete is moving, so because of this, front court drills were not introduced until later into the rehabilitation programme.

As with any rehabilitation programme, it was governed by how the athlete reacted to any new intervention that was made. A needs analysis allowed the team to identify exactly what the athlete would be required to do in order to compete successfully and therefore the rehabilitation programme was structured to reflect as many aspects of this as possible.

This was a multi-disciplinary approach to his rehabilitation involving strength and conditioning, nutrition, sports medicine, physiology and psychology. It was very important to take into account the mental aspect to rehabilitation and injury which can be very intense for athletes. It is essential to understand their personal needs and requirements to feel ready to participate. The use of goal setting is a significant tool that can be implemented in their rehab programme. By setting both short- and long-term goals, the athlete has targets to work towards and can see any progress that is being made, which helps with motivation as rehab can be quite arduous and mentally draining.

The athlete progressed very well and was able to compete in the Commonwealth games, winning an individual gold medal and a men's double silver medal.

to the rehabilitation process and overload the athlete, leading to repeated injuries.

During the rehabilitation phase, other factors such as diet, physiology and psychology should also be considered as the combination of such factors may have a significant impact on the efficacy of rehabilitation. Daily, weekly and monthly monitoring must be established in order to show a documented progression through the different stages of rehabilitation.

Take-home rehab messages:

- Maintenance of specific strength and CV fitness during rehab;
- Multi-disciplinary approach essential – usually contributions from physio, doctor, strength and conditioning coach, nutrition and psychologist;
- Manipulate one variable at a time and assess with monitoring system;
- Planned systematic incremental loading pattern.

Nick Matthew OBE

When you are long-term injured you have to have something to focus on to motivate you and starve the boredom. Sometimes the long-term goal of being successful and winning matches again can feel so far away that you have to set short-term goals as well to keep you going day to day. If you only focus on the long-term goal it can feel so distant that it can turn into a negative. You need to set daily goals to keep the momentum of your motivation.

CONCLUSION

Injuries, either acute or through repetitive micro trauma, can have career-ending implications for squash players if not managed correctly. Consequently the physiotherapist plays a pivotal role in both preventative strategies and fast tracking return to play following injury. As with any aspect of performance, it is essential that the physiotherapist works in conjunction with the rest of the multi-disciplinary team including the athlete themselves to provide a holistic approach to the athlete's performance management.

Fig. 4.4 Nick Matthew shows an example of the unorthodox body positions players have to get into to play squash at the very top level.

REFERENCES

Benson, B.L., Rolnick, A.M., Ramos, C.G. (1981). An epidemiological study of squash injuries. *Am J Sports Med*, 9, 103–106.

Butler, R.J., Plisky, P.J., Southers, C., Scoma, C. and Kiesel, K.B. (2010). Biomechanical analysis of the different classifications of the Functional Movement Screen deep squat test. *Sports Biomech*, 9, 270–279.

Chard, M.D., Lachmann, S.M. (1987). Racquet sports patterns of injury presenting to a sports injury clinic. *Br J Sports Med*, 21, 150–153.

Clavisi O. and Finch C. (1999). Striking out squash injuries—what is the evidence? *Int J Consumer Prod Safety*, 6(3), 145–157.

Cullen, P.T. and Silko, G.J. (1994). Indoor racquet sports injuries. *Am Fam Physician*, 50, 374–380.

Finch, C.F. and Eime, R.M. (2001) The Epidemiology of Squash Injuries. *Int Sport Med J*, 2(2), 1–11.

Fong, L.P. (1994). Sports-related eye injuries. *Med J Aust*, 160, 743–750.

Hawkins, R. and Fuller, C.W. (1999). A prospective epidemiological study of injuries in four English professional football clubs. *Br J Sports Med*, 33, 196–203.

Herrington, L., Hatcher, J., Hatcher, A. and McNicholas, M. (2009). A comparison of star excursion balance test research distances between acl deficient patients and asymptomatic controls. *The Knee*, 16, 149–152, 2009.

Hewett, T.E., Myer, G.D., Ford, K.F., Heidt, R.S,. Colosimo, A.J., McLean, S.G., van der Bogert, A.J., Paterno, M.V. and Succop, P. (2005). Biomechanical measures of neuromuscular control and valgus loading of the knee predict anterior cruciate ligament injury risk in female athletes: A prospective study. *Am J Sports Med*, 33, 492–501.

Hill J., Howatson G., van Someren K., Leeder J.D.C. and Pedlar C. (2014). Compression garments and recovery from exercise-induced muscle damage: a meta-analysis. *Br J Sports Med*, Sep, 48(18), 1340–6.

Leeder, J.D.C., Gissane, C., van Someren, K., Gregson, W. and Howatson, G. (2012). Cold water immersion and recovery from strenuous exercise: A meta analysis. *Br J Sports Med*, 46, 233–240.

Locke S., Colqunhoun D. and Briner M., (1997). Squash racquets. A review of physiology and medicine. *Sports Med*, 23(2), 130–138.

Macfarlane, D.J., Shanks, A. (1998). Back injuries in competitive squash players. *J Sports Med Phys Fitness*, 38, 337–343.

Micheli, L. and Curtis, C. (2006). Stress Fractures in the Spine and Scarum. *Clin Sports Med*, 25, 75–88 .

Minick, K.L., Kiesel, K.B., Burton, L.B., Taylor, A., Plisky, P. and Butler, R. (2010). Inter rater reliability of the Functional Movement Screen. *J of Strength Conditioning Res*, 24, 479–486.

Montpetit R. (1990). Applied physiology of squash. *Sports Med*, 10(1), 31–41.

Nadler, S.F., Malanga, G.A., Feinberg, J.H., Rubbani, M., Moley, P. and Foye, P. (2002). Functional performance deficits in athletes with previous lower extremity injury. *Clin J Sport Med*, 12, 73–78.

Pforringer W. (1980). So you think you are safe playing squash. *Squash Player Int*, 14–15.

Plisky, P.J., Rauh, M.J., Kaminski, T.W. and Underwood, F.B. (2006). Star excursion balance test as a predictor of lower extremity injury in high school basketball player. *J Orth Sports Phys Ther*, 36, 911–919.

Takarada Y., Sato Y. and Ishii N. (2002). Effects of resistance exercise combined with vascular occlusion on muscle function in athletes. *Eur J Appl Physiol*, 86, 308–314.

van Dijk C.N. (1994). Injuries in squash. In: Renstrom P.A., ed. *Clinical Practice of Sports Injury Prevention and Care*. London: Blackwell Scientific Pubs; pp. 486–494.

CHAPTER 5

PERFORMANCE NUTRITION: APPLYING THE SCIENCE

Chris Rosimus and Stephanie Shreeve,
English Institute of Sport

Fig. 5.1 Laura Massaro attributes a large part of her success to a good nutrition plan.

WHAT THE PLAYERS THINK

Nick Matthew OBE

A good diet allows you to be consistent with your training, sleeping and recovery between matches or sessions. Like any-thing, one good meal is not going to make a difference, you have to have good eating habits and make sure these are consistently applied. I have never bought into nutritional fads – I feel constant good food habits are more beneficial and also easier to maintain at home or abroad.

During tournament I will eat around 25 per cent more carbs than normal. Some people say carbs are the devil but when you are playing a squash tournament you need that extra energy source. When I was young I used to have carbs for every meal. I realize now that was overload and gradu-ally worked out that you need to alter your diet depending on how hard your training was at that point. It's not about getting the maximum amount of fuel; it's about getting the appropriate amount of fuel.

It is important when you are in places where it may be risky to eat the fruit or salads that you have supplements with you to replace the nutrients you may have lost. I don't like having to rely on supplements and prefer a good balanced diet, but sometimes you do have to adapt your pattern and use supplements to ensure your body is getting everything it needs.

James Willstrop

You work so hard as a player you need to enjoy your food – you need a good balance and not to become obsessive about it.

Laura Massaro

When you are travelling to all different countries you can sometimes over-analyse your diet and do your own head in – some-times you have to use a bit of common sense and just get the best available to you. It is difficult when your match finishes late at night – this is where recovery shakes and meal replacement drinks are priceless.

If you do become leaner you have to make sure you are not losing power as a consequence. When you are training hard all the time you get hungry, and at this point the hardest thing for me to control is portion size.

Fig. 5.2 James Willstrop is a great believer in the power of food, but he also thinks you should not become obsessive with your diet.

Fig. 5.3. Due to the high levels of energy used in squash is it essential to refuel the body properly.

WHAT THE COACHES THINK

Dave Pearson

When I played we didn't understand the science of eating – you just ate what you thought you needed. Traditionally we thought because we burnt so many calories playing the sport then we could eat as many carbs as we liked! A few years ago Nick Matthew started to bulk up a bit too much by eating too many carbs, he changed his diet and now is in the best shape he has ever been in.

The nutrition plan needs to be tailored to each sport and each athlete as everyone will have different needs and different solutions required. When travelling the world as a squash player a sound nutritional strategy is absolutely vital for success. Players need to be careful with what they eat – but also careful they don't become obsessive and let it take over their thoughts 24/7.

Paul Carter

When I was playing we didn't know about nutrition – we would eat three square meals a day and presume that was OK – but these days it's also essential that players do allow themselves a treat at times. The key to good nutritional support is early education at the junior level – it will then become a daily habit for the players as they progress through their career. When working with juniors it is also vital to educate the player's parents around nutritional planning.

Players need to plan their eating habits when travelling. If they do not get what they are used to eating it will have a negative physical and a massive mental effect on them. When travelling to some countries you have to be careful eating buffet food or food that has been washed in the local water.

David Campion

They say you are what you eat! Good nutrition is absolutely vital to succeed in squash. Nutrition is a very scientific process and enables the players to measure the effect their diet is having on them physically.

THE NUTRITIONAL DEMANDS OF SQUASH

Squash is a high-intensity sport, requiring multiple bouts of vigorous sprint activity (Wilkinson, McCord and Winter, 2010). A squash player's ability to perform high-intensity, variable movements is a key determinant of success at the elite level of competition (Wilkinson et al., 2012). The body composition of a squash player may affect athletic performance and carrying excessive body fat may increase injury risk and impair agility and speed. However, minimal body fat levels may negatively impact endurance and immunity (Meltzer and Hopkins, 2011), which may result in reduced performance and increase the risk of illness. Athletes who wish to optimize athletic performance by reducing their body fat levels and maintain lean mass are advised to follow a structured nutritional intervention that promotes a gradual body mass loss of 0.5–1kg per week. Moreover, preservation of lean body mass (LBM) is desirable to a squash player in order to prevent unwanted losses of strength, speed and power. In consideration of this, achieving an appropriate energy balance is essential, as adequate nutrient intake will support health, training load and performance. In addition, as squash is predominantly an indoor sport with little structured outdoor training, players may be at increased risk of vitamin D deficiency (Angeline, Gee, Shindle, Warren and Rodeo, 2013), due to the lack of exposure to ultraviolet radiation from the sun.

MAXIMIZING PERFORMANCE

The human body requires a balanced intake of nutrients to stay healthy. Whether you are an elite athlete or recreational exerciser, adequate nutrient intake is essential to support muscle growth and repair, maintain bone health, and provide fuel to support performance and boost the immune system. To ensure optimal nutrition is achieved, elite athletes should consume a variety of nutrients from multiple sources to ensure all essential micro- and macronutrients are consumed. This is important in order to support the physical demands placed on the body through sport. The body receives energy from carbohydrate (4 kcal/g), protein (4 kcal/g), fat (9 kcal/g) and alcohol (7 kcal/g). Furthermore, athletes should aim to start training and competition in a hydrated state, and consume fluid as appropriate to the intensity and duration of exercise performed to ensure the degree of dehydration has no negative impact on performance.

Carbohydrate requirements for squash

Carbohydrates (CHO) are the preferred source of fuel during exercise as they are easily oxidized and utilized as energy. Dietary CHO are classified by their structure (Monosaccharides, disaccharides, oligosaccharides and polysaccharides) and are available in two forms: sugars or starch. These are broken down and absorbed into the bloodstream as glucose. The body stores carbohydrate in skeletal muscle (approximately 500g) and the liver (approximately 100g) in the form of glycogen. During high-intensity exercise, glycogen is converted into glucose and delivers fuel to working muscle and the brain via the bloodstream (Fig. 5.4).

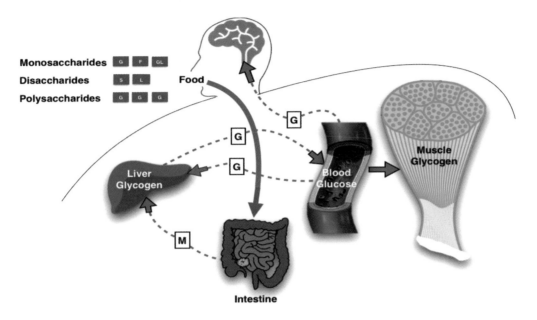

Monosaccharides

Disaccharides

Polysaccharides

Fig. 5.4 Carbohydrate metabolism.

FUELLING BEFORE, DURING AND AFTER
SQUASH

Ensuring adequate glycogen stores before
exercise is important for the athlete. A high
muscle glycogen concentration will allow the
athlete to perform at their optimal intensity
for a sustained period of time, whereas low
muscle glycogen can lead to early fatigue and
a subsequent drop in performance. With this
in mind, carbohydrate-feeding strategies are
an important consideration for all squash
players.

3–4 HOURS BEFORE EXERCISE

The pre-exercise meal is important for a
variety of reasons (Table 5.1). The main
purpose for it is to provide the athlete
with sufficient energy to perform, particularly
CHO. Daily CHO intakes can vary between 3
and 12g/kg per day. It is important to note that
carbohydrate intakes are highly variable for
each individual and there is no 'one size fits all'
approach, as requirements may vary depend-

ent upon competition schedule, training load
and body composition.

In general, a meal providing a relatively
high amount of CHO should be consumed
approximately three to four hours before
exercise and provide approximately 1–3g/kg
of CHO. For example, a 70kg squash player
would require between 70g–210g of CHO

**Table 5.1. The goals of the
pre-exercise meal. (Table adapted
from Hawley and Burke, 1998)**

- Top up muscle glycogen stores;
- Restore liver glycogen stores after an
  overnight fast;
- Ensure the athlete starts exercise in a
  hydrated state;
- Prevent hunger.

Table 5.2. Pre-exercise meal examples based on a 70kg athlete.

- 100g cereal, 300ml milk, 1 banana;
- 4 slices of brown bread with jam and 1 apple;
- 2 bagels with honey, 1 fruit yoghurt and 1 glass of fruit juice;
- 1 baked potato with 200g baked beans;
- 300g pasta with tomato-based sauce;
- 125g couscous, 200g sweetcorn and 1 fruit yoghurt.

approximately three to four hours before training or competition. This meal should also include a moderate amount of protein and be low in saturated fat (less than 3g), but is predominately CHO. Meal examples are listed in Table 5.2. Moreover, research has been conducted investigating the effect of carbohydrate loading in the days preceding exercise.

A study of nine New Zealand level squash players were recruited to complete a simulated squash match on two occasions: following a forty-eight-hour high-carbohydrate diet (11.1g/kg–1); and following a calorie-matched low-carbohydrate (2.1g/kg–1) diet. The match simulation was designed to mimic a five-game match lasting approximately one hour. They found that the higher CHO intake was associated with significantly faster time to complete the games (2340 ± 189 s vs 2416 ± 128 s, p = .036). Blood glucose and lactate concentrations were also significantly higher in the high-carbohydrate condition (p = .038 and p = .021 respectively). These results suggest that ingestion of a diet high in carbohydrate (>10g/kg body weight) preceding simulated competitive squash produces increased rates of carbohydrate oxidation

and maintains higher blood glucose concentrations. These metabolic effects were associated with improved physical performance (Raman, Macdermid, Mundel, Mann and Stannard, 2014).

RECOVERY

One of the main goals of post-exercise recovery is to replenish glycogen stores via CHO ingestion. This is particularly important to sustain performance levels if the athlete has multiple training sessions or matches during the course of a day. Resting muscle glycogen stores range between 500 and 600g (Bosch et al., 1996; Costill et al., 1981) but can decrease during high-intensity exercise of relatively short duration (Van Beelen, Wouterse, Masselink, Spijker and Mesman, 2011). If adequate CHO is consumed, muscle glycogen is typically restored within twenty-four hours (Burke et al., 1995; Costill et al., 1981). This process can be accelerated if CHO is consumed alongside protein, due to elevated insulin levels that stimulate glucose uptake and activate muscle glycogen synthase (Cartee et al., 1989; Jentjens and Jeukendrup, 2003; Wallberg-Henriksson et al., 1988). If the athlete only has a short period of time between training or match play, it is advised that high-carbohydrate snacks that are easily digested are consumed as soon as possible post-exercise (Table 5.3). If the athlete has a longer period of time between bouts (twelve to twenty-four hours), then it is less critical to consume CHO immediately post-workout.

Protein

Protein is an essential component of an athlete's diet, key to building and repairing muscle to promote recovery and enhance training adaptation. Athletes have believed for a very long time that large intakes of

Table 5.3. Immediate post-exercise recovery snacks that provide CHO and protein.

- Low-fat chocolate milk;
- 500ml isotonic sports drink and 1 small pot of low-fat yoghurt;
- 1 banana and 300ml semi-skimmed milk;
- Tuna sandwich in white bread;
- 2 slices of toast with jam and peanut butter;
- 1 bowl of soup and 1 bread roll;
- 1 baked potato with cottage cheese and ¼ tin of baked beans.

protein are necessary for optimal athletic performance; however, more is not necessarily better. Dietary protein recommendations for a sedentary individual are ~0.8g/kg per day, with typical athletes consuming 1.2–2.0g/kg of bodyweight of protein per day dependent on the exercise type, intensity and duration of training. During periods of hypertrophy or reduced calorie intake athletes should consume approximately 1.7g/kg of bodyweight per day whilst 1.2–1.5g/kg of bodyweight is sufficient to support training and recovery.

The timing of protein post-training sessions is particularly important, with athletes aiming to consume 10–20g immediately after every training session. Protein intake is particularly important after intense court sessions and S and C sessions. The addition of carbohydrate (1g/kg of bodyweight) is essential post-exercise to speed the delivery of protein to the muscles and replenish glycogen stores. The use of rapidly digested whey-derived protein supplement (recovery shakes) is a practical option for training/competition as many athletes experience a suppressed appetite or need to coordinate with other post-training session commitments. Then they can plan to have their main meal within one or two hours post-session.

Animal proteins have a high biological value; they contain all the sixteen essential amino acids required for optimal recovery. Larger quantities of plant based proteins need to be consumed to provide the equivalent amounts of protein.

SUMMARY

Protein is an essential macronutrient for athletes.

Consume 10–20g post-training session, particularly post-S and C sessions.

The use of whey-based recovery drinks are a suitable practical option for optimizing protein recovery post a training session, especially if experiencing a supressed appetite.

High protein rich sources are meat, fish, dairy and eggs, while plant-based protein sources include tofu, beans, pulses, nuts and seeds.

Table 5.4 Example of 10g of protein per portion size.

- 30g lean meat or poultry;
- 40g fish;
- 125g tofu, lentils, beans;
- 2 small eggs;
- 200g yoghurt;
- 40g hard cheese;
- 50g nuts and seeds.

Table 5.5 Fluid replacement guidelines.								
Weight loss (kg)	0.25	0.50	0.75	1.0	1.25	1.5	1.75	2.00
Volume to drink (ml)	400	750	1125	1500	1875	2250	2625	3000

HYDRATION

During exercise, the production of sweat helps to regulate body temperature. Sweat rates are determined by the environment conditions, duration and intensity of the exercise. There is large inter-individual variation in sweat rates, but typical maximum sweat rates are approximately 2–3L/hr. The current position stand on fluid replacement during exercise highlights the need to prevent excessive (>2 per cent) body mass loss, to minimize any compromise in performance (Sawka et al., 2007).

While squash matches are usually of relatively short duration, they can be played in hot and humid conditions. Dehydration is a common problem in squash athletes, particularly in tournaments, with sweat losses measured at 1333–2370mL per hour in male elite squash players. Most were unable to match their fluid intake during the match, resulting in dehydration of 1.3–2.2 per cent of body weight (Brown et al., 1998). During a squash match, fluid intake is limited to the periods between games. Players must optimize opportunities available to consume fluid and ensure volume is sufficient. Fluid should be consumed before and after the match, particularly if further competition or training is planned for later in the day.

It is vital for athletes to start matches and training well hydrated and utilize every opportunity to drink sufficient fluids to minimize losses. Water is a good choice; however, athletes should consider using sports drinks, which provide carbohydrate and electrolytes, as these help their body retain fluid. Also ensuring fluids are cold and sweetened will encourage fluid intake (Sawka et al., 2007).

Monitoring hydration status

Regular monitoring of morning urine colour will give a quick indication of the current hydration status. The darker the fluid, the more likely that the athlete is dehydrated and needs to increase fluid intake immediately. The aim is for a large volume of light straw-coloured urine. Those individuals who maintain a pale yellow urine colour always are typically within 1 per cent of their baseline hydrated body mass. Urine colour does not offer the same precision and accuracy as urine specific gravity or osmolality, but it is likely effective in athletic settings.

It is vital to understand the volume of fluid that is lost during a training session or game. An easy way is to weigh in before and after training in minimal clothing (after towel-drying), and for each 1kg lost in body weight replace with 1.5L of fluid.

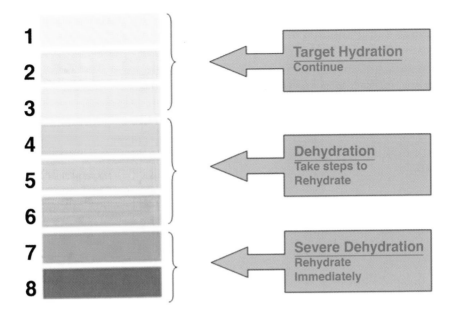

Fig. 5.5 Monitoring of morning urine colour.

SPECIAL CONSIDERATIONS: THE VEGETARIAN ATHLETE

A well-designed vegetarian diet can meet the requirements for energy, carbohydrates and protein for athletes. Vegetarian diets can be very high in fibre with the inclusion of many beans, legumes, fruits, vegetables and wholegrain cereals. High-fibre diets have high satiety values (make you feel less hungry) and therefore may struggle to meet total energy requirements. In athletes with high energy demands the use of lower-fibre cereals (cornflakes, white bread, pasta and rice) may be needed to help to meet large energy demands.

Protein

Whilst animal products contain complete proteins (all sixteen essential amino acids are present), plant sources of proteins are limited by one or more essential amino acids. Combining foods that do not contain essential amino acids with other foods that contain the missing amino acids is an important part of recovery from training.

MAXIMIZING PROTEIN INTAKE
Good vegetarian sources of protein include:

- Eggs, milk and milk products (cheese, yoghurts). Vegans should choose calcium and vitamin B12 fortified milk alternatives such as soy.
- Tofu, falafel, beans, lentils, textured vegetable protein, peanut butter and nut spread, tahini, hummus, nuts and seeds.
- Replace meat with tinned beans in recipes, for example try a vegetarian chilli or lentil lasagne.

Calcium

Dairy foods are the richest sources of calcium but if these have been excluded then fortified soya products such as milk, cheese and yoghurt are excellent calcium-rich alternatives. Other vegetable sources include leafy greens (spinach, watercress, broccoli), figs, almonds, brazil nuts.

Iron

There are two forms of iron in the diet – haem iron (found in animal-derived foods) and non-haem iron (found in fortified cereals, legumes, green leafy vegetables). Haem iron is well absorbed by the body (15–35 per cent) whereas non-haem iron is not as readily absorbed (2–8 per cent). It is important for any athlete to be aware of iron-rich foods and factors that inhibit or enhance iron absorption, but particularly a vegetarian athlete. Iron plays an important role in energy generation, growth and immunity, and it is especially important for teenage athletes or female athletes who are menstruating.

MAXIMIZING IRON INTAKE

Vegetarian sources high in iron include iron-fortified breakfast cereals, beans, nuts, legumes, and green leafy vegetables. Vitamin C increases the absorption of iron, and to maximize the absorption of iron meals should include a vitamin C source such as tomato, peppers, chilli, kiwi fruit, berries or oranges.

Tea and coffee contain tannins, which will limit the amount of iron absorbed from foods. Tea and coffee should be kept outside of meals to increased absorption of iron (two-hour spacing is recommended).

Summary

- A varied diet is essential to maximize intake of zinc, iron, calcium, vitamin B12 and riboflavin. Choose a wide variety of breads, cereals, fruit, vegetables, legumes, nuts, seeds, milk and milk products (or alternatives) to maximize nutrient intake and availability.
- Iron is essential for athletes, and with poor bio-availability it is important to achieve sufficient levels of iron through a variety of different iron-rich food sources. Increase Vitamin C and avoid tea and coffee around meals.

SUPPLEMENTS AND ERGOGENIC AIDS

Although dietary supplements and nutritional ergogenic aids, such as nutritional products that enhance performance, are highly prevalent, the fact remains that very few improve performance (Rodriguez, Di Marco and Langley, 2009). However, the use of sports foods such as protein powders, energy bars and meal replacement products may be a practical option and support an athlete's diet, particularly during competition in the subcontinent when food quality and variety may be limited. Alongside these, the use of sports drinks that provide carbohydrate and electrolytes to aid hydration may be beneficial.

Evidence-based supplements

CREATINE

Creatine is currently the most widely used ergogenic aid among athletes wanting to build muscle and enhance recovery (Bemben and Lamont, 2005b; M, 2006; Rawson and Volek, 2003; Volek and Rawson, 2004). Creatine can aid in the rapid rephosphorylation of adenosine diphosphate (AD) back to adenosine triphosphate (ATP) by the creatine kinase reaction during high-intensity exercise, especially if the bouts of intense activity are repeated with short rest periods between them (Bemben and Lamont, 2005a).

To our knowledge, only one study has investigated the use of creatine in squash. In this study by Romer et al. (2001), nine squash players performed an on-court ghosting routine that involved ten sets of two repetitions of simulated positional play, each set interspersed with thirty seconds passive recovery. Experimental and control groups supplemented four times daily for five days with creatine or a placebo, separated by a four-week washout period between each trial. The creatine group improved mean set sprint time by 3.2 per cent with Sets 2 to 10 being completed in a significantly shorter time following creatine supplementation compared to the placebo condition. These findings provide encouraging evidence that creatine supplementation may improve exercise performance in competitive squash players. Given the high-intensity nature of squash competition and training in addition to periods of strength and conditioning work undertaken by elite level squash players, the use of creatine as an ergogenic aid to promote recovery and adaptation to training may be desirable.

CAFFEINE

The effects of caffeine in reducing fatigue and increasing wakefulness and alertness have been recognized for many centuries (Burke, 2008). These properties have been targeted by shift workers, long-haul truck drivers, members of the military forces, athletes, and other populations who need to fight fatigue or prolong their capacity to undertake their occupational activities (Burke, 2008).

From a sporting perspective, the potential ergogenic effects of caffeine may be more closely related to its role as a CNS stimulant and the associated decreased perception of effort (Dunford M, 206; Rodriguez, DiMarco and Langley, 2009). Although no squash-specific research is available, the effect of caffeine in other sports has been investigated. A study found that Rugby Union players ingesting 6 mg/kg/bw recorded an improvement in 20 and 30 metre sprint performance respectively (Stuart, Hopkins, Cook and Cairns, 2005). In addition, a study of tennis players found that caffeine ingestion might improve skill execution. Following intake of 3mg/kg/bw, players showed improved forehand stroke during ninety minutes of simulated tennis activity (Strecker, 2007). Further research involving the squash population may be desirable to establish its possible ergogenic effect on squash performance.

TART CHERRIES

As previously mentioned, optimal recovery post-match is desirable to help maintain subsequent performance and minimize the risk or impact of fatigue-related injury. With this in mind, there is emerging evidence that ingestion of tart cherries may help prevent symptoms of muscle damage. Consumption of about forty-five cherries a day has been shown to reduce circulating concentrations of inflammatory markers in healthy men and women (Jacob et al., 2003; Kelley, Rasooly, Jacob, Kader and Mackey, 2006). Considering the natural anti-inflammatory and antioxidant capacity of tart cherries, it is plausible that cherry consumption before and after eccentric exercise may have a protective effect (Connolly, McHugh, Padilla-Zakour, Carlson, and Sayers, 2006).

QUALITY ASSURANCE

When choosing notional supplementation, it is essential to ensure that the product has been adequately tested for banned substances. For elite or professional athletes, it is possible that they will be requested to participate in a random drugs test, particularly in and around a competition. To help minimize any risk, best practice before taking any nutritional supplementation is to consult with a registered performance nutritionist who can advise appropriately.

MINIMIZING THE IMPACT OF ILLNESS AND INJURY

Immunity

Athletes are at increased risk of infection (especially upper respiratory tract infections) during heavy training periods and competition. The cause of this increased risk is not completely understood but could be due to a number of factors, such as increased exposure to pathogens, environmental factors, stress and poor nutritional strategies.

It is vital to ensure to implement appropriate nutritional strategies before, during and in recovery of training and competition to reduce negative effects on immunity. Poor diet or deficiencies in total energy intake, carbohydrate, protein and key micronutrients have been shown to have negative effects on immunity.

CARBOHYDRATE

An athlete who consumes less than recommended carbohydrate levels is at greater risk of illness. Exercising in a glycogen-depleted state has been shown to negatively impact many aspects of immune function with greater activation of stress hormones. Consuming a normal mixed diet with a good combination of carbohydrates, proteins and fats alongside optimal recovery strategies post-training sessions will all enhance carbohydrate stores.

Ingesting carbohydrate during extended training sessions can significantly blunt any aspects of acute exercise-induced immune depression. An intake of 30–60g/hour through commercially available sports drinks will provide adequate carbohydrate intake, whilst simultaneously supporting hydration levels.

PROBIOTICS

Probiotic supplementation regulates the intestinal microbial flora and enhances gut immune function. The gut microbial flora interacts with other cells in the body to exert health benefits on the skin and upper respiratory tract, which can provide additional immunity support during heavy training periods.

It is encouraged to take probiotic supplementation during heavy training blocks and also the two weeks prior to travel, whilst travelling and during competition to optimize immunity during these times. Probiotics are only effective if taken daily, so regular consumption is key.

ANTIOXIDANTS

Deficiencies in micronutrients (vitamins and minerals) will have a negative effect on immunity, so ensuring the diet provides the recommended levels is vital, and once this deficiency has been corrected immune function is typically restored. For ultra-endurance athletes mega doses of vitamin C and E have been shown to reduce infection incidences; however, for those who are not deficient it does not show any significant improvements.

Recent evidence suggests that taking excessive single antioxidant doses can blunt the adaptation response to training. It is recommended to avoid using high doses of antioxidants during training periods and use only during competition. Alternatively functional foods, such as cherry and blackcurrant juice, which are naturally high in antioxidants but are mixed with other substances, do not have a similar blunting effect.

Special considerations: Travelling

Travelling abroad is typical for many athletes, with many having regular occurrences throughout the season. Planning ahead is the key to success, to eliminate as much disruption to routine as possible.

Key areas to plan ahead for are:

- Eating logistics: self-catering or catered through hotel;
- Climate: hot humid conditions affect hydration so additional fluids will be needed to maintain hydration;
- Food quality and safety: some countries have lower standards of food hygiene, so take care to avoid gastrointestinal upsets.

When an athlete is travelling long haul, it is advised to set their watch to local time as soon as possible when boarding the flight, so sleep and eating times can be adjusted to the new destination. They should take plenty of activities on board the flight to keep awake and to avoid eating when bored. Meals should be pre-ordered (if possible) and plenty of adequate snacks taken onto the flight, as many in-flight meals and snacks are not that healthy.

Ideal snack options for flight include:

- Pre-prepared pasta or rice pots;
- Bread roll/bagel with lean meat filling;
- Fresh fruit;
- Dried fruit and nut mixes;
- Cereal/seed bars;
- Rice cakes;
- Malt loaf.

Pressurized cabins and air-conditioned environments increase fluid loss from the skin and the lungs, so the advice is to drink plenty on the flight. Drink fluid regularly, approximately 300ml/hour (avoid alcohol or caffeine), and carry an empty water bottle in hand luggage and ask the cabin crew on the plane to fill it up to ensure fluid is available at all times.

Nutrition for bone health

Since squash is an indoor sport, with little structured outdoor training, it must be recognized that individuals who predominantly perform indoors are at increased risk of vitamin D deficiency (Angeline et al., 2013), due to the lack of exposure to ultraviolet radiation from the sun. Sunlight is a major source of vitamin D resulting from the conversion of 7-dehydrocholesterol to vitamin D3 within the skin (Fig. 5.6).

Vitamin D deficiency is common – in America approximately 1 billion of the general public are classified as vitamin D deficient (Holick, 2007). Vitamin D is synthesized in the skin upon direct exposure to sunlight, and is responsible for the regulation of calcium, phosphate and parathyroid hormone (PTH). An optimal level of vitamin D to support athletic performance is unknown. However, a serum level of 25-hydroxy vitamin D less than 20 nmol/L is considered deficient for the general public. In athletes, vitamin D deficiency may impair muscle function, compromise the immune system and increase the risk of bone-related injury due to increased bone resorption and subsequent decreased bone density (Need, Horowitz, Morris and Nordin, 2000).

VITAMIN D SUPPLEMENTATION

There are few studies that investigate the vitamin D status of athletes. However, a study of elite Australian female gymnasts (aged ten to seventeen years) showed that fifteen athletes recorded serum levels of 25-hydroxy

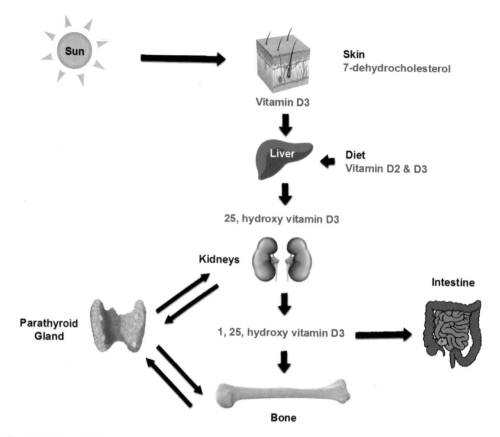

Fig. 5.6 Vitamin D metabolism.

vitamin D3 of less than 75 nmol/L with a further six displaying levels below 50 nmol/ (Lovell, 2008). Moreover, a study of club-level athletes who supplemented with 20,000 and 40,000 IU D3 for twelve weeks effectively restored inadequate vitamin D levels in 57 per cent of subjects, with differences between doses for serum 25-hydroxy vitamin D3 seen after six weeks, but with no significant difference observed between doses at twelve weeks (Close et al., 2013).

This suggests that sports performed indoors contribute to suboptimal vitamin status of athletes and that appropriate supplementation protocols should be considered to optimize the bone and immune health of athletes, particularly during the winter months when exposure to sunlight is further limited. This is an important consideration in the prevention of bone-related injury, with research of female military recruits showing that vitamin D supplementation significantly reduced the risk of stress fracture (Lappe et al., 2008).

Fatigue

There are a number of different factors that can cause fatigue, such as depletion of muscle glycogen stores, dehydration, inadequate sleep and recovery. Ensuring optimal nutritional strategies throughout training and competition will reduce fatigue and any negative effects on performance.

Table 5.6 Practical application		
Before	7am	Breakfast cereal, slice of toast with jam, yoghurt, and fresh fruit. Start drinking bottle of fluid;
	9am	Cereal bar and a banana. Continued fluid sips during warm-up;
During	10am	Bottles of water and sports drink, to drink during breaks;
Post	11.30am	500ml of low-fat milk/recovery shake with piece of fruit such as banana. Replace lost fluids;
	1.30pm	Jacket potato with cottage cheese and tuna, side salad. Yoghurt.

RECOVERY

Post-exercise recovery is a challenge to athletes to ensure restoration of muscle glycogen, replacement of fluids and electrolytes lost in sweat. Post-court sessions it is vital to replace carbohydrate – 1g/kg body mass (70g if 70kg athlete) alongside 10–25g of protein will have a substantial effect on refuelling and recovery post-exercise. Aim for recovery food to be consumed within 20–30mins post exercise.

FUELLING

When at competition, eating large meals before a match is not ideal so ensure eating regular smaller snacks throughout the day, to avoid any gastrointestinal discomfort when playing. Eat a larger meal three to four hours before a training session or game; a smaller snack such as fresh fruit, cereal bar, fruit and yoghurt, bread with honey or jam can be eaten approximately one hour before. Refuelling during the game with a carbohydrate sports drink will support hydration but also maintain energy levels and limit the reduction in muscle glycogen.

FATIGUE DUE TO HYDRATION

Being dehydrated will also negatively affect fatigue levels, and is simple to correct. It is best not to rely on thirst but to drink regularly to avoid any possible dehydration. With limited time during games to drink between games, it is more crucial to pay extra attention to hydration before competition starts, and ensure post-match that all lost fluids are replaced. During exercise, monitor changes in body mass – a loss of 1kg = 1L of fluid – so aim to drink 150 per cent (1.5L) post-exercise within the next few hours to fully restore fluid balance. Have fluids available at all meals and keep a water bottle handy throughout the day. Drinking is a habit and needs to be practised.

HOW TO ASSESS HYDRATION STATUS

It is vital to effectively monitor hydration during training and competition; however the techniques need to be easy to use, safe, portable and inexpensive.

URINE SPECIFIC GRAVITY

The specific gravity of urine refers to the density (mass per volume) of a sample in comparison to water. Any fluid that is denser than water has a specific gravity greater than 1.000, with normal urine specimens ranging from 1.013 to 1.029. When dehydrated, urine specific gravity exceeds 1.030.

Specific gravity can be measured quickly and accurately with a handheld refractometer. A few drops of a urine specimen are placed

OSMO Score	Hydration Status	Immediate Action
Less than 350	Extrememely overhydrated	No need for extra fluid
350 - 450	Slighty overhydrated	No need for extra fluid
450 - 750	Well hydrated	Drink when thirsty
750 - 880	Slightly dehydrated	300ml water before warm-up & 300ml after warm-up
900 - 1000	Dehydrated	600ml water & 1-2 electrotabs
More than 1000	Very dehydrated	600-750ml water with 2 electrotabs

Fig. 5.7 Hydration regimen based on urine osmolality.

on the stage of the refractometer, and it is pointed towards a light source, which passes through the urine specimen. The device and the technical skill required may hinder the use of this equipment.

However, urine specific gravity (as measured with a refractometer) has a high correlation to urine osmolality (as measured with an osmometer) and they may be used interchangeably. The ease of use of a portable osmometer may make it the preferred method for urine analysis.

URINE OSMOLALITY

Urine osmolality is a measure of total urine solute content in a given volume of fluid. Analyses require an osmometer, and with a portable osmometer is a refractometer calibrated in mOsmols/kg H2O from 0–1500mOsmols. It is recommended to keep hydration levels below 600mOsmols, with anything over 600

indicating the start of slight dehydration and a reading of over 1000mOsmols consistent with dehydration. Morning urine samples are most commonly used, since the first urine of the day is often the most concentrated. If the osmolality of the morning sample is within acceptable limits, then there may be less cause for concern. Fig. 5.7 outlines a rehydration regimen based on urine osmolality.

BODY WEIGHT CHANGES

The measurement of body mass change represents a commonly used, safe technique to assess hydration status, especially during dehydration that occurs over a short period of time (1–4 hours). Bodyweight change provides the simplest and most accurate index of hydration status in real time. Weigh in before and after training in minimal clothing (after towel-drying), and for each 1kg lost in bodyweight replace with 1.5L of fluid.

OPTIMIZING PHYSICAL CONDITION

Strategies

Body composition may affect skill and technique. For squash players, carrying excess body fat may result in early fatigue, poor tolerance to heat and suboptimal recovery. Squash players who wish to optimize athletic performance by reducing their body fat levels and maintain lean mass are advised to follow a structured nutritional intervention that promotes a gradual body-mass loss of 0.5–1kg per week. This can be achieved by a moderate energy deficit of 500–1000 kcals per day alongside appropriate strength and conditioning training to preserve lean body mass (LBM) (Garthe, Raastad, Refsnes, Koivisto and Sundgot-Borgen, 2011). Preservation of LBM is desirable to the squash player, to prevent unwanted losses of strength, speed and power. Research supports preservation of LBM through increased protein intakes between 1.4–2.0g per kg of bodyweight (Tipton and Phillips, 2013).

During any weight-loss intervention, achieving an appropriate energy balance is essential, whilst providing enough nutrients to support health, training load and performance. This can be particularly challenging for squash players during travel to competition. When an athlete's lack of knowledge may inhibit them from maintaining an optimal dietary intake (Economos, Bortz and Nelson, 1993), this potentially may result in nutrient deficiency.

CASE STUDY

This case study outlines the effect of nutritional intervention on body composition, vitamin D status and physical performance of a female squash player.

Methods

Over a six-week period, a professional female squash player followed a calorie-controlled diet to provide a daily energy deficit of 500 kcals. Full blood count, vitamin D, physical performance assessments were carried out at baseline and Week 6 of intervention. Body composition was assessed at baseline, Week 3 and Week 6 using skinfold calipers and the body assessment methods.

Results

All assessments of body composition improved from baseline with a significant reduction in skinfolds: data and statistical test (p = 0.036). The greatest changes compared to baseline in serum markers were 25-hydroxy vitamin D3 (68.3 per cent) and ferritin (31.2 per cent). These were accompanied by improvements in total cholesterol, LDL cholesterol and variations in immune markers. The intervention had a positive effect on all physical performance measures, with Reactive Strength Index (RSI) and on-court speed showing the greatest improvements from baseline.

Conclusion

The combination of energy restriction, adequate nutrient intake and appropriately structured strength and conditioning training is an effective way to gradually reduce body fat and improve the body composition of a female athlete.

Practical methods of assessing body composition

Body composition assessment in athletes and anyone who is involved in physical activity is of great importance as a determinant of their performance.

There are a number of body composition assessment methods, all of which have their pros and cons. The assessment of body composition is across three different approaches to body composition assessment: the Level I method is based upon cadaver analysis, but any methodology that is able to assess body composition in athletic environments will be an indirect method – Level II or, doubly indirect, Level III.

DUAL ENERGY X-RAY ABSORPTIOMETRY

Dual energy X-ray absorptiometry (DXA) has been suggested as the 'gold standard' for estimating human body composition. DXA measures three components of body composition – bone mineral content, fat tissue mass, and lean tissue mass (as well as regional fat distribution) – with high precision and accuracy. It passes filtered X-ray beams through the individual and maps the mass and composition of each pixel as either bone mineral content, fat tissue mass or lean tissue mass.

However, there is a small radiation dose associated with whole-body DXA, which makes this method unsuitable for routine monitoring of athletes. It is best considered a research tool rather than a routine method of assessment in athletic populations.

DENSITOMETRY

Body density measurements using either hydrodensitometry (underwater weighing – UWW) or air displacement plethysmography (ADP) estimate percentage body fat based upon a two-component model, dividing the body into fat mass (FM) and fat free mass (FFM). It assumes a constant density for each component, and calculates percentage body fat from whole body density.

UWW entails the athlete to be fully submerged in a suspended seat in a tank, calculating body density from body volume measurements. ADP relies on the same principles, but measures body volume in a sealed air capsule, rather than underwater. Although this method is very accurate, it is also complex, time-consuming and expensive. In addition, it requires special equipment and trained technicians.

There are also variations in body percentage fat reported for gender between UWW and ADP. Compared with results from UWW, ADP underestimated the per cent of body fat by approximately 8 per cent in lean females and overestimated it in higher-fat males. Therefore caution is needed when interpreting the results from these methodologies, particularly in lean athletes.

BIOELECTRICAL IMPEDANCE ANALYSIS

Bioelectrical impedance analysis (BIA) is a commonly used method for determining body composition, since it is non-invasive, reliable and inexpensive, using portable equipment. The BIA method is based on the conduction of electrical current in the body and differences in electrical conductivity between the fat and water components of the body.

Although BIA has been widely used to estimate body composition, its accuracy is limited, with many studies suggesting that it overestimates body percentage fat. BIA values are affected by numerous variables including body position, hydration status, consumption of food and beverages, ambient air and skin temperature, recent physical activity. Reliable BIA assessment requires standardization and control of all these variables.

SKINFOLDS

Skinfold calipers are commonly used in sport to assess body composition because they are non-invasive and inexpensive. The caliper measures the compressed thickness of a double fold of skin plus the underlying adipose (fat) tissue. Measurements are carried out by indenting skeletal landmarks, where landmarks are found by palpation or measurement. Commonly seven or eight sites are used: triceps, subscapular, biceps, iliac creast, supraspinale, abdominal, thigh and calf .

The results can be presented as a sum of skinfolds (number in millimetres) or this can be converted into a percentage body fat. Most practitioners working with athletes would present the results as a total sum of skinfolds. This is because there are many generalized equations that can be used to determine percentage body fat, which can be less accurate and sensitive to change.

The International Society for the Advancement of Kinanthropometry (ISAK) has developed international standards for the anthropometric assessment. A skinfold assessment should only be conducted by a practitioner who has an up-to-date ISAK qualification.

Simple techniques should not be rejected because they appear unsophisticated. Skinfold measurements provide a simple, easy, and quick yet highly informative assessment of fatness in athletes.

SUMMARY

When evaluating the best methodology for assessing body composition it is important to understand which is the most effective and easiest to implement. The most practical method (for those who are qualified) is skinfold assessment, as it is non-invasive, inexpensive and easy to complete.

Fig. 5.8 James Willstrop and Nick Matthew take their diets very seriously, but also both agree that 'treats' are not a bad thing!

REFERENCES

Ackland, T.R., Lohman, T.G., Sundgot-Borgen, J., Maughan, R.J., Meyer, N.L., Stewart, A.D., Müller, W. (2012). Current status of body composition assessment in sport: review and position statement on behalf of the ad hoc research working group on body composition health and performance, under the auspices of the I.O.C. Medical Commission, *Sports Medicine*, 42, 227–49.

Angeline, M.E., Gee, A.O., Shindle, M., Warren, R.F. and Rodeo, S.A. (2013). The effects of vitamin D deficiency in athletes. *The American Journal of Sports Medicine*, 41(2), 461–464. doi: 10.1177/0363546513475787.

Armstrong, L.E. (2005). Hydration Assessment Techniques, *Nutrition Reviews*, 63, S40–S54.

Bemben, M.G. and Lamont, H.S. (2005a). Creatine supplementation and exercise performance: recent findings. *Sports Medicine*, 35(2), 107–125.

Bemben, M.G. and Lamont, H.S. (2005b). Creatine supplementation and exercise performance: recent findings. *Sports Medicine*, 35(2), 107–125.

Bolanowski, M., Nilsson, B.E. (2001). Assessment of human body composition using dual-energy x-ray absorptiometry and bioelectrical impedance analysis, *Medical Science Monitor: International Medical Journal of Experimental and Clinical Research*, 7, 1029–1033.

Brown, D. and Winter, E.M. 1998. Fluid loss during international standard match-play in squash. In *Science and Racket Sports II* (eds A. Lees, M. Hughes, I.W. Maynhard). London: E. and F.N. Spon.

Burke, L. (2007). *Practical Sports Nutrition*. Champaign, IL: Human Kinetics.

Burke, L.M. (2008). Caffeine and sports performance. *Appl Physiol Nutr Metab*, 33(6), 1319–1334. doi: 10.1139/H08-130.

Burke, L. and Deakin, V. (2010). *Clinical Sports Nutrition*. Australia: McGraw-Hill

Close, G.L., Leckey, J., Patterson, M., Bradley, W., Owens, D.J., Fraser, W.D. and Morton, J. P. (2013). The effects of vitamin D(3) supplementation on serum total 25[OH]D concentration and physical performance: a randomised dose-response study. *British Journal of Sports Medicine*, 47(11), 692–696. doi: 10.1136/bjsports-2012-091735.

Connolly, D.A., McHugh, M.P., Padilla-Zakour, O.I., Carlson, L. and Sayers, S.P. (2006). Efficacy of a tart cherry juice blend in preventing the symptoms of muscle damage. *British Journal of Sports Medicine*, 40(8), 679–683; discussion 683. doi: 10.1136/bjsm.2005.025429.

Dunford M, S. M. (206). *Dietary supplements and ergogenic aids*. Chicago: American Dietetic Association.

Economos, C.D., Bortz, S.S. and Nelson, M.E. (1993). Nutritional practices of elite athletes. Practical recommendations. *Sports Medicine*, 16(6), 381–399.

Garthe, I., Raastad, T., Refsnes, P.E., Koivisto, A. and Sundgot-Borgen, J. (2011). Effect of two different weight-loss rates on body composition and strength and power-related performance in elite athletes. *International journal of sport nutrition and exercise metabolism*, 21(2), 97–104.

Holick, M. F. (2007). Vitamin D deficiency. *The New England Journal of Medicine*, 357(3), 266–281. doi: 10.1056/NEJMra070553.

Jacob, R.A., Spinozzi, G.M., Simon, V.A., Kelley, D.S., Prior, R.L., Hess-Pierce, B. and Kader, A.A. (2003). Consumption of cherries lowers plasma urate in healthy women. *The Journal of Nutrition*, 133(6), 1826–1829.

Kelley, D.S., Rasooly, R., Jacob, R.A., Kader, A.A. and Mackey, B.E. (2006). Consumption of Bing sweet cherries lowers circulating concentrations of inflammation markers in healthy men and women. *The Journal of Nutrition*, 136(4), 981–986.

Lanham-New, S.A., Stear, S.J., Shirreffs, S.M., Collins, A.L. (2011). *Sport and Exercise Nutrition*. Wiley-Blackwell.

Lappe, J., Cullen, D., Haynatzki, G., Recker, R., Ahlf, R. and Thompson, K. (2008). Calcium and vitamin d supplementation decreases incidence of stress fractures in female navy recruits. *Journal of Bone and Mineral Research: the official journal of the American Society for Bone and Mineral Research*, 23(5), 741–749. doi: 10.1359/jbmr.080102.

Lovell, G. (2008). Vitamin D status of females in an elite gymnastics program. *Clinical Journal of Sport Medicine: official journal of the Canadian Academy of Sport Medicine*, 18(2), 159–161. doi: 10.1097/JSM.0b013e3181650eee.

Martin, A.D., Drinkwater, D.T. (1991) Variability in the of body fat: Assumptions or techniques. *Sports Medicine*, 11, 277–288.

Maughan, R.J. (1993). An evaluation of a bioelectrical impedance analyser for the estimation of body fat content. *British Journal of Sports Medicine*, 27, 63–66.

M.W. (2006). Food drugs and related substances *Nutrition for Health, Fitness and Sport* (5th edn). New York: McGraw-Hill.

Meltzer, S. and Hopkins, N. (2011). Nutrition for Technical and skill-based Training. In *Sport and Exercise Nutrition* (eds S.A. Lanham-New, S.J. Stear, S.M. Shirreffs and A.L. Collins), 1st edn. United Kingdom: Wiley-Blackwell.

Need, A.G., Horowitz, M., Morris, H.A. and Nordin, B.C. (2000). Vitamin D status: effects on parathyroid hormone and 1, 25-dihydroxyvitamin D in postmenopausal women. *The American Journal of Clinical Nutrition*, 71(6), 1577–1581.

Raman, A., Macdermid, P.W., Mundel, T., Mann, M. and Stannard, S.R. (2014). The effects of carbohydrate loading 48 hours before a simulated squash match. *International journal of sport nutrition and exercise metabolism,* 24(2), 157–165. doi: 10.1123/ijsnem.2013-0108.

Rawson, E.S. and Volek, J.S. (2003). Effects of creatine supplementation and resistance training on muscle strength and weightlifting performance. *Journal of Strength and Conditioning Research/National Strength and Conditioning Association,* 17(4), 822–831.

Rodriguez, N.R., Di Marco, N.M. and Langley, S. (2009). American College of Sports Medicine position stand: Nutrition and athletic performance. *Medicine and Science in Sports and Exercise,* 41(3), 709–731. doi: 10.1249/MSS.0b013e31890eb86.

Rodriguez, N.R., DiMarco, N.M. and Langley, S. (2009). Position of the American Dietetic Association, Dietitians of Canada, and the American College of Sports Medicine: Nutrition and athletic performance. *Journal of the American Dietetic Association,* 109(3), 509–527.

Sawka, M.N., Burke, L.M., Eichner, E.R., Maughan, R.J., Montain, S.J. and Stachenfeld, N.S. (2007). American College of Sports Medicine position stand. Exercise and fluid replacement. *Medicine and Science in Sports and Exercise,* 39, 377–90.

Sparks, A. and Close, G.L. (2013). Validity of a portable urine refractometer: The effects of sample freezing. *Journal of Sports Sciences,* 31, 745–749.a.

Strecker, E., Foster, E.B., Taylor, K., Bell, L. and Pascoe, D.D. (2007). The effect of caffeine and ingestion on tennis skill performance and hydration status. *Medicine and Science in Sports and Exercise,* 39, 43.

Stuart, G.R., Hopkins, W.G., Cook, C. and Cairns, S.P. (2005). Multiple effects of caffeine on simulated high-intensity team-sport performance. *Medicine and Science in Sports and Exercise,* 37(11), 1998–2005.

Tipton, K.D. and Phillips, S.M. (2013). Dietary protein for muscle hypertrophy. *Nestle Nutr Inst Workshop Ser,* 76, 73–84. doi: 10.1159/000350259.

Van Beelen, P., Wouterse, M.J., Masselink, N.J., Spijker, J. and Mesman, M. (2011). The application of a simplified method to map the aerobic acetate mineralization rates at the groundwater table of the Netherlands. *J Contam Hydrol,* 122(1–4), 86–95. doi: 10.1016/j.jconhyd.2010.11.006.

Volek, J.S. and Rawson, E.S. (2004). Scientific basis and practical aspects of creatine supplementation for athletes. *Nutrition,* 20(7–8), 609–614. doi: 10.1016/j.nut.2004.04.014.

Wilkinson, M., Cooke, M., Murray, S., Thompson, K.G., St Clair Gibson, A. and Winter, E.M. (2012). Physiological correlates of multiple-sprint ability and performance in international-standard squash players. *Journal of Strength and Conditioning Research/National Strength and Conditioning Association,* 26(2), 540–547. doi: 10.1519/JSC.0b013e318220ddbb.

Wilkinson, M., McCord, A. and Winter, E.M. (2010). Validity of a squash-specific test of multiple-sprint ability. *Journal of Strength and Conditioning Research/National Strength and Conditioning Association,* 24(12), 3381–3386. doi: 10.1519/JSC.0b013e3181f56056.

CHAPTER 6

EFFECTIVE MENTAL TRAINING FOR PERFORMANCE

Kirsten Barnes, Canadian Sport Institute Pacific

Fig. 6.1 All successful players take time to train their minds as well as their bodies.

WHAT THE PLAYERS THINK

Nick Matthew OBE

During a match being psychologically robust has allowed me to focus on what I need to do to win. There will be times when you need to focus all your attention to one opponent – but you can't get hung up on one person. Personally when training between tournaments I will mentally focus on how I can better my overall game in order to beat all opponents. The focus is always on what I can do to get better, rather than worrying about something else you can't control. Most of the time you don't know who you will be playing until the day before – so there is no point wasting mental energy worry about it until you know. I keep concise notes on all my opponents I can refer to the night before or the morning of the match. I tend to read these notes and then focus on the strengths and weaknesses of my opponent in the practice session the morning of the match.

After the practice session in the morning I like to pull together a three-point game plan for the upcoming match. Firstly I focus on what I am strong at, and then I focus on what specifically I need to do to win this match – may be opponent-specific (what are my tactics against this specific player) or may be court-specific (if it's a cold dead court I really concentrate on how to get my length and ensure I am getting up the court). And finally I think about one strength of my opponent's that I need to stop them doing – it's a balance between focus on your own and your opponent's strengths and weaknesses – the key is how to get the blend right. I always have faith in my plan and give the strategy time to start working. However, if it is clearly not going well I always have a plan B ready – and this is always a very simple message to go back to the basics of the game and avoid complication (move your feet, step up and take the ball early, hit the back wall with your length).

My psych told me off for only talking to him when things have gone wrong! I believe players should be proactive in their psychology and not just react to negative situations. When it comes to psychology you should have an organized strategy and create specific goals way before the events - before the Worlds I had a specific mental six-month plan with various stages and outcomes to achieve along the way.

James Willstrop

When I was younger I focused too early and too much on the upcoming match – this began to stress me out! Now I will of course think about it the night and morning before, but I will only start to really sharpen my thoughts around an hour before the match.

Laura Massaro

At the start I worked with my psych on issues taking place off the court and that definitely improved my squash. Four years ago we did a lot of self-belief sessions analysing whether I truly believed I was good enough to be the best in the world. Two weeks later I won my first ever gold event and beat world number one Nicol David for the first time.

I had a lot of limiting belief factors. Once I got rid of these I could just play the best squash I was able to without these factors affecting me. I work every day on being more mentally positive. I worked with my psych and realized I am not just defined as Laura Massaro the squash player, I'm a complete person. This was really important to me - it can't be healthy to just think about sport 24/7. Being happy off court is vital to being able to perform on court.

Fig. 6.2 Every day Laura Massaro works on the mental side of the game.

Fig. 6.3 Psychologically squash is one of the toughest sports; the world's top players possess incredible mental strength during both training and match play.

WHAT THE COACHES THINK

David Pearson

You do of course need to be constantly mindful of your key opponents. But when training and practising players need to focus on their positives – if you worry too much about your opponent it can become like a weight on your neck. When going into a match a top player will be focusing on his opponent's strengths and weaknesses; but more importantly focusing on how his strengths can expose the weaknesses, and how he can defend against the strengths.

Inevitably you will be thinking about your next opponent during tournaments, but if you think about this all the time you will be mentally exhausted before the match has even started. Two or three hours before a match a player should watch a few rallies of the opponent to get a mental picture of what the match is going to be like. You should only really starting thinking intensely about your opponent about an hour before the match.

Paul Carter

Practice sessions need to be mentally challenging as well as physically. They should replicate the sport in all aspects to be most effective.

David Campion

Mentally players need to have the drive to do things they are not good at – it is too easy for players to practise and train where they are already strong. Goal setting is vital for player development, especially at a younger age. These should be a mixture of process and outcome-based goals.

INTRODUCTION

What we learn about ourselves in the daily training environment can make us better competitors and people. The psychology of any sports training environment should be one that fosters a resilience mindset for the athletes' sport career and life. The root of any successful performance in sport is the quality and quantity of training the athlete or team does, and squash is no exception. Great match play comes off the back of solid training and the way to make it through long tough matches successfully is by putting in the long tough hours of training.

This chapter will provide some insight and tools for successful mental training in the daily training environment as well as support for the successful transfer from training to match play. The training environment puts huge demands on the body and mind; as a player you are asked repeatedly to do the same shots over and over again, train in the gym and work in a fatigued state. You also have the opportunity to make mistakes and learn from them, to push the limits beyond that of a match, to test yourself and ultimately develop your resilience as an athlete and an increased awareness of your capabilities.

Resilience, or mental toughness, is constantly being developed during the thousands of training hours you do throughout the year. As reflected in the Jones *et al.* (2002) definition of mental toughness the notion of developing resilience is about, 'having the natural or developed psychological edge that enables you to generally cope better than your opponents with the many demands (competition, training and lifestyle) that sport places on a performer and specifically being more consistent and better than your opponents in remaining determined, focused, confident and in control under pressure' (p.209). Developing mental toughness as

part of the physical training programme is a crucial factor to effective, sustainable training as well as successful match play. As the world of squash continues to advance in technology, mental performance is increasingly impacting game play. The benefit of player resilience is as important as the technical, tactical and physical training and experience of players.

BUILDING MENTAL RESILIENCE

Mental training attitude

There are a few overarching concepts regarding mental training that are important to consider prior to working on the actual mental skills. The aim of this first section is to share some principles and approaches for building resilience within an effective, individualized training programme. The following five concepts will be presented, and these concepts are by no means thoroughly explored so please take the time to look further into these areas for your own development (the appropriate book references will be provided for further information).

- Growth mindset
- Relentlessness
- Deliberate Practice
- Optimism
- Mindfulness Acceptance Commitment (MAC).

These five concepts are some of the most researched and developed in the area of building mental resilience. They are worth considering, and hopefully embracing as part of your attitude towards your physical, mental and emotion development as a player in your daily training and in your match preparation.

Table 6.1 Growth vs fixed mindset. (Adapted from Dweck, 2006)	
Growth Mindset	**Fixed Mindset**
Intelligence can be developed;	Intelligence is static;
Leads to a desire to learn and therefore a tendency to…	Leads to a desire to look smart and therefore a tendency to …
…embrace challenges	…avoid challenges
…persist in the face of setbacks	…get defensive or give up easily
…see effort as the path to mastery	…see effort as fruitless or worse
…learn from criticism	…ignore useful negative feedback
…find lessons and inspiration in the success of others;	…feel threatened by the success of others;
As a result they reach ever-higher levels of achievement.	As a result they may plateau early and achieve less than their full potential.

Growth Mindset

The quality of your daily training is critical to any successful performance, and your attitude towards yourself, as well as what you believe you can do, profoundly affects the way you train and live your life. The intensity of training, the fatigue built up through the week, and often the monotony of repetition can affect one's daily mindset and attitude. Understanding and embracing a 'growth versus fixed mindset' (Dweck, 2006) could make all the difference in the world.

The 'growth versus fixed mindset' as explained by Dweck (2006) emphasized several important components for success in sport and life. These are highlighted in Table 6.1. She also pointed out that 'you have a choice. Mindsets are just beliefs. They're powerful beliefs, but they're just something in your mind, and you can change your mind' (Dweck, 2006, p.16).

As a player or coach, consider where your mindset is and how you can get the most out of yourself in training by accessing aspects of a growth mindset. Playing squash (or any other high level in sport) is a choice, not a sacrifice. Embracing a mindset that allows you to train effectively and enjoy the process will not only improve your training, but your life. What a powerful way to train and improve with each shot in every session.

Relentlessness

To be successful against opposition means that training has to be hard. The more you can challenge yourself, the better you will be in match play. Divine (2014 and 2013) highlighted the importance of continually pushing boundaries in your training through structured challenges that make you uncomfortable. Be prepared to get comfortable being uncomfortable, and learn about yourself in the training environment. Divine (2014) went on to say how people are so much more capable than they think. He called this potential 'your

20x Factor, you are capable of at least twenty times what your current paradigm allows you to believe' (Divine, 2014, p. 9). The training environment is the place to push limits to a breaking point in order to expand your comfort zone. Consider what the 20x factor might be for you in your training programme. Discussing what this might be with your coach and whoever is writing your training programme could help make training the hardest and most rewarding thing you do.

The training environment is also where you can make mistakes and fail because you are pushing the limits to the very edge. Failing is part of everybody's learning and training experience. Making mistakes and not achieving your goals is a reality of all sport performances and part of the resilience-building process. Dealing with physical and emotional pain and learning to bounce back from setbacks are also attributes of mental toughness (Jones et al., 2002) that you should learn to embrace as you push your own limits in training.

Get ongoing and regular feedback from your coach and those people around you who understand what you are working towards. Do not forget your own improvement. Do your own self-reflection and evaluation of your training (what went well? what needs to be better?) and adjust your goals based on that evaluation. These are all steps in a simple performance cycle: set goals and make a plan with clear intentions, take action, get feedback and reflect on that plan. The process is crucial for ongoing growth and development as a player (Fig. 6.4). This is not about being perfect. It is about being productive, present and in a process towards achieving your goals.

Deliberate Practice

Deliberate practice, paired with constant feedback, is another quality of successful

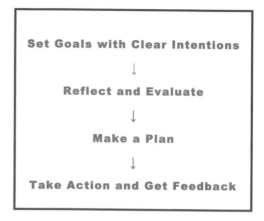

Fig. 6.4 A schematic plan of the performance cycle.

training environments. Deliberate practice entails isolating the specific elements of squash, repeating them over and over again, and getting feedback in the process to allow you to develop appropriately to your needs and excel further in training and match play.

Coyle (2009) explains how deliberate practice enhances the neurological circuitry in our brains. Through repetition, the amount of myelin (the insulation that wraps around nerve fibres) grows, allowing neurons to fire with more speed, strength and accuracy, which means stronger, faster and more fluent movement and thoughts. This is just what you want for squash, Coyle adds – 'Struggle is not optional – it's neurologically required; in order to get your skill circuit to fire optimally … you must make mistakes and pay attention to those mistakes' (p.44) – as is continuing with repeatable practice of the smaller technical components of your game. This keeps your circuits firing, and myelin functioning and growing.

Deliberate practice also reinforces the competitive nature of brain plasticity – a 'use it or lose it' principle – and the way the brain maps what we do gets stronger through repetition, as explained by Doidge (2007). Create purpose and intent for yourself by taking time before every training session to be clear in what you are going to work on that session and continue to break down the bigger technical aspects of your game to smaller components that you can work on every day.

Optimism

Optimism is relevant to the quality of the daily training. Having a positive perspective helps to shift attention towards what you can control, gives you the capacity to cope in times of difficult challenges, and inner strength (Orlick, 2008).

Optimism is explained best by Seligman (2006, 2011) who is a leading expert in this field. Seligman highlighted that optimistic people are those 'who don't give up and have a habit of interpreting setbacks as temporary, local and changeable' (Seligman, 2011, p.102). 'They are unfazed by defeat and when confronted by a bad situation, they perceive it as a challenge and try harder' (Seligman, 2006, p.5). Pessimist characteristics tend to reflect the opposite. Seligman believes that optimism can be learned and we can choose the way we think.

Optimism therefore plays a crucial role in pressure moments within the training environment both on and off the court. If we continue to allow ourselves to focus on problems, we will actually have more problems. Conversely, asking yourself what you can change in order to improve brings an element of control and alters your perception, which leads to success and optimistic growth.

The MAC approach

There is an integrated approach in psychology that helps athletes develop a mindful and non-judging awareness of thoughts, feelings and actions. This performance enhancing approach is called Mindfulness, Acceptance, Commitment (MAC) (Gardner and Moore, 2006).

Mindfulness stems from eastern philosophical traditions and is a mental awareness with a non-judgemental focus on thoughts, emotions and stimuli occurring in the present moment. It emphasizes that a mindful, task-focused attention is one that observes the distraction, whether it is external (around you) or internal (in your head) but does not evaluate it (good or bad, right or wrong) (Gardner and Moore, 2006).

Acceptance is being aware of those distractions, particularly internal distractions such as negative mood or uncomfortable thoughts and appreciating this as a normal part of a sport and human experience (Gardner and Moore, 2006). When negative mood is experienced, there is no need to avoid it. Accept it without judgement, knowing that it is time-limited and will pass. Through the acceptance of your thoughts and feelings, you will ultimately make better performance decisions.

Commitment is a willingness to engage in behaviours that keep you on track towards your goal(s), as well as reinforce the personal values you hold, in order to be a successful player. Acknowledging your ineffective thoughts and feelings and redirecting your actions with task-relevant behaviour helps to improve the moment and the quality of your training.

Mindfulness, acceptance, commitment is about paying attention to your thoughts and feelings, accepting them non-judgementally (not dwelling on the negative) and then effectively shifting or redirecting your thoughts and feelings with useful actions to alter your behaviour.

MENTAL TRAINING SKILLS

There are four key areas of mental development that will complement the previously mentioned resilience attitudes. The four areas are:

- Self-awareness and motivation
- Focus
- Effective behaviour under pressure
- Increasing self-belief.

One final area that will be touched on is performance lifestyle. The way in which we 'live' our lives while training and competing can have a significant impact on the effectiveness. Some high-level reminders of quality living while training as a squash player will be touched upon.

Throughout this section there are sample templates and tables for you to use in a way that best suits you. They can be used in their entirety or you can take relevant information from them to use on a regular basis and build into your training programme. Lastly, while the information that follows has been presented in separate sections, every section is connected to the other. When you work on something in one area of mental performance it will have a direct positive impact on another.

Self-awareness and motivation

SELF-AWARENESS

Developing self-awareness is key to quality training. Knowing how you work with those around you and being able to communicate information about yourself to others contributes to an effective, productive and sustainable daily training environment. Covey (1989) explained self-awareness as enabling us to stand apart and examine not only the way we see ourselves in terms of our own attitudes and behaviours but also how we see other people. Emotional intelligence is also worth exploring as this looks further at the impact of emotions; specifically, being able to recognize and manage your own emotional state, as well as being able to notice the emotional states of others and use this to form healthier relationships with others.

Developing self-awareness can begin by creating a personal vision statement for yourself (Table 6.2). A personal vision statement is something that is an expression of your vision and values – knowing why playing squash is important to you, what it means to you and having personal values that support your vision can help guide difficult decisions that you may be faced with. At the heart of all successful sport achievements is the passion that explains why you are committed to the sport. Supporting your passion and commitment with your vision, values and a 'top mission goal' for the season starts to increase your self-awareness and optimism. Committing these thoughts to paper (or electronically) makes it real and acts as a reminder to you of 'why' you are doing this. During slumps in training your vision can often be what helps you pull yourself back up and keep persevering.

An additional awareness-raising exercise that you might find helpful is to establish a morning and evening routine (see Table 6.3). Routines help make useful behaviour automatic and can help you in your preparation and recovery for training and competition. Routines are never permanent, but rather a flexible, adaptable framework. In this case, morning and evening routines are there to help set you up for your day and maximize your evening/night recovery.

MOTIVATION

Generally more time is spent training than in match play. Maintaining motivation on

Table 6.2 Personal vision and values.
My PERSONAL VISION for playing squash:
_____
_____
_____
My TOP 3 values as an athlete, and one thing I can do regularly to make sure I am LIVING each one:
1. _____
2. _____
3. _____
My MAIN goal for this year:
_____
_____
_____

a day-to-day basis can mean the difference between improvement gains and not. Your internalized motivation to succeed and your ability to bounce back from setbacks with even more determination are qualities of highly motivated athletes (Jones et al., 2002; Hunt-Davis and Beverage, 2011; Divine, 2014). Therefore, the challenge of any daily training environment for a squash player is how to get the best out of yourself every training session.

Years of sport psychology research has repeatedly demonstrated the positive relationship between goal setting and motivation and achievement (Weinberg and Gould, 1995).

Goal setting is about supporting your vision with action. Setting goals creates direction, clarity and daily purpose. Knowing what you are trying to achieve each day can relieve boredom and introduce new challenges, and over time with deliberate practice small gains are made contributing to greater achievements. To stay motivated, begin by reflecting on what you wrote in the previous section – your vision and main goal(s) for the season. Hopefully you feel a sense of excitement when you read this to yourself. Now, consider the combination of the three types of goals explained below to help map out what your more specific goals could be.

Table 6.3 Morning and evening routine.

My **MORNING** routine:
What I do to best prepare for the day:

_____

_____

_____

_____

_____

_____

_____

_____

_____

_____

> *Some questions to consider ...*
>
> ■ What am I excited about and looking forward to doing today?
> ■ What is my purpose today?
> ■ What are the key things I will work on today to move me closer to my purpose?

My **EVENING** routine:
What I do to finish the day and get ready for tomorrow:

_____

_____

_____

_____

_____

_____

_____

_____

_____

> *Some questions to consider ...*
>
> ■ Was I 'on' and in the zone today or 'off' and unbalanced?
> ■ What contributed to how I felt?
> ■ What were three things that went well today? (and do again tomorrow)

OUTCOME GOALS: 'WHY' . . . I AM DOING THIS

These goals are often directly linked to your personal vision and top mission goal for the season. They typically focus on the result of a competitive event such as winning or achieving place in a tournament or even beating a particular opponent. Achieving these goals depends not only on your ability and effort but also that of your opponent. You may have played the match of your life and lost or missed out on a spot in the semi-final because on the day someone else was better than you. Despite the fact that outcome goals may not always be in your control, they lie at the heart of *why* we enjoy the competitiveness of playing and should exist at part of your annual, long-term goal planning.

PERFORMANCE GOALS: 'WHAT' . . . I WANT TO ACCOMPLISH/ACHIEVE

These goals focus on achieving a standard or particular objective which is specific to you and measured against your own previous performances. These goals tend to be under your control, as they are referenced against something that you achieved on a previous occasion, for example improvement in physiological testing or video evidence of your backhand drop shot getting stronger and more accurate. Performance goals ask the question *what*. What do you need to improve on, by how much and by when? This helps you guide the work you do to reach a higher standard and get you closer to achieving your outcome goal(s).

PROCESS GOALS: 'HOW' . . . I WILL DO THIS

These goals comprise of all the technical, tactical, physical, mental and lifestyle components that make up a squash player's daily existence in their quest for improvement. Process goals focus on the specific aspects of what you are working on in order to improve. Process goals may be anything from the technical aspect of your swing to improving your shot consistency or increasing your speed by doing specific movement drills. It could also be the discipline to write down your reflections from each training session, or getting the one hour of rest for recovery you need during the middle of the day. Successful process goals answer the question *how*. How can you get better in reference to *what* the performance goal is, for example: if I want to improve my forehand drop shot how am I going to do this?

Process goals are essential because they drive deliberate practice. They bring you in to the present moment and steer your efforts reminding you about what you need to be working on. This is important because too often, especially when fatigue is high, players run the risk of simply going through the motions of training. When this happens, it is hard to guarantee the quality of the training session and often runs the risk of injury. Not being fully present prior to training is going to happen from time to time, but being able to reduce how often this happens by creating purpose and intent prior to the session will positively impact the work you do. Asking yourself a simple question such as 'what am I going to work on today?' can bring you in to the present moment and create a mindful approach to what you are about to do, leaving other issues or concerns checked at the door. Use Table 6.4 to begin working on your goals. Involving your coaches in the process of setting goals is a good idea. Being on the same page and knowing that you are working together on key aspects of your game is important for improvement and achievement.

Focus

Maintaining an ideal level of focused intensity during training sessions is key to quality and

Table 6.4. Goal setting.	

Outcome Goal(s) for this season: (end of season ranking and/or tournament placement or wins against opponents) _____

Performance goals: *What are the key areas of my game I want to work on in the next 2–3 months:*	Process goals for each performance goal: *How I will work on this goal, my action:*
1.	
2.	
3.	

sustainable training. This requires a combination of knowing what your optimal level of focus is, how to refocus if distracted as well as knowing what you like to do to 'recharge' your batteries when the session is done (Orlick, 2008). Bringing a focused intensity to training helps to establish an optimistic and positive pattern in performance that can be carried into competition.

When focusing effectively you are in a relaxed state of being alert. Your mind is able to focus appropriately on the relevant information so you can make accurate decisions and respond effectively. When pain and fatigue of training or life's experiences are overwhelming, often the negative emotions, questioning and self-doubting thoughts creep in to our head. Your focus is distracted and

directed to listening to what the negative voice has to say: 'my legs feel tired today' or 'why can't I get this shot right?' which makes it difficult to remain committed to what you are there to do.

Distractions that shift focus away from the task can be internal, such as the voice inside your head, or external such as other people, noise, conditions of the court, or things happening elsewhere. Both fatigue and nerves can also cause you to be far more susceptible to noticing irrelevant information, making poor decisions and being consumed by the negative. Table 6.5 begins the process of distraction awareness by helping you identify those things that distract you in training and what happens to you when you get distracted.

Table 6.5 Dealing with distractions.
1. What distracts you?
2. Are the distractions internal or external?
3. What happens physically, mentally and behaviourally when you get distracted?
4. What do you notice about yourself?

Focusing and refocusing techniques

Once you are aware of distractions and their impact, you can begin to develop strategies to positively focus and refocus if distracted. It is not a very reliable strategy to just hope that something will work on the day so making time during training to practise strategies will help you be prepared for matches.

The MAC approach, mentioned earlier, is an overarching framework that can help with effective focusing and refocusing. If the training session begins from a place of mindfulness where your thoughts and feelings are focused on what you are about to do, then you set yourself up for a purposeful session. Equally,

if you arrive at training with a head full of thoughts or negative emotions, MAC can be helpful to bring you into the present moment. Specific strategies that can help focus or redirect your thoughts to refocus are:

■ Positive Cues: Having effective and strategic words, phrases or prompts can help focus on the task at hand. They can be visual (something you look at), verbal (something you say to yourself) or physical (something you do). Cues include technical cues (about your stroke or shot), tactical cues (your game plan) and motivational cues (to help you push through a tough rally or recover from a mistake). Your positive self-talk strategies are sometimes referred to as power statements (Divine, 2014). Identifying these can redirect your negative thoughts and help you develop productive ways to focus on your training. Developing these takes time, awareness and some reflection post-training to find what works best for you.

■ Breathing: Remember to breath! As simple as this sounds, when your focus starts to shift away and your negative mindset creeps in breathing can help to bring you back to the moment and control your emotions. The area of bioneurofeedback is increasingly showing how breathing can impact your physical and mental state (Werthner et al., 2013). Breathing exercises can serve two main purposes: for relaxation/recovery and effective focusing/refocusing in training and competition. The evidence surrounding breathing exercises suggests that when time is taken to engage in slow rhythmical breathing (guided either by a type of music, biofeedback device, or your own counting mantra such as 'in, 2,3,4, pause, out, 2,3,4) this slows the heart rate and breathing rates. A state of coherence is achieved, which helps to turn off the stress response. Breathing exercises for recovery and focus are aimed at turning off your active sympathetic nervous system. This allows the body and mind to relax by engaging the calm parasympathetic nervous system, which supports the recovery process. When breathing exercises are built into daily training you are also training effective brain wave activity, for example: being alert and ready to go vs daydreaming.

■ Switching off: Being able to switch off is important, as often players feel that to be successful and committed they have to 'eat, sleep and breathe' squash. It is incredibly important to give your brain a rest and create down time. Directing your brain away from squash helps to keep things in perspective, and can create a positive focus on other areas of your life, which can ultimately have an enhancing effect on performance back on the court.

EFFECTIVE BEHAVIOUR UNDER PRESSURE IN TRAINING

Handling situations where you feel pressured and dealing with adversity comes with the territory – in any sport. Feeling under pressure usually means something is about to happen that you care about and is important to you. Pressure can also be associated with the demand of the situation outweighing your preparation or perceived ability (e.g. training with a better player) or when unexpected events happen or when appropriate resources aren't available, such as equipment. When you experience pressure situations your beliefs and attitude, your past experiences and personality all play a role in how you interpret and respond to pressure. Your interpretation or appraisal of a pressure situation can be one

of threat or opportunity. The way in which pressure affects you can be a combination of mental (self-doubt, worry or confusion), physical (butterflies, tense muscles or increased heart rate) and behaviour (short temper, forgetting things, pacing or showing up late) symptoms (Jones and Moorhouse, 2007).

Sources of pressure will always occur; they will vary from player to player and will come from different places within and outside of squash. In the training environment, pressure is more often chronic than acute. The 'ongoing' aspect of training (and life around training) can create situations where players start to break down and often don't even realize this until it is too late. Training is supposed to put the body and mind under pressure and this activates the sympathetic nervous system (flight or fight) for longer periods of time compared to that of a match. This is different to the pressure and nerves of competition, which can come on very strong, but should subside as play begins or when the match is over. During training it is important to develop your own mental strategies to manage day-to-day pressures. Having stress in your squash life is inevitable and should be seen as a good thing. When pressure is embraced and perceived positively you are able to use it to your advantage, adapt to change and make correct decisions (Jones et al., 2001. 2007).

Handling Pressure Effectively

While the training environment never fully replicates the physical, mental and emotional states of competition, there are still opportunities in training to develop pressure coping strategies and build resilience. Start by noticing what puts you under pressure, how you usually interpret this pressure (as a threat or opportunity), how this pressure makes you feel and how you respond (see Table 6.6).

Table 6.6 Identify your sources of pressure: how pressure affects you and your response.			
Source of pressure	Interpret pressure and impact on me	How I typically respond	How I should respond
Training at the end of the week – fatigue from the week	Makes me worried and question what I am doing and feel grumpy and irritable	Go quiet and don't interact with anyone, especially the coach	Let the coach (or someone) know how I am feeling and get their help to understand the training and work through (push through) training that day

Next, there are three types of strategies for handling pressure effectively (adapted from Jones and Moorhouse, 2007):

1. Go to the source: If you can identify the pressure that is causing you stress, you can attempt to stop it or reduce the impact of that pressure, such as having that tough conversation with your coach. Taking time to plan for most eventualities can be a great way to manage situations when they arise. 'What-if' planning can be great for discussing possible scenarios that could occur, and then developing plans to deal with them. The more you plan, the better, even if only half the things you plan for happen.

2. Appraisal: If going to the source of pressure is less of an option – or not in your control – then your interpretation of the pressure (either as a threat or opportunity) is hugely important. 'How you think about or appraise pressure determines whether you are stressed by it' (Jones and Moorhouse, 2007). You have a choice about how you appraise pressure. The challenge is being able appraise or reappraise the situation as an opportunity in order to be effective in the moment, excited and use the pressure to your advantage. When you appraise negatively or get in to a negative mindset you are more susceptible to irrational thinking or cognitive distortions such as catastrophizing, jumping to conclusions, black and white thinking or taking things personally. Peters (2012) explained how two regions of the brain, the amygdala (emotion centre) and the frontal lobe (thinking brain) need to work together to lessen the negative impact of pressure. However, the emotion centre of the brain, which he refers to as the 'inner chimp', is five times stronger than other parts of our brain, and wants to be in control by overriding the thinking brain. The aim is to manage the 'chimp' and engage the thinking brain. Consider in Table 6.7 how you might reappraise you own negative or irrational thought and begin your own process of challenging your own thinking that causes you stress.

Table 6.7 Convert irrational thinking to rational thinking.	
Irrational thought	**Rational thinking and positive affirmations**
I always struggle with this workout, I hate it, I can't do it	I did this 2 weeks ago; Let's take it one minute at a time and use one of the cues that helps me get through it

3. Coping Strategies: Coping strategies can help you manage pressure and control nervous energy so you can prepare and focus on training, assist in your recovery and improve overall body awareness. Coping strategies can be one of or a combination of mental, physical or behavioural.

Mental coping:

- Different forms of meditation for mental relaxation
- Mindfulness training
- Imagery (see Table 6.8 for different uses of imagery in squash)

It is helpful to be in a place that allows you to be comfortable, focused and have your eyes closed (not to do while driving).

Physical coping:

- Yoga
- Progressive muscle relaxation

- Breathing exercises – for overall relaxation as well as physical preparation pre-game or pre-serve

Mental and physical:

- Find a relaxation and imagery script that works for you

Behavioural coping:

- Routines – performance routines (see Table 6.9) as well as daily preparation routines (morning and evening routines mentioned earlier)
- Post-match reflection

Everyone has a will to win but very few have a will to prepare
Vince Lombardi

Avoid leaving preparation to chance. Routines are a flexible but planned process to preparing for the training day or match. Routines help you to:

Table 6.8 Different uses of imagery.	
Imagery Use	**Examples**
Mental practice of technical skills	Mentally rehearse aspects of your technique e.g., shots, movement on court Your own:
Improving confidence and positive thinking	Mentally rehearse previous, successful performances e.g., rally-winning shots, recovering from being down Your own:
Tactical rehearsal and problem solving	Mentally rehearse tactics related to game plan or positive recovery at critical moments or poor referee call Your own:
Controlling emotional arousal and anxiety	Mentally rehearse relaxing images in combination with a deep-breathing technique to stay focused on what you want to be thinking about, great squash playing or something else Your own:
Performance review and analysis	During post-match or training session review, which may include the use of video you can imagine (relive/replay) what was good or what needs to be better next time Your own:
Preparation for performance	In preparation for any performance you can mentally rehearse your routine which can include warm-up and game plan. You can also imagine different court conditions or scenarios, opponents, officials, recovery from a mistake Your own:
Within performance routines	Mentally rehearse closed skills like serves and your pre-serve routine Your own:
Maintaining mental freshness during injury	There is considerable evidence that suggests using imagery while away from your sport due to injury or illness to help activate the muscles and create a sense of familiarity and connection with your sport while not being able to physically train or compete Your own:

- Stick to what you know works, avoid last-minute unnecessary change and unhelpful distractions
- Be flexible, though, in your preparation, sometimes you must adapt to varying circumstances

- Create familiarity and calmness
- Keep you in the moment
- Bring a sense of clarity and awareness to what you are doing

	What you do	What you like to Think about/ Focus on/how do you like to feel
Table 6.9 Pre-, during- and post-match routines and interaction with coaches and support staff.		
One to three days before: (what works well in your preparation for a match)		
Night before:		
Morning of/ X hours before:		
Warm-up off court Warm-up on court		
10–15 min before:		
Knock-up: Start of game:		
Game plan: Between games (including input from coach):		
Between matches:		
Post-match input from coach(es):		
Post-match input from support staff:		

INCREASE SELF-BELIEF

The positive relationship between belief and performance is significant. One only has to look back in time at great sporting achievements, such as Roger Bannister breaking the four-minute mile when everyone around him said it could not be done. Self-belief is a key factor underpinning sustained performance in the game of squash.

The training environment is a great place to begin the process of growing self-belief. By acknowledging the good things that happen every day in training you are building confidence and slowly over time cultivating belief in yourself. Self-belief must be genuine and unshakable. Those who have 'real' self-belief tend to possess an inner belief that does not require regular external reinforcement or acknowledgement. They do not need to tell others of their achievements, they do not take things personally and they welcome ongoing feedback to development their abilities (Jones and Moorhouse, 2007) – they have a growth mindset.

Table 6.10 Building blocks of belief.

Identifying your achievements and why you were successful

Achievement	Evidence
Winning club championship.	Took each match one at a time and didn't jump ahead mentally to the next round.
Finish the hardest workout I have ever done.	Determination to do it, perseverance even when I wanted to stop.

Identifying your achievements:

You often do not take time to acknowledge the things you have achieved and thus nurture your belief, and in doing so you prevent yourself from building on strengths and limit your ability to repeat those successes on a regular basis. In an effort to develop self-belief, it is important to take time to remember and reflect on those moments of achievement (no matter big or small). In Table 6.10 you should identify your achievements, both recent and from the past. Next to each achievement, highlight a quality that helped you achieve that particular goal. The achievement is now history, but the quality you possess lives on and will be what you will need to draw upon for future success. Take a moment and begin your own building blocks of belief.

Continue to develop your self-belief by identifying at least one good moment from daily training. There is a natural tendency for most players to spend more time critiquing their game. This will not (and should not) change, as part of any successful player's journey is constantly looking at what needs to get better and working on all aspects of your game. But what you can also do is notice what is going well. Do not ignore your improvements! To help with this process, see the sample sheet 'daily training reflections'. Use the daily training diary sample sheet (Table 6.11) – or your own version of this – and take a moment at the end of each training session to reflect on how training went that day. This provides a constant record of how things are going and gives you the chance to reinforce your strengths and build your own belief every day by noticing the little things that went well.

Life off the court

The life of a high performing squash player is one that often exists in a bubble. The high

Table 6.11 Daily training diary.

DAILY TRAINING PREPARATION AND POST-TRAINING REFLECTION

DATE:

What is the session?

What will I work on?

How did the session(s) go?

End of day training reflections:
What went well?

What will I work on tomorrow?

COMMENTS

Did I start the training session well hydrated?

YES / NO

Did I start the training session well fuelled?

YES / NO

Was I switched on and ready to train with purpose?

YES / NO

Did I remain focused during training?

YES / NO

Was I able to regain focus if I needed to?

YES / NO

DATE:

What is the session?

What will I work on?

How did the session(s) go?

End of day training reflections:
What went well?

What will I work on tomorrow?

COMMENTS

Did I start the training session well hydrated?

YES / NO

Did I start the training session well fuelled?

YES / NO

Was I switched on and ready to train with purpose?

YES / NO

Did I remain focused during training?

YES / NO

Was I able to regain focus if I needed to?

YES / NO

volume of training, travelling and tournament playing means there is little time available to do much else. However, taking time to consider things that may co-exist with squash training should be considered. Successful athletes believe not only in the power of the mind and the physical work that must be done, but in the importance of having a life outside of sport to help avoid an 'overly' singular focus on sport. Areas to stay on top of include:

- AM and PM daily routines;
- Nutrition – daily healthy eating as well as pre- and post-training hydration and appropriate food intake;
- Rest and recovery – during the day, between training sessions;
- Sleep – getting the right amount of sleep;
- Planning your time – when you have appointments to get to and errands to run;

- Strong relationships with friends and family – including positive and supportive communication.

Keep in mind there are Performance Lifestyle advisors and career counsellors who understand high-performance sport, and who can help explore options around your squash for you to think about while being an athlete and for life after competitive squash.

CONCLUSIONS

It is important to believe in what you are doing, to understand why you are doing it, to learn from every experience and to ultimately feel like you have done all you can to prepare when you enter the court. Being effective in your daily training environment, from the

Fig. 6.5 Self-belief is a vital trait to succeed in squash. Without being arrogant or complacent, Nick Matthew will not allow any doubts to enter his mind before a match.

moment you wake up in the morning to when you leave the club at the end of training, helps you stay in control of your destiny and believe in the journey you are on.

Working on your mental performance is an integral part of your daily training. The body and mind do not exist in isolation; therefore as you train physically, technically and tactically remember to integrate aspects of mental training and performance lifestyle into your programme. Develop your growth mindset and embrace opportunities to push your boundaries. Be relentless in training, especially when under pressure. Set challenging, effective goals and create a deliberate practice approach to every session. Be optimistic in all aspects of your squash game as well as your life. A positive outlook will engage parts of the brain that keep you focused, present, mindful and emotionally in control. This allows you to get the best out of yourself every session. You have the opportunity every day to build mental resilience in performance and life.

REFERENCES

Covey, S. (1989). *Seven Habits of Highly Effective People*. London: Simon and Schuster.

Coyle, D. (2009). *The Talent Code*. New York: Bantam Books.

Divine, M. (2014). *Unbeatable Mind. Forging Mental Toughness*, www.unbeatablemind.com.

Divine, M. (2013). *The Way of the Seal*. New York: Readers Digest Association.

Doidge, N. (2007). *The Brain that Changes Itself*. New York: Penguin.

Dweck, C. (2006). *Mindset. The New Psychology of Success*. New York: Ballantine.

Gardner, F. and Moore, Z. (2006). *Clinical Sport Psychology*. Champaign, IL: Human Kinetics.

Hunt-Davis, B. and Beverage, H. (2011). *Will it Make the Boat Go Faster?* Leicester: Matador.

Jones, G., Hanton, S. and Connaughton, D. (2002). What is this thing called 'Mental Toughness'?: An investigation of Elite Sport Performers. *Journal of Applied Sport Psychology*, 14, 205–218.

Jones, G., Hanton, S. and Connaughton, D. (2007). A Framework of Mental Toughness in the World's Best Performers. *The Sport Psychologist*, 21, 243–264.

Jones, G. and Moorhouse, A. (2007). *Developing Mental Toughness. Gold Medal Strategies for Transforming your Business Performance*. Oxford: Spring Hill.

Orlick, T. (2008). *In Pursuit of Excellence. How to win in sport and life through mental training*. Champaign, IL: Human Kinetics.

Seligman, M. (2006). *Learned Optimism: How to Change Your Mind and Your Life*. New York: Vintage.

Seligman, M. (2001). Building Resilience. *Harvard Business Review*, April 2011.

Weinberg, R. and Gould, D. (1995). *Foundations of Sport and Exercise Psychology*. Champaign, IL: Human Kinetics.

Werthner, P., Christie, S. and Dupee, M. (2013). Neurofeedback and Biofeedback Training with Olympic Athletes. *Neuroconnections*, Summer 2013.

CHAPTER 7

THE PSYCHOLOGY OF MATCHPLAY

Simon Hartley, Be World Class

Fig. 7.1 Squash is both physically and psychologically draining; being mentally robust is essential to succeed.

133

WHAT THE PLAYERS THINK

Nick Matthew OBE

I used to think nerves were a bad thing until I read a quote on the EIS gym wall saying if you're not nervous going into a match then you're not ready. This now makes me think if I am nervous it's a positive and signals that I am mentally ready. Of course you're more nervous in the big match with the crowds and the telly – when this happens I think about my three-point game plan and try to simplify it in my mind to focus on a specific point and remove the negative thoughts.

When the going is tough and my lungs are burning I look at the short-term and just at that rally I am playing. If I win that tough rally then I get the ball in my hand and I can take a moment to recover and reset my mind. I did some work with Elary Hanley (legendary International Rugby League Player) and he always said to me 'brains not brawn' – meaning when you are breathing out of your backside it's easy to just focus on what is happening physically and just hit and run – at this point you have to work even harder to mentally focus and stick to your plan.

James Willstrop

When I was younger I focused too early and too much on the upcoming match – this began to stress me out! Now I will of course think about it the night and morning before, but I will only start to really sharpen my thoughts around an hour before the match.

I do get nervous and that is natural. I deal with pre-match nerves by focusing on what I need to do in the upcoming match and recalling the work I have put in to get here. I feel that focusing on what you want the outcome of the match to be can be too much out of your control. I prefer to focus on how I am going to get there (tactics, strategies and so on). This helps me channel my thoughts positively.

The pain in training is harder for me to deal with than the pain in match play. When you're playing a match there are a lot of external stimuli to push you (such as team mates, ranking points, prize money). So for me it's harder but probably more important to get yourself mentally up for a hard training session. When doing a physically brutal training session I rationalize it by telling myself that the pain is not forever; you're either going to die or finish the session – it will end somehow! Sometimes the pain during the match prevents you from applying a tactic – you have to just accept the pain and reassure yourself by knowing you have done the hard work in training – that is why training hard is essential mentally.

Laura Massaro

If you over-think a match the night before it can disrupt your sleep pattern, which can definitely affect the way you play. And if you over-think a match before you play it can be mentally draining and you can turn up to the match already tired.

I like to write my plan down the morning of the match so it is crystal clear in my mind. When planning my match tactics I use a theory called ICE – Identify, Commit, Execute. If I fully commit to my plan I am confident I will win 9/10 matches. Going back and focusing on my written-down plan gives me complete clarity and helps me deal with nerves. If I become completely result-driven this can create nerves. I am better focusing on the performance than the result. During matches I have a piece of paper in my towel with key words on (such as Good Body Language, Bounce, This Rally) to help me focus back on my plan if things are going off track.

The pain I deal with in training gives me confidence to deal with the pain during a match. Because I train so hard I know that if I am in pain then so is my opponent, and gain mental strength by knowing this.

Jenny Duncalf

The morning before a match my coach will feed in a way that replicates my opponent that day. When I do get nervous I just let it happen - it's nature's way of getting you ready for the match. When I was No.2 in the World, I played Laura in the quarters of the Worlds. I felt very nervous and shared

this with my coach. Just sharing these feeling helped them go away.

When being coached I like information to flow both ways and create a journey together. I completely trust my coach and want him be honest and tell me what needs to be changed. The best coaches are extremely passionate about the sport and truly care about the player and they bring that intensity with them in the coaching session. I have good and bad periods with my coach, but as with any relationship you have to work at it to keep it successful.

As long as my opponent is feeling the same as me – I actually enjoy the pain! Some players seem to have a natural ability to block out the pain and not let it affect them.

Fig. 7.2 Psychologically Nick Matthew is one of the toughest players the game has ever seen, time and again showing mental strength to win matches that appear to be beyond his reach.

WHAT THE COACHES THINK

David Pearson

At the end of the day I feel the main sports pyschology goes on between the player and the coach. A coach truly knows the personality of the player and what will or won't work. To be a very good psychologist you need to really know the player, not just superficially – you need to know what makes them tick day-in and day-out.

Having nerves makes you ready to play at 0–0. Having no nerves can be a sign you are being complacent – which is a bad thing no matter who your opponent is.

Paul Carter

Practice sessions need to be mentally challenging as well as physically. They should replicate the sport in all aspects to be most effective. If you know who you are playing at the weekend you should be thinking about and planning your sessions, with your opponent's strengths and weaknesses in mind.

Between the knock-up and the start of the match it's about calming the player – you can only do that if you know the player you are talking to. You can over-pump up your player – you need to know what level of arousal works for each player, particularly the optimal state of arousal of your player – they will all be different. Creating the required level of anticipation is very much individualized. A good coach will equip a player with a strategy to help cope with nerves. This strategy will involves simple tactics that aim to stop any panicking.

Having the ability to deal with pain is what differentiates between good and world-class players. You have to train to the level of pain felt in matches – without this when you feel pain in matches it's a novel feeling and you may not be able to cope with it.

David Campion

Psychologists have helped our players focus on what they can actually change. Players can sometimes worry about things they can't control, creating unnecessary worry and distraction. Psychology guides our player to focus on the process and not worry too much about the outcome – creating a here-and-now mindset.

Players will always get nervous and that's a good thing because it shows they care about the result. The top players will rationalize these feelings and turn them into a positive thing.

Players have an incredible ability to suffer physical pain – this comes from their unquenchable desire to win squash matches. I don't know whether people are born with the ability to deal with pain or not, but all the top players are definitely talented at it.

Fig. 7.3 James Willstrop firmly believes that hard training sessions help prepare you not only physically, but mentally, for the brutal matches.

INTRODUCTION

Most players and coaches recognize that our mind is pivotal to our performance. In many cases, players have very similar levels of skill, tactical know-how and athleticism. The difference between them is often dictated by what goes on between their ears. For some players, walking onto court can change their mindset. The simple act of walking through the glass door often presents them with a challenge. How do you manage your headspace in competition? How can you control your thinking and feeling state, rather than letting it control you?

Our mind can be incredibly powerful. If we can direct it, the mind is a valuable asset. However, when it is out of control, it can cripple us. What happens when things don't go our way? What do we do when doubts creep in? How do we respond when we make

mistakes? What do we do when the game swings away from us and it looks like we might lose it? During this chapter, we will look at how to control our thinking and feeling states, so that we can optimize our performance.

THE CRUX

Ultimately, the psychology of performance hinges on one simple principle. In order to perform well, we need to be focused on the right thing at the right time. To do that, we need to be present – in the moment. When players find themselves 'in the zone' it is normally because they become immersed and absorbed in the moment. They are completely focused on the task at hand. Of course, the opposite is also true. When we are not completely focused on the right thing at the right time, we tend to make errors.

Life teaches us that we experience the world through our senses. More specifically, our experience of the present is sensory; we see it, hear it, feel it, smell it and taste it. When we are performing in sports, our experience tends to be dominated by our vision, auditory and kinaesthetic senses. Therefore, to become immersed in the moment, we need to see, hear and feel our performance ... not think it.

Interruption

I am sure I am not the only one that has driven considerable distances in my car and been seemingly unaware of what I have been doing. I have arrived at my destination, with no idea of what cars I have been sharing the road with, or the decisions that I made to get there. I cannot even remember which songs have been playing on the stereo. I was on 'auto-pilot'. Clearly my eyes were open and the visual information was received by my brain. My ears could hear the music. I even made decisions about braking, accelerating and turning. I navigated and responded to traffic. However, in truth I was partially disengaged with it. There was something between me and the sensory experience; something interrupting the process. That 'something' was my thoughts. I often think of this phenomenon as 'thought blindness' (although it clearly affects more than our vision). Mack and Rock (1998) refer to it as 'inattentional blindness'. Simply put, it means we are not really registering what is happening around us. Our thoughts are becoming a distraction.

Over the years I have spent a considerable amount of time working with elite professional cricketers. Batsmen have an interesting challenge. They need to select and play shots against deliveries that often exceed 80 miles per hour. The generally accepted definition of a fast bowler is one who bowls consistently at over 90 miles (145km) per hour. A cricket pitch is just 22 yards (20m) long. That gives batsmen around half a second to pick up the trajectory of the ball, decide which shot to play, and then to execute it. As if that were not hard enough, the best bowlers not only get the ball to swing laterally through the air, but also to deviate off the pitch. In that time the batsman must make up his mind whether to defend the ball, attack it, leave it to pass the stumps or, if it is aimed at his chin, take evasive action (*The Economist*, 2012). This cannot be done consciously, because conscious contemplation takes at least half a second, by which time your stumps may have been uprooted. Therefore, in order to select and execute a great shot, the batsmen recognize the need for a 'clear mind' – one that is free from thought. To play great shots, the batsman needs to watch the ball early and keep focused on it throughout.

Through your own experience you will know that thoughts can be cumbersome. They often take a relatively long time to form. Neural physiologist Benjamin Libet (2004) suggests that it takes 0.4–0.5 seconds to switch on conscious thought. In fast-paced sports, such as cricket and squash, this means that if you have to think about it, it is too late.

This is further complicated when we engage our internal dialogue. Our thoughts are often verbal and linguistic. We tend to think in words. Therefore, it is common to experience a conversation between our ears. However, this dialogue is not always made up of whole sentences or even whole words. Our thinking can happen faster than the formation of the words. In essence, we begin the next thought before we fully form the first. Therefore our thoughts can be snippets of conversations, partially formed sentences and clipped words. Sometimes, we experience this as a half-whisper or the fleeting shadow of a thought. Although this may all sound pretty innocuous, it is these glimpses of thoughts that interrupt our focus. They appear in those crucial micro-moments during our performance. Instead of being focused on what we are seeing, hearing and feeling, we end up being momentarily 'blinded' and distracted by these semi-complete thoughts.

Switching Focus

Of course we do need to think during the performance. Players need to make decisions during a rally, as well as between points and between games. I am not suggesting that players should not think. However, thinking needs to be done at the right time!

In reality, focus is an incredibly dynamic concept. The cues that we need to focus on are in constant flux. Players have to switch their focus between a multitude of different stimuli at the click of a finger. Jon Hammermeister (2011) has referred to the need for rapid and appropriate shifting of attention as 'mental agility'. Doing this successfully requires the athlete to be entirely immersed and absorbed in each moment.

What does this look like in practice? Many game sports coaches refer to the PDA (Perception, Decision, Action) cycle to describe the way in which a player's attention shifts during the game (Vickers, 2007; Hartley and Walker, 2011). Let us walk through the basic process for a squash player.

- Firstly they perceive. They read what is going on around them. If their opponent has just played a shot, the player might assess the weight and height of the shot, the opponent's position and their movement.
- All of this information (and much more) will then inform their decision. What does the player do based on their perception?

Where will they move? What shot will they look to play?
- Once they have made their decision, they will execute their action: make their move and play their shot.

Obviously, as a player moves through this cycle, their point of focus must change. When they are in the 'perception phase', their focus needs to be wide and primarily external. They need to pull in information from the world around them. They must focus on what they see, hear and feel from their environment. As they enter the 'decision phase', that focus must switch and become internal. When we make decisions, our focus is inevitably directed at our own thoughts.

Once a player has decided upon the most effective action they need to be able to execute it. To execute our skills and play high-quality shots, we need to have a very specific and narrow point of focus. In some cases that might need to be predominantly external (focusing on an external cue, such as looking at the ball) and in some cases it is primarily internal (focusing on the feeling cues from our body, which helps us to regulate the power that we use and therefore the weight of the shot). Interestingly England Head Coach, Chris Robertson, talks about 'shot responsibility' (Hartley, 2012). He explains that, in the moment when a player takes a shot, they should be entirely immersed in the shot. That moment should be their 'quiet time' when everything else except the shot disappears into the background; it is a moment devoid of anything else.

CONTROLLING THE SWITCH

The ability to control our focus throughout that cycle can separate players. Controlling focus and rapidly changing our focus is a skill. Therefore, it requires practice. Let us take this a stage further. High-level coaches are also aware that the PDA cycle actually has more phases in expert performance. It is not simply a case of perceiving, then deciding and then executing. As players become more experienced they often have a secondary perception and decision phase before they execute their action (Hartley and Walker, 2011; Neumann and Sanders, 1996). Through experience, players are able to process information and make decisions more quickly. More experienced players tend to narrow the number of potential shots they consider, which simplifies the decision-making process. With additional time, players have the ability to reassess before executing their action. Is it still the right shot? Is the opponent in the position that I expected them to be in? If they are, I may simply confirm my initial decision and go with it. If not, I may need to change tack and play a different shot.

In a match situation, we are not given more time to cater for the extra perception phase, the reassessment and another decision. The ball does not slow down to allow us to fit in these extra processes. Therefore, we have to be able to run the processes more quickly and to change our focus more quickly. If we fail to focus back onto the shot quickly enough, we deny ourselves that important 'quiet time' in which to execute the shot. Tactically of course we can help ourselves by starting the whole process as early as possible. Physically we can also ensure that we are able to move quickly and therefore give ourselves more time at 'the sharp end' – the final approach into the shot and shot execution. However, we also need to ensure that we can switch focus quickly and effectively. In short, we need to get our focus on the right thing, at the right time, as *early* as possible.

World-class Focus

In a recent conversation with Chris Robertson, he described the way that truly world-class players actually have a third perception and decision-making phase before executing their shot (Hartley and Walker, 2011; Hartley, 2012). At the very last moment before playing the shot, they will make a final reassessment. Perhaps they were planning to play a drop shot. Has their opponent come up behind them quickly? Is the drop shot still on? Should they opt for a flick to the back of the court instead of the drop?

The ability to make late decisions separates players in a vast number of open-skill sports, where athletes react to their opposition. When we make late decisions and execute skills later, we give the opponent less chance to respond. Novices find that hard to do because they may not have the ability to switch their focus between perception, decision and action at lightning speed. Not only do they require longer in each phase of the cycle (it takes them longer to perceive and assess, and longer to make their decisions), it also takes them longer to pin their focus firmly on executing their skill (Hartley and Walker, 2011).

Easier Said Than Done

I often describe focus as a torch beam. Focusing on the right thing at the right time means we shine that beam where we need it. Is our torch beam focused on the opponent, the decision, or the feel of the shot when it needs to be? The challenge for many athletes is actually to take control of the beam and *decide* where the beam will shine. What is it that you need to focus on? Can we direct the spotlight quickly and then hold it on that cue long enough to execute the skill? Controlling this beam can be a challenge. That challenge tends to be exacerbated if we are scared (Easterbrook, 1959; Horn, 2008). Imagine walking along a path in the dark with a narrow flashlight beam. If you are scared, you react differently. If you hear something go bump behind you, the likelihood is that you will spin round and shine your light on it to see what made the noise. This draws your beam from the path you are supposed to be following. If you were comfortable walking the path, or you could see pretty clearly, you would be much less likely to take your beam off the path.

In sport, if we are not feeling confident we tend to start over-thinking (Rotella, 2005). This draws our focus internally (Blanke, 2007) and we become absorbed by our thoughts. As Chris Robertson suggested, a player should arguably be 100 per cent focused on the ball as they prepare to execute the shot. If they are not focused on the ball, the chances of playing a decent shot are pretty remote. If the player is thinking about the mistake made in the last shot (instead of shining their spotlight on the ball), the focus will be shining on their own thoughts.

The moment during the PDA cycle where a player is fully immersed in the shot is a state that is also referred to as a 'mindless' state (Rotella, 2005). When we examine the demand in this detail, it is possible to see the extent of the mental challenge. Squash players not only need to switch their focus from one cue to another, they also need to switch between thinking and 'non-thinking'.

Just Focus on the Shot

How can we reduce the number of errors? One solution is very simple: 'Just focus on the shot'. Obviously, it is easy to say, but not necessarily easy to do. Fortunately, our brain is actually wired to help us. Although it may not sound like an advantage at first, our conscious brain can only do one thing at a time. This enables us to control what we do focus on. Athletes often ask me, 'How do I stop thinking negative thoughts?' Inevitably, telling ourselves to stop thinking about it does not tend to work. Here is a little exercise to illustrate the point. Your challenge is to stop thinking about the colour blue. Do not think about anything blue – not blue skies, blue seas or blue anything. Of course, it does not tend to work. The simple answer is to start focusing on something else. Try thinking of something red, like a shiny red Ferrari, red roses, ripe strawberries or red apples. Are you still thinking about blue?

When we play a shot it makes sense to shine our torch beam on the shot; to see it, hear it and feel it. This means different things to different players. Some players might focus on feeling balanced, or feeling the weight of the shot through the racket. Others prefer to watch the ball onto the racket head or listen to the sound of the shot. When players really listen to their shots, they will often recognize the differences in the pitch as the ball hits the strings. Is it a dull thud or a 'ting'? We can often detect when our timing is slightly off by the sound and rhythm. Every player has different cues that make sense to them. When they focus in on these cues, they often execute their skills really well. I often spend considerable time helping players to find the points of focus that work really well for them.

Focus Follows Interest

A little while ago I had a conversation with a tennis player who was struggling to perform in competition. More specifically, they found it a real challenge to focus on their processes because they were consumed by the result. They were investing their focus in the score.

Their mind was so tied up in trying to win the game that they failed to focus on hitting the ball well. If we think of focus like a torch beam, this player's beam was alternating between the scoreboard and their own thoughts.

> 'Damn, I'm two points behind. I need to win the next point ... Oh ****, I've just lost another point. I can't lose this, I just can't. I can't get beaten by an opponent that's twenty places below me in the rankings. How will that look?... What is my coach going to say?... What will the press say? Come on, get it together'.

Throughout this process, the player is not focused on the shots. They are not truly watching the ball, or feeling the weight of the shot. Therefore, they are not executing it well. In our conversation, I said something to the player that they found bizarre.

> I said, 'You have to be more interested in how you play the shot than where the ball lands.'
> 'That's ridiculous', he replied, 'because if the ball lands outside the white line it's out and I lose points. If it lands inside the white line it's in and I get points.'
> 'Yes', I said, 'I know all that. However, you have to care more about how you hit the ball. Your focus follows your interest. You have to be more interested, and care more, about how you hit it. That way you'll focus on the shot completely and you'll play it really well. You'll play it with the right weight, trajectory, direction and spin. When you do that, it is more likely to land where you want it to.'

There is a common mental pattern that occurs in the minds of many athletes. It often starts when they are overly focused on the result. Sometimes the player will experience

this as a feeling they call 'pressure'. When we feel 'under pressure' there is a tendency to over-think our performance and try too hard. We become absorbed by our thoughts. We think the performance, rather than seeing, hearing and feeling it. As a consequence, we tend to make more errors. Most athletes find that this leads them into a downward spiral; they over-analyse the mistake, beat themselves up about it, think more and try even harder. The net result is usually a bigger mistake. The answer of course is to focus on the process – to care more about how they play the shots. So, what makes this a challenge for players?

DELVING DEEPER

So, why is it that the tennis player was more interested, and cared more, about the result? Like many of the athletes I have worked with, this particular player felt that they needed to win. There is a difference between needing to win and wanting to win. Athletes often feel that they need to win because their sense of self-worth depends upon the result. It is not hard to see why. Most elite athletes have been playing their sport since they were children. For most of their lives they have known themselves as 'a squash player'. Being 'a squash player' becomes central, and dominant, to their identity. In some cases, it is the only thing they perceive that they have ever been any good at.

When we tie our identity to one role, we may start to feel a need to be good at it. Many players will use their results to judge whether they are good enough or not. Therefore, winning becomes critical. If we do not win, we conclude that we are rubbish at the one thing we really identify ourselves with. 'If I am a squash player and I'm losing, I must be a rubbish squash player'. For many athletes, a game of squash becomes a means of self-validation. They use their results to answer the question, 'Am I a success or a failure?'

Humans have a tendency to seek respect and recognition. Many people do this through their profession or social networks. It is common for many athletes to use their successes in sport as a form of social currency in their peer group. The problem of course is that when results do not go our way, we start to struggle. Our mind starts to get anxious. What happens if I do not win? Will people respect me? If we perceive that our success in life depends on our results on the squash court, we become really vulnerable. Pinning our success as a person on results puts us in a very fragile position. Matches, and even points, can take on a new meaning.

What's the Job?

My ears prick up when I hear players taking about 'Big Matches', 'Big Games' or 'Big Points'. On one occasion I asked an England player, 'How many points is a 'big point' worth?' The player looked confused. 'Well, one', came the reply. 'How many points are the others worth?' I continued. 'They're worth one as well'. The principle here is that the points are all equally valuable. Therefore, it makes sense to perceive them as equally important and play them with the same focus. If we perceive them differently, we are likely to feel differently about them too and potentially change our focus. If we think they are more important, there is a chance we will become more anxious about them and start to over-think them.

The key here is our perception. If we view the next game as 'a big game', we may begin to see it as career-defining, or even life-defining. We might start to think that our job is to achieve our dreams, to make all those years of

training worthwhile, to repay those who have invested so much in us, to meet the expectations or to realize the dreams of those around us. In reality, none of those things are our job. The game of squash looks pretty simple to me. I do not think the job is to win. I know that might sound rather strange, but it is true. I think the job is simply to score as many points as we can, and concede as few as we can (Hartley, 2013). And that is it! I would argue that this is equally true for a recreational player as it is for the World No.1.

It may sound like a cop-out to say that the job is not to win. Surely that is what competitive sport is all about, right? I agree that players want to win and it is what they aim for. However, winning and losing is outside of our control. There are a myriad factors that influence the result — not least the opponent and the officials. The processes, however, are within our control. We control our thoughts, focus, decision-making and execution. We do not control the result, or other people's judgements, or their expectations, or what the press say. Our job is to control the processes, not the outcome. Our perception of pressure often comes when we get the job wrong.

De-fusing the Bomb

If players use their performances and results on the squash court to inform their self-worth, there is a very good chance that they are attempting to fill a void. Humans often look to some form of external validation when they do not provide themselves with internal validation. Business executives often use their job title, their salary scale, the size of their car or house to tell themselves that they are successful.

It is pretty common for us to use other people's feedback to provide the validation.

When we do this, we tend to become overly concerned about what others might think or what they say about us. In this position, we are also vulnerable. Put simply, we place our view of ourselves at the mercy of something external. If the business executive loses his job with the fancy job title and the salary, he may conclude that he is a failure. Equally, if we rely on other people's validation, we hand them control for our sense of self-worth.

To diffuse this, we need to be able to construct our own view of ourselves based on who we are and what we do. The Ancient Greek aphorism, 'Know thyself', is one of the Delphic maxims inscribed on the Temple of Apollo at Delphi. It has been a central pillar in philosophy, and certain theories of psychology, through the ages. Knowing ourselves is fundamental if we are to accept ourselves. Simply put, we need to know who we are, not just what we do. If I asked, 'Who are you?', would you reply by saying, 'I am a…'? Many people only know themselves by their roles. If I defined myself by my roles, I might say, 'I am a father, a husband and a performance coach'. But that does not tell you who I am, it tells you what I do. The truth is, these roles are temporary. There was a time before I became a husband or father. However, I was largely the same person I am now. Although there are things about me that have changed since I got married and had children, the essence of who I am transcends these roles.

To find out who we are, we need to look deeper. What are you like as a person? Are you kind, helpful and generous? Are you selfish or selfless? *Perhaps it would be more useful to ask, when are you kind, helpful, generous and selfless?* What are your core values as a human? Are you honest and trustworthy? Do you compromise these values? Are there times when you might 'flex the truth', for example to avoid embarrassment or hurting someone's feelings maybe?

It is when we begin to reflect on these things that we start to gain a sense of who we are. In order to accept ourselves, we need to know ourselves and like ourselves. We need to know that we are a decent human being – that we make a positive contribution to our world. To make a positive impact, we do not need to be world leaders or Nobel Peace Prize winners. We can make a contribution in every interaction. Are the people around us better because we are in their lives? This understanding becomes our foundation. It allows us to realize that we do not need to win squash matches or impress other people in order to accept ourselves. We do not become a better person by winning. We do not become a worse person when we lose. We do not need to win to be successful in life. Although society offers us definitions of success (such as winning, wealth and fame), ultimately we decide whether we are successful or not. We choose what constitutes success. With a wider, more grounded view of success, we free ourselves of the need to win, without losing our desire to win.

PULLING THIS TOGETHER

Very simply, our performance hinges on our ability to focus on the right thing at the right time. We need to immerse ourselves in the moment and become absorbed in the processes. In sports such as squash, the focus changes constantly and at the blink of an eye. We need to be able to switch our focus rapidly between our perceptions, decision-making and executing the shot. Crucially, in those moments when we take the shot, we need to keep a clear mind. In these moments, we need to focus on seeing, hearing and feeling the shot… not thinking. Our focus follows our interest. So, to focus on the process we need

Fig. 7.4 James Willstrop has an exceptional ability to keep digging deep mentally and retain composure in moments of extreme pain and pressure.

to care more about how we play the shot than we do about where it lands. This becomes tricky if we tie our ego, our identity and our self-worth to our results. If we depend on external validation, we often get caught in a trap. To fill the void, we need to provide the validation ourselves. We need to understand that we are a good person and a valuable member of humanity. In order to allow ourselves to focus fully on the shot, we often need to know ourselves and accept ourselves first.

REFERENCES

Abernethy, B., Summers, J.J., and Ford, S. (1998). Issues in the measurement of attention. In *Advances in Sport and Exercise Psychology Measurement* (ed. J.L. Duda). West Virginia: Fitness Information Technology, pp. 173–195.

Baghurst, T., Thierry, G. and Holder, T. (2004). Evidence for a Relationship Between Attentional Style and Effective Cognitive Strategies During Performance, *Athletic Insight* 6(1). Available www. athleticinsight.com/Vol6Iss1/AttentionalStyles andEffectiveCognitiveStrategies.htm (accessed 15 February 2012).

Blanke, G. (2007). How to Stop Overthinking Your Life and Start Living, *Real Simple,* August 2007.

Bond, F.W. and Flaxman, P.E. (2006). The ability of psychological flexibility and job control to predict learning, job performance, and mental health, *Journal of Organizational Behavior Management*, 26, 113–130.

Clingman, J.M., and Hilliard, V.D. (1990). Race walkers quicken their step by tuning in, not stepping out. *The Sport Psychologist,* 4, 25–32.

Collins, J. and Hansen, M.T. (2011). *Great By Choice.* London: Random House.

De Oliveira, R.F., Damisch, L., Hossner, E-J., Oudejans, R.R.D., Raab, M., Volz, K.G. and Williams, A.M. (2009). The bidirectional links between decision making, perception and action, *Progressive Brain Research*, 17(4), 85–93.

Duncan, J., Phillips, L. and McLeod, P. (2005). *Measuring The Mind: Speed, Control and Age*. London: Oxford University Press.

Easterbrook, J.A. (1959). The effects of emotion on cue utilization and the organization of behavior. *Psychological Review*, 66, 183–201.

Economist, The (2012). In The Blink Of An Eye, *The Economist*, 23rd April 2012, Available www.economist.com/blogs/gametheory/2012/04/decision-making-cricket.

Elliott, B. (2006). Biomechanics and Tennis, *British Journal of Sports Medicine*, 40(5), 392–396.

Gallwey, T. (1986). *The Inner Game of Tennis*. London: Pan Books.

Gill, D.L., and Strom, T.E. (1985). The effect of attentional focus on performance of an endurance task. *International Journal of Sports Psychology*, 16, 217–223.

Hamilton, J. (2008). Think you're multi-tasking? Think again, *NPR online*, 2nd October 2008.

Hammermeister, J,. Pickering, M, and Lennox, A. (2011). Military Applications of Performance Psychology Methods and Techniques: An Overview of Practice and Research, *Journal of Performance Psychology*, 3, 3–13.

Hartley, S.R. (2011). *Peak Performance Every Time*. London: Routledge.

Hartley, S.R. (2012). *How To Shine; Insights Into Unlocking Your Potential From Proven Winners*. Chichester: Capstone.

Hartley, S.R. (2012). Switching Focus; A Crucial Skill, *Journal of Performance Psychology*, 4, 23–33.

Hartley, S.R. (2013). *Two Lengths of the Pool: Sometimes the simplest ideas have the greatest impact*. Arkendale, UK: Be World Class.

Hartley, S.R. and Walker, S. (2011). Switching Focus in Tennis: Playing in 'The Zone', *Podium Sports Journal*, September 2011. Available http://www.podiumsportsjournal.com/2011/09/18/switching-focus-in-tennis-playing-the-zone (accessed 15th February 2012).

Horn, T. (2008). *Advances in Sport Psychology*. Champaign, IL: Human Kinetics.

James, W. (1890). *The principles of psychology*. New York: Henry Holt.

Libet, B. (2004). *Mind Time; The Temporal Factor in Consciousness*. Cambridge, MA: Harvard University Press.

Mack, A., and Rock, I. (1998). *Inattentional blindness*. Cambridge, MA: MIT Press.

Maxeiner, J. (1987). Concentration and distribution of attention in sport. *International Journal of Sport Psychology*, 18, 247–255.

Moran, A.P. (1996). *The psychology of concentration in sport performers*. Exeter, UK: Psychology Press.

Nideffer, R.M. (1976). Test of Attentional and Interpersonal Style. *Journal of Personality and Social Psychology*, 34, 394–404.

Nideffer, R.M. (1980). Attentional focus-self assessment. In *Psychology in Sports* (ed R.M. Swinn). Minneapolis, MN: Burgess, pp. 281–291.

Ravizza, K and Hanson, T. (1998). *Heads Up Baseball: Playing the Game One Pitch at a Time*. Columbus, OH: McGraw Hill.

Rotella, R.J. (2004). *The Golfer's Mind*. New York: Free Press.

Rotella, R. J. (2005). *Putting Out Of Your Mind*. London: Pocket Books.

Summers, J.J., and Ford, S. (1995). Attention in sport. In *Sport psychology: Theory applications and issues* (eds T. Morris and S. Ford). Chichester: Wiley, pp.63–89.

Taylor, J. (2010). Understanding Focus in Sports, *Psychology Today*, 13th July 2010. Available http://www.psychologytoday.com/blog/the-power-prime/201007/sports-understanding-focus-in-sports (accessed 15th December 2010).

Taylor, J and Wilson, G.S. (2005). *Applying Sport Psychology: Four Perspectives*, Champaign, IL: Human Kinetics.

Vickers, J.N. (2007). *Perception, Cognition and Decision Training; The Quiet Eye In Action*. Champaign, IL: Human Kinetics.

Weissman, D.H., Roberts, K.C., Visscher, K.M. and Woldorff, M.G. (2006). The neural bases of momentary lapses in attention, *Nature Neuroscience*, 9, 971–978.

Wulf, G., McNevin, N. H., Fuchs, T., Ritter, F., and Toole, T. (2000). Attentional focus in complex skill learning. *Research Quarterly for Exercise and Sport*, 71, 229–239.

CHAPTER 8

THE SCIENCE AND ART OF COACHING

Danny Massaro (with David Pearson), University of Central Lancashire

WHAT THE PLAYERS THINK

Nick Matthew OBE

The key to good coaching is knowing the player you are coaching – you are not just coaching a technique you are coaching a person and it is vital to know what makes that player tick. When you are a kid sessions are very coach-led and you must have faith in what your coach is saying – but it's still healthy for the player to ask sensible questions and find out why they are being told to do certain things. As you get older and more experienced there should be a much great player input and it becomes very much a partnership.

I can see through false positive feedback – having positive feedback is of course good – but I would prefer honesty than falseness. In a session I'll get a lot of information from my coach at the start, then we work together to find the key. A lot of information is good as long as you find the thing that actually makes the difference to your performance. Simple feedback is the ultimate goal as it is the easiest to process, but sometimes you have to go through all the information together to find the nugget

James Willstrop

A coach should have a presence when delivering information, but it should be a two-way street. The coach should be respected at all times and the information taken on board by the player, but essentially it should be collaborative and involve a two-way dialogue.

Laura Massaro

I like to have a picture of the future – I like to know why we are doing a certain exercise and how it's going to improve me as a player. I like to know why we are making technical changes so I then have trust in the change when using it in a match. When I changed my grip last year, I was told what to do and why – then worked it out for myself – it's about a feeling as much as anything else. A good coach will not give too much information and will give positive feedback during the session. Key words will be delivered. Too much feedback and stoppages take me out of my rhythm and I can lose the feeling.

As a player you need to know that your coach is passionate about making you improve and cares about you as an athlete and a person.

Fig. 8.1 David Pearson (right) is one of, if not the, most successful squash coaches in history – producing multiple world individual and team champions, including three times world champion Nick Matthew (left). David is a strong advocate of the 'art' aspect of coaching.

Fig. 8.2 Both Nick Matthew and Laura Massaro still have coaching sessions on a very regular basis; between them they own four World, four British Open and nine British Closed Titles, but they both believe having respect and a good honest relationship with your coach are essential to their success.

WHAT THE COACHES THINK

David Pearson

Don't use excuses to not change techniques – a lot of coaches will wait until the closed season and this may be too late. If you spot a technical issue stopping tactics from being delivered don't be afraid to deal with it there and then. A good coach will be able to spot technical problems with the swing. They don't just watch the game, they watch the detail; an outstanding coach is the one with the ability to solve this problem. Spotting technical problems can be quite easy – changing them is another story. The two world champions I coached in 2013 went back to the absolute basics in technical terms – both Nick and Laura completely changed their grips. It doesn't matter who you are working with as a coach, don't be afraid to strip it all back to the beginning.

In between games you are there to support – give no more than two tactics and one technique advice – do not overload.

Different players like different coaching styles between games, and good coaches will change the way they are between games according to the player. It is essential between games that your nerves are not observable by the player.

A coach shouldn't be afraid to stop a session and talk things through. In a technical learning session it should be 50/50 between verbal interaction and physical activity. A good session does not always end in a good sweat!

Malcolm Willstrop

Since my players are usually with me from a very young age for a long time, technical matters are part of the long haul, just as most teaching is. Coaching visiting – and often more established – players as I do, I would still offer technical advice when appropriate, but perhaps less forcibly than with younger players, whose technique I am shaping from the beginning.

Fig. 8.3 Jenny Duncalf has spent thousands of hours being coached; she is considered one of the finest technical players on the world tour.

INTRODUCTION: THE RISE OF NEUROSCIENCE

In the past decade there have been huge advances in the ability to study the brain, a topic called 'neuroscience'. Armed with ever more powerful 'neuroimaging devices', neuroscientists have discovered certain truths about our brains. Perhaps the major truth is that of 'Neuroplasticity', which is the fact that the brain structure grows and changes throughout our whole life. Linda Page stated in her groundbreaking book *Coaching with the Brain in Mind,* 'We now know that how we think can modify the brain that we use to do our thinking. Coaching clients can learn to think in ways that change their capacity to feel, think, and act – and ultimately to shift who they are in the world' (Rock and Page, p.18).

Neuroscientist Jeffrey Schwartz (Rock and Page, p.18) gave an interesting perspective of the coaching process: 'Oh I see what coaching is … it is a way of facilitating self-directed neuroplasticity.' In other words, coaches help people to change their own brain/mind structures by challenging their players with questions, tasks and discussion. The premise is that people change their own brain structure depending upon what and how they think, ultimately self-coaching their own brain into an appropriate adapted state. In squash terms this may be a player finally being able to think for themselves more often in pressure situations, or 'click' in their understanding of a technique or tactic.

Neuroscience has supported the complex nature of coaching and given weight to the individual and complex nature of the brain and mind. Most of this chapter on coaching squash pushes in the direction of revealing how very personal and human coaching is and neuroscience has been able to support that. Rather than trying to simplify the individual, social and contextual complexity of humans and the way we interact, neuroscientists are revealing deeper layers of complexity. They are learning from coaching – the science is being led by the art.

In the preface to his book *Proust was a Neuroscientist* Jonah Lehrer reveals details of how artists anticipated the discoveries of neuroscience over a century ago.

> Their imaginations foretold facts of the future. Of course, this isn't the way knowledge is supposed to advance. Artists weave us pretty tales, while scientists objectively describe the universe. In the impenetrable prose of the scientific paper, we imagine a perfect reflection of reality. One day, we assume science will solve everything.

He goes on to propose a fuller perspective:

> Unlike scientists who began to separate thoughts into their anatomical parts and although these artists witnessed the birth of modern science – Whitman and Eliot contemplated Darwin, Proust and Woolf admired Einstein – they never stopped believing that the truths of consciousness must begin from the inside, with what it really feels like.

Whether you lean towards coaching as a science or more as an art, I hope this chapter reveals a good balance for you and you can accept both sides into your outlook.

THE NATURE OF COACHING

> There's so much more to coaching squash than merely teaching someone how to hit the ball.
>
> Jonah Barrington, p.76.

In search of the Holy Grail!

Of all the chapters in this book, this one is probably the least black and white, yet still informed by research and collective experiences. Over the past twenty-five years, coaching has really taken off as a topic to be analysed and dissected. Like many of the other forms of sports science in this book, coaching itself has begun to be treated as another form of science, where research is undertaken to push closer towards a model of improved coaching. The thing is, coaching is all very human and no matter how much we try to quantify and 'find the many truths' of coaching, we will never find them. Taking from the philosophy of Ken Wilber, one of the world's most published philosophers, only 'partial truths' exist. We can have fun searching for them, though remembering not to get too fundamental about it, an affliction that many have fallen foul of. Coaching is always about interpretation. It is a personal process, specific to situations, affected by moods and dependent upon levels of maturity within the people involved. There exists no definitive rulebook; there never will be. Only a journey into the unknown, quite like life itself.

It is important to remember there really is not one superior formula to coaching squash or indeed any sport. No equation exists for a coach that can guarantee success with players. Yet what is available in the following passages is a road map of possibilities well informed and backed by research and experience. As a coach you may not agree with or be able to apply all aspects, yet hopefully it will benefit your imagination and craft in some significant way.

Contradictions and Uncertainty

The paradox for the coach is that whilst they seek certainty they must learn to enjoy and accept it is an uncertain process. Armed only with a loose (or in some cases strict) philosophy and various depths of knowledge, the coach is deluded if they think they can make the process a certain one (for example, if you do this more, you will win; if you don't do this you will lose).

It would be foolhardy to claim that coaches all have the same talents and impact on player development. Just as you get different quality doctors or different classes of schoolteacher you certainly have wide ranges of talent in coaches too. It remains a mystery why some people just 'have it' and some do not, no matter how much we try to explain it. A coach can just fit a certain relationship and situation at a certain time, yet in different circumstances they just cannot make it click. It is a rare coach that is able to thrive in all situations at most times of their career. Some just never seem to make it work despite having great knowledge and ideas. There are past players who slide effortlessly into coaching well, whilst others just struggle. Some people develop into the role better over years of effort and learning yet some just do not.

The difficulty can be the contradictions. Coaching is about things you can see as much as things you cannot see. It is about changing, as much as staying true to your roots. Coaching is about patience as much as it is about urgency. It is about confident direct leadership and letting others lead. Strangely, it is about winning whilst losing and losing whilst winning, the big picture and the small. Coaching involves guesswork as much as it involves facts, intuition versus intellect. Coaching can be scientific but it is mainly an art. That wonderful ability to find the right words to say just at the right time is as artistic as any painter stroking a brushstroke just in the appropriate place. Like art it is about interpretation and instinct, a faith in the unknown. Armed with only a vision of how things can become, coach and player must trust each other, share understandings and hold mutual respect close. Overall, coaching is about relationships more than formal instructions.

David Pearson

When I was national coach I was often asked by the Performance Director at the time to write down everything I did so that other coaches could copy it. I used to say that there was no point to that because lots of my coaching skill was based on me and my personality. Things you can't write down. For example I am told I have a good way of relaxing players, I don't know why and I wouldn't be too interested in knowing why. It may be a natural part of me or a skill I've acquired over time. I tend to read people well as a session progresses and I adapt accordingly. It's those little adaptations that matter, that sense when it's important to change what you're doing or keep on with the same thing.

A Matter of Opinion

Which of these do you list as the top six most important attributes a coach needs to be?

Stubborn	Positive	Learner
Leader	Listener	Intelligent

Charming	Warm	Eloquent
Educated	Funny	Worrier
Organiser	Researcher	Loving
Confident	Planner	Spiritual
Friendly	Protective	Judgemental
Streetwise	Wise	Strict
Forgiving	Honest	Interesting
Motivating	Strong	Popular
Respected	Patient	Driving
Enthusiastic	Calm	Older
Up to date	Maverick	Perfectionist
Fun	Cool	Human
Analytical	Loyal	Pragmatic
Faultless	Knowledgeable	Male
Female	Muslim	Christian
My nationality	Past professional	

This is a very personal choice for you, the reader. You have so many individual experiences, values and beliefs; you know this task has no correct answer. There is no hierarchy or combination above any other. Each of these single words could have a whole book or books written about them. There could be strong justifications for every word being more important than the next in terms of what an expert coach requires. This is an important point to be appreciated. Too often there is an assumption that to 'coach the right way' is to do this or that. There is always a new piece of validated research or a tale of success that pertains to be a whole truth or at least a key part of the whole. Methods such as detailed observation, longitudinal study, structured interview and many more qualitative and quantitative investigations into topics relating to the coaching process are used well, yet for every 'aha' moment and every 'pattern' that is revealed, nothing can rightly preach to be the only way to go.

The same confusion goes for specific areas such as skill development, nutrition, strength and conditioning, talent identification, parental roles, psychology and so on. Even paradigms such as 'old school' being less or more superior to new methods also shift from situation to situation. Only one thing remains certain, which is that not much is certain within the art and science of coaching.

Map Makers

> We must see people in terms of their future potential, not their past performance.
>
> Sir John Whitmore, p.16.

Essentially coaches are 'map makers'. They point the way for the player. A player's journey is a process of exploration, taking many wrong turns as well as right ones. It can be a shared journey but the player must be the one to travel first. The finest players lead their coaches through their journey, not the other way. Coaches after all are just coaches. It is the player that counts. They play! This is a principle many coaches do not grasp in this age of the 'supercoach'.

A good question to ask, as coaches seek to put more and more detail on maps by adding research, reflections and advice, is: are they depriving performers of a much-needed struggle? By over-enthusiasm, over-worrying, feeling responsibility and craving their own kickback of success, maybe coaches are creating over-complicated maps smothered with too much detail, consequently depriving players of the freedom to go and explore for themselves. Most often the learnings are in the exploration and in particular wrong turns and getting lost on their journey. If this is the case, then the art of appropriate map making is a far more important skill to acquire than merely piling up information and coaching jargon.

David Pearson

We have replaced wisdom with knowledge. We have lost the human feel and tried to replace it with too much evidence and information. All the best players I have ever worked with made it because of who *they* were and how damn hard they worked, their character too. Yes I helped them a lot but like Peter Nicol always used to tell me: 'He's the player, he's the one who goes out and does it, not the coach.'

Wisdom is Earned, Knowledge is Cheap

> Knowledge is knowing that a tomato is a fruit; wisdom is knowing not to put it in a fruit salad.
>
> Brian O'Driscoll,
> Irish Rugby Union Captain

Football coach Jose Mourinho speaks at the heart of a modern issue in sports coaching, and squash is no exception:

> I think we are in a moment of contradictions. Because there is a wave of opinion that says because the knowledge is available for everyone – the distance between you and the knowledge is nothing – we have got generations of people well-informed, well-prepared. I disagree. I feel a lot, when I read what people sometimes write, that it's not like this, because when the knowledge is at the disposal of everybody, some people are in a comfort zone. When the knowledge is not at your disposal, you have to think. And you have to produce knowledge. If you want a good training session because you want to coach defence in a low block you have

200 sessions [pointing to the computer, where they are accessible on the internet]. If you don't have this you have to produce it yourself. So I see lots of replicas. You got to the fifth division, or Under-10s, the two centre-halves open, the goalkeeper gives the ball to the central midfielder, the central midfielder isn't technically good, he loses the ball. But they keep going in the same direction. We are in the moment of stability because the knowledge is available to everyone and we have stopped in a comfort zone.

(Telegraph/Gary Neville, 2014).

Mourinho's sentiments are echoed by David Pearson:

When I started coaching in the early eighties you were thinking on your feet a lot, I suppose I've just carried on trusting myself to work it out. I have hardly ever read a coaching book or manual in my life. I read all sorts of other things like history and war stories but as for information on coaching I have tended to avoid them. As fascinating as they are and I know it may be a fault but I have always liked to work things out and trust my own intellect. I've had many coaches talk a great game over the years and been at conferences where I have been told 'how to coach' but I rarely see them make the impact themselves apart from talking about it.

Coaches tell me all the right things why their players lost and which tactics they did or did not employ correctly. They have great suggestions for drills and exercises and tell me all the psychological theories of what is going on. It's all interesting and they are very convincing when you listen, sometimes I wonder how on earth I can coach with all this about me. But, and it's a big but – rarely do I hear someone

explain why problems occur from a technical angle or how to specifically improve things within that individual person out there playing. We can all be good at sounding clever and regurgitating things we've read but actually coaching, changing players and improving problems over the years – that is coaching to me. And the players know it too.

Coaching Pressure and Lack

There has always been an expectation that a coach is someone who helps people improve yet nowadays there seems to be a lot of added pressure placed on coaches to make a significant difference. We have seen coaches given far more media attention, far more qualifications and education, and many more coaching positions have been rewarded with full salaries or good hourly rates of pay. This all brings expectation and a pressure to live up to the role as 'chief influencer'. Results are required and time to deliver reduced. Coaching criticism is rife. There is always an expert pointing out the alternative method, always a piece of research suggesting you need to be more up to date, and when things are good always a bit of social media to boost your ego in unhealthy proportions. This can bring stress to the environment, which is rarely good. So it is really important that coaches have strategies in place to reduce the 'pressure' that will come their way.

The feeling of 'lack' is a destroyer of many things. It dents your confidence and brings paranoia. It stiffens your creativity and makes you vulnerable to academic elitism, coaching folklore and quick fix marketing gimmicks. It takes away faith in oneself to just be you.

Lack feeds 'hero worshipping' of those who appear not to lack! With the rise in coach education and the chopping down of sport into all its tiny expert components, it gets harder to operate confidently by just being yourself. It is hard to feel complete as you are encouraged to reflect, philosophize and force improvement upon yourself. I witnessed this pressure coming in through the late 1990s. The need to evolve and adapt is of course a key part of life, but to do it from a position of 'lack' or 'should' is unhealthy and a trap to be avoided. Be interested, be curious and listen but most of all think for yourself.

David Pearson

Hopefully you will finish this chapter a little more accepting of yourself and the way you currently operate.

Building on the Uniqueness of the Individual

This definition provided by the International Coaching Federation points towards the personal qualities required to coach in the original sense of the word individuality:

Coaches are trained to listen, to observe and to customize their approach to individual client needs. They seek to elicit solutions and strategies from the client: they believe the client is naturally creative and resourceful. The coach's job is to provide support to enhance the skills, resources and creativity that the client already has.

In the appropriately titled book *You Haven't Taught Until They Have Learned*, John Wooden, one of the most revered coaches in the history of sports, offers his insight into individual player needs:

I am not going to treat you all the same. Giving you the same treatment does not make sense because you're all different. The good Lord, in all his infinite wisdom, did not make us all the same. Goodness gracious, if he had the world would be a boring world don't you think? You are different from each other in height, weight, background, intelligence, talent, and many other ways. For that reason each one of you deserves individual treatment that is best for you. I will decide what the treatment will be. It may take the form of gentle encouragement or it may be stronger. That depends on you.

They are all different. There is no formula. I could name players, all who were spirited but in a different way. You can't work with them exactly the same way. You've got to study and analyse each individual and find out what makes them tick. Some you may have to put on the bench more. Others you have to pat on the back more. I wish there was a formula. The same thing won't work with every team. It depends on the personnel. So you have to know the individuals you are working with.

A strong recent example of the need to consider individuality is the reference to 'genetics' in David Epstein's award-winning book *The Sports Gene*. For much of the past ten years there has been a push towards '10,000 hours of practice' being a bare minimum to reach peak performance no matter what your genetic makeup. Suddenly, evidence suggests that number or indeed any set total, is not as certain as previously populated; as Epstein says, 'there is no magic formula'. He brings powerful scientific arguments in relation to gender, race, willpower, age and physiology, which again adds complexity to standard folklore. He uses science to reveal deeper layers of complexity than we previously thought:

I learned that some skills that I thought were innate – like the bullet-fast reactions of Major League hitters – are learned, and others that I thought were entirely voluntary acts of will, like the compulsive drive to train, have important genetic components. I learned that the best genetic and physiological research in sports often contradicted my intuition about elite sports performance.

We know in squash that we have all types of people, from all types of backgrounds, culture and race that have gone on to make the very best of players. Saying that, some have struggled and have been fighting the genetic tide so to speak. Others are clearly blessed in certain areas and like horses in horseracing and sprinters in sprinting, some have the breeding to fit squash's particular demands of twisting at speed and keeping going at it! The beauty of 'game sports' like squash, however, is that there are so many facades to the sport that gains can be made in many areas, not least technical, psychological and tactical areas. This is where the shrewd coach can thrive by mapping pathways based on unique visions for each individual.

SQUASH-SPECIFIC NEEDS:
Each player will have personal strengths and weaknesses in the major areas of squash: technical, psychological, tactical and physiological.

PLAYING STYLE AND PERSONALITY NEEDS:
Players play and see squash in different ways and use squash to meet different personal needs. Below are just four possibilities:

■ *Hard worker*: small improvements over the long term, dedicated, wants honest feedback, effort-based, long-term thinking,
strong-willed, discipline pays off in the end

■ *Naturally gifted*: game seems to come easy, quick improvements, variety of skills, develops own ideas, short-term success especially in juniors, flowing movements, good 'squash brain'

■ *Structured thinker*: likes a plan and information, logical, likes a discussion, plays in patterns, 'we can work it out' approach, likes patterns, built by design, difficulty with creation

■ *Unstructured creative*: random ideas, experimental, new shots, fun-based, likes play and game-based practices, finds structure hard to stick with, spontaneous.

Each player will have a natural way they approach trying to win a squash match. It is imperative the coach and the player understand this and then agree where they want to develop. Rarely will a complete change of approach work and likewise a rigid approach will keep a player limited. Maturity in your natural style is usually best recommended where a player knows their own strengths but is willing to adapt where necessary over the years. This will closely be related to a player's natural *personality* and the wise coach will understand the importance of matching both and coach accordingly, because this is where deep motivation lives. Without a player feeling motivated and energized no journey will ever be completed.

PERSONAL AND LIFESTYLE NEEDS:
It is said that 'good coaches coach players yet great coaches coach people'. A player is not a machine outside of human existence; they are simply a person who plays squash. A coach's ability to understand, take an interest and offer support in personal and lifestyle factors that the person has is very important to the whole process. Areas to consider are:

- Welfare
- Family connections
- Finance
- Health
- Maturity (moral development)
- Living conditions
- Social skills
- Personal history
- Connectedness and belonging
- Life skills, such as cooking, cleaning
- Organizational skill
- Cultural/religious beliefs
- Emotional intelligence
- Self-identity and self-esteem
- Personal relationships
- Educational.

Measurement and investigative tools

There are many subjective and objective methods of discovering, recording and quantifying player needs. Examples include:

- Game analysis (post-game and real time)
- Performance profiling
- Psychological profiling
- Physiological testing
- Biomechanical analysis
- Situational analysis
- SWOT analysis
- Intuitive (gut) input
- Family and friends input
- Input from others who know the athlete and are trusted to give well-informed judgements (other coaches, ex-professionals, some competitors, officials)
- Observational – spending time with players in diverse situations
- Discussion and interview
- Questionnaires
- Coaching conversations
- Personal conversations.

When appropriate evidence and opinion has been compiled, patterns should appear giving well-formed judgements on which interventions are most needed.

Ongoing Change and Adaptation

Remember that players *evolve* and their needs will be constantly changing. Whilst people generally do not change in their *core*, they will be changing on the surface and coaches must keep pace. Players grow in experience and standard, they age, they mature, their life situation alters and they expect different things in life for themselves. The challenge of the game changes also as players evolve, rule/equipment changes come in and the overall standard of squash goes up. So constant monitoring of needs of your player and a frequent reflection into yourself as a coach are most vital for progression. As Mark McClusky, author of *Faster Higher Stronger: How Sports Science is Creating a New Generation of Superathletes* (2014) states, 'Your ability to learn faster than your competitors may be the only sustainable competitive advantage.'

Simple but not easy!

The only simplicity for which I would give a straw is that which is on the other side of the complex.

Oliver Wendell Holmes, p.109.

The final point to dwell on here is that 'simplicity' often lies at the other side of 'complexity' and sometimes as coaches collect more experiences it is hard to grasp that. This book itself will be throwing more layers of complexity into your understanding of squash yet the hope is that you can take that complexity and eventually simplify it through practice.

As All Blacks and World Cup-winning coach Steve Hansen stated, 'Our job is to make the complex simple. The simpler you can make it for somebody, the easier it is to do it.'

PERSONAL COACHING COMPETENCIES

Anyone can become angry – that is easy. But to be angry with the right person, to the right degree, at the right time, for the right purpose, and in the right way – that is not easy.

Aristotle

Coaching Intelligence is Emotional Intelligence

'Emotional Intelligence' was popularized by Daniel Goleman in 1995. Goleman, a man who was awarded the American Psychological Association's Lifetime Achievement Award for his work on brain and behavioural sciences, explained that emotional intelligence is 'the capacity for recognizing our own feelings and those of others, for motivating ourselves, and for managing emotions effectively in others and is a most vital predictor of success.'

The four categories of Emotional Intelligence (EI) include Self-Awareness, Social Awareness, Self-Management and Relationship Management.

Goleman argues that above IQ, Emotional Intelligence (EI) is the key intelligence required for humans to be fully functioning. Each cornerstone of EI is vital in coaching and is a highly relevant structure to build coaching skills upon. You will be taken through most of the twenty-one emotional competencies and how they apply to the needs of a squash coach. The last eleven competencies are more specifically about the relationships with others whilst the initial ten are more to do with personal development.

Table 8.1 The two main building blocks of trust are sincerity and reliability. (Adapted from O'Connor, 2007, p.18)

Self-Awareness	Social Awareness
■ Emotional self-awareness	■ Empathy
■ Accurate self-assessment	■ Organizational awareness
■ Self-confidence	■ Service orientation
Self-Management	**Relationship Management**
■ Emotional self-control	■ Developing others
■ Trustworthiness	■ Inspirational leadership
■ Conscientiousness	■ Influence
■ Adaptability	■ Communication
■ Optimism	■ Change catalyst
■ Achievement orientation	■ Conflict Management
■ Initiative	■ Building bonds
	■ Teamwork and collaboration

Self-Awareness

Awareness is the beginning of all growth. Awareness of a problem is the beginning of the solution. Awareness transforms that vague something into a specific action you can correct or improve. Sometimes when we feel like we are 'getting worse' we are finally ready to get much better.

> Dan Millman,
> Body Mind Mastery, p.21.

EMOTIONAL SELF-AWARENESS

Having the skill to feel what is rising inside you is where emotional mastery begins. Recognizing feelings enables you to control them and this is vital to the squash coach.

Yes, this is something I've got better at over the years. You get a knack of recognizing feelings in yourself and how they affect you. For example, I will suddenly feel happy or inpatient or bored and these things need to be nipped in the bud if they have a negative effect on the player. When I am watching a player in an important match I really need to make sure I am in the right emotional state when I go and speak with them. It's no good a player telling me later that I was too stressed or negative during the play, I've got to recognize it in myself before I speak with them.

> David Pearson

ACCURATE SELF-ASSESSMENT

This is about knowing your own strengths and weaknesses as a person and consequently as a coach. How open are you to receive feedback from others about what you do well and what you need to improve upon? It is how you perceive yourself and your limits and then how open are you to self-development.

I have been told I am very self-reflective, perhaps too much at times, especially in my early years of coaching. I feel I have a good grasp of my current limits as a coach and also where I excel. This has enabled me to play to my strengths in the areas I am strong and admit to the weaker areas of my coaching style. I like this because it takes away pressure to be 'all things to all men'. I encourage players to go to other coaches and seek advice from other areas because I am very aware of my narrow area of influence. I always aim to improve and grow my coaching strengths through experience, reading, observation and education but not in a quest to be perfect in every area. This way I feel more honest with players, less responsibility to have all the answers and much more open to criticism and feedback where I can improve.

> Danny Massaro

SELF-CONFIDENCE

A hugely important factor in any leadership situation is to know you have the capacity within you to get the job done. A self-confident coach thinks 'Yes, I am the best person for this, I know what I am doing and I can accomplish what needs to be done here.' Consequently, players feel this sense of certainty and they settle, knowing that belief is all around.

Yes, to me this isn't about being cocky or a know-it-all but about absolute belief in your convictions as you converse with a player. I know for a fact that much of the things I coach work. I've seen it work for real and I have seen the results. A player must get a sense from you that you are supremely assured in your views when you discuss things with them. I have had to take players who were much better than me, who have won much more than I did as a player and basically explain they were wrong! That takes confidence because you know these people are clever and have done many good things in the past but you must let them know by your passion and beliefs that you can put your point forward. Last year after Laura Massaro had won the British Open, I had to confront her and explain I thought her grip would be better a bit further round. I worried about that beforehand but decided to express my views anyway. Laura believed in me and she spent eight weeks practising how to hold the racket!

David Pearson

Self-Management

EMOTIONAL SELF-CONTROL

This is the ability to control those rising emotions especially during matches and at competitions. If you are easily 'wound up' then you are an easy target from your own players, officials and others. Having the ability to keep cool under pressure, refrain from negativity and allow feelings to rise and pass through you is a key coaching intelligence. This is not always easy and on occasion it is useful to let emotions go but very rarely is it the pathway to excellence.

This is one of the hardest ones especially with family. I found my emotional control much harder with my daughter Jenny (Duncalf). Generally though, I have been able to get better at being calmer during matches. I have little strategies I use like thinking of the bigger picture or singing songs to myself which helps. I think it's really important to keep under control because the player needs you to be think-ing clearly, they are the ones going through the actual stress. I've seen some parents and coaches causing all sorts of problems because they're too emotional – swearing,

arguing, blaming and making wide-of-the-mark accusations. Players need calming and assuring 90 per cent of the time, not being blamed, henpecked and shouted at.

David Pearson

TRUSTWORTHINESS

SINCERITY

Table 8.2 Sincerity and reliability	
Low sincerity, high reliability	**High sincerity, high reliability**
Low trust because while the coach is able to keep promises, she does not.	Trust established. The coach is both capable and willing to keep promises.
Low reliability, low sincerity	**Low reliability, high sincerity**
No trust. Coach not willing and not able to keep promises.	Little trust. Coach wants to keep promises but is not able to.

RELIABILITY

Reliability is about 'practising what you preach'. It is a consistency between what you tell your players you will do and what you actually do. You can keep secrets and at the same time be tough and confront issues that need addressing. Trust leads to a refreshing openness to talk about feelings and personal issues that players often need to release. Trust helps strengthen and deepen a bond between player and coach and often it is in these bonds where real coaching influences lives.

Without trust you can forget it in terms of what I call 'real coaching'. A player has to be able to open up as a coach does with a player. There can't be any white elephants in the room. If I think a player isn't fit or I think their lifestyle is not right or their behaviour is poor then I will tell them. You deliver it in a certain way when the time is right but it must be discussed. Most players take it if they trust you, because they know you mean well. I've not been able to get that bond with everyone I've coached and generally because we couldn't get that 'openness' improvements haven't been what I think they could have. This is where the player has to take a leap of faith sometimes and really commit to a coach and their ideas.

David Pearson

CONSCIENTIOUSNESS

This is the want 'to do a good professional job'. Coaching is a profession and like all professions involves the drive to produce certain standards of reliability and quality. Coaching is not a careless activity, far from it. An effective coach will reflect and plan for each performer they work with. There will be a certain level of effort and attention to detail, a desire to improve the situation according to discussed time frames. There is a certain commitment to the process and the player will be able to recognize this in your attitude before, during and after coaching sessions.

I aim to give every single player I ever go on court with my full attention. I happen to like sessions evolving naturally but this doesn't mean I am not thinking and pondering before sessions how best to help a player. It is an enthusiasm to give all you've got, to be interested in the player and let them know they are getting your full attention and care. I'm knackered when I stop but find each lesson fascinating. Totally regardless of the level of player

it is my professional obligation to do my best for them, whoever they are. Coaching is giving.

David Pearson

ADAPTABILITY

I remember seeing an elaborate and complicated automatic washing machine for automobiles that did a beautiful job of washing them. But it could do only that, and everything else that got into its clutches was treated as if it were an automobile to be washed. I suppose it is tempting, if the only tool you have is a hammer, to treat everything as if it were a nail.

Abraham Maslow, p.68

One of the most popular leadership models that has been applied to sports coaching is Packianathan Chelladurai's multi-dimensional model (1978) and is all based on adaptability. In summary, the leader is expected to vary their leadership style according to two sets of equally potent and at times conflicting forces:

1. Situational demands: what does the situation require here? Example: a player needs to be told strongly what to do because there is a mini crisis.

2. Member's preferences: how does the player like to be led? What do they prefer a leader to be? Example: a player likes to be in charge, making their own choices, but enjoys support and direction when they ask for it.

LEADERSHIP

Chelladurai (1984, 1990) proposed that there are five types of leadership behaviour:

1. *Training and instruction:* behaviour is aimed at improving performance.
2. *Democratic:* allows decisions to be made collectively.
3. *Autocratic:* gives the leader personal authority.

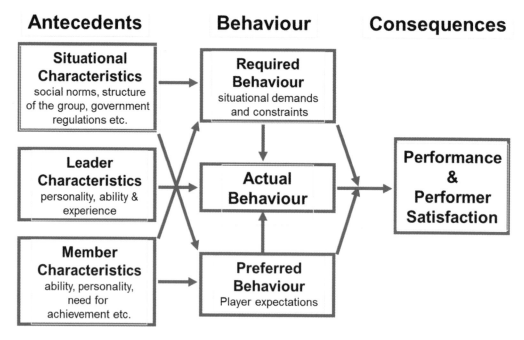

Fig. 8.4 The multi-dimensional model.

4. *Social support:* shows concern for the well-being of others.
5. *Rewarding:* provides team members with positive reinforcement.

A coach who can show the adaptability and skill to match their leadership style with what the 'situation requires' and what the 'player prefers' is likely to have greater coaching impact.

> *A good recent example of this was with Nick Matthew in the final of the World Open 2013. It was two games all with Gregory Gaultier and basically I felt Nick had lost his length. Greg was struggling physically on the day and in my mind all Nick had to do was hit the back wall. Normally I let Nick talk a lot between games because this is what he prefers, I tend just to listen and suggest one or two things. On this occasion the situation required me to take control. I shouted at*

> *him and emphasized it with a swear word or two, which I never normally do. He was shocked and for one of the first times in his career didn't say a word. He went on and nailed the tactic and won well.*
>
> David Pearson

OPTIMISM AND INITIATIVE
> *What doesn't kill you on the court makes you stronger on the court.*
>
> Nick Matthew OBE

There is no doubt that having positive expectations and an appreciation of current opportunities is a major emotional competency required in coaching. Carol Dweck, Educational Researcher and author of bestselling book *Mindset*, calls it having a 'Growth Mindset'.

> *The passion for stretching yourself mentally, physically and emotionally and sticking to it, especially when it's not*

going well, is the hallmark of the Growth Mindset. The Growth Mindset is only concerned with ongoing improvement.

Carol Dweck

We are all different but I can grow and change anything through application and experience. I will try my hardest to keep pushing my talents. Why worry about hiding deficiencies when I could be overcoming them. Why repeat things that aren't working when I can be changing and experimenting with new ideas. I want to be stretched. Nothing ventured, nothing gained. If at first you don't succeed, try and try again. Success is learning and developing my abilities as a player and person. In the end I always get better.

Laura Massaro

GROWTH MINDSET PATTERNS OF THE BEST SQUASH PLAYERS

Growth Mindset players and coaches realize the tour is more difficult than they thought it would be, but it's what they want to do, so that only makes them more determined. They enjoy touring as they always return home with learnings from playing and watching other players they admire. They actively seek out coaches and trainers who will be honest with them about what they need to work on. They then go and do that work and have it checked by experts. They find things to be pleased with from almost every performance and practice, yet sense where improvements must be made. They want coaches they can grow with over time and so see the bigger picture of 'pay off' in the future (one to six years). There is a confidence to experiment in 'league' and 'practice' matches in order to improve over the long term. Losing and winning is very important to them but does not define them. They very rarely overreact to results because performance issues take priority. A low fear

of failure exists because they can't really recognize failure as too defining because effort is the king aim and they know they control that.

Sooner or later players like this move up the rankings and start to leave peers behind. They begin to consistently worry higher-ranked players who begin noticing they are in the midst of someone who is going to keep improving. Sudden surprising and rapid bursts of improvement come because of all the accumulated hard work that has been building up. Enjoyment of tour stays high, excitement high and they begin to earn the respect of expert coaches and players, not that they seek it or need it. They may begin to 'believe the hype' as their confidence naturally grows but not to the point of arrogance, just confidence. They continue up the rankings, get picked for their country and win caps and medals.

Setbacks inevitably arrive such as injuries, and these are used as opportunities to work on other things such as psychology, technique, strength and relationships. They keep a very good life balance where they work hard but rest well and generally feel internally satisfied with their careers and lives. They continue to seek improvement to the end of their career and are always willing to adapt, change and mature at the pace required to stay on top of their game.

You have to believe in players no matter how hard it gets sometimes. The player must be prepared to change and dedicate to the long-term process, and coaches can help them with this by being optimistic themselves. In the space of two years I went from an average club player to playing for England and that has stuck with me. You can always improve and without your coach believing in you how can you expect a player to believe in themselves? There is always something to improve and it can happen in a click one day. Lots of work and patience can suddenly pay off in one match and then you're on to the next level. I call it faith.

David Pearson

The art here is to help develop a Growth Mindset together with the players themselves, so you both have it. Lots of it will come through the attributions you give to success and failure. At times it will be important to blame yourself and also take personal credit for things. Other times we need to accept failure was not our fault but maybe bad luck or opponents were too good. The key is that motivation remains high to go away and continue to improve. A coach can help direct attention and awareness to the reasons, excuses or attributions that work best at that time for a particular player. Making an appropriate excuse or alternatively directly laying responsibility on the player is a balance most required by both player and coach.

You've got to be clever when to pick your battles with players and when to ease off and make excuses for them. A month before Nick Matthew won the World Open Championships last year, he lost very heavily to Gregory Gaultier in the US Open final. It was a crushing blow. It would have been easy to pick holes in Nick that night and panic, blaming this and that but I relaxed about it and said Greg was just on another planet, nothing you could do, Nick. Whilst we walked home together that night Nick told me he was ready and glad of the lesson he had just had and Greg had peaked too early to win the Worlds. Whilst not necessarily true (although it did turn out that way) I was really struck by Nick's reaction and how he used it as a positive experience and kept his spirits up with only a month to go.

David Pearson

ACHIEVEMENT ORIENTATION AND SERVICE ORIENTATION

Pete Carroll, current coach of the Seattle Seahawks and NFC Coach of the year explains the importance of visualizing achievement and what it represents to you: 'Constantly we work with visualization, with envisioning what we could become. All power comes from the ability to envision what you want to become. How could you possibly get there unless you can picture it? You wouldn't know when you had arrived' (Byrne, p.80).

This is basically a passion for excellence, in this case coaching. This is the basic internal drive to achieve success with your players in whatever form success takes for you both.

In our Culture we tend to equate thinking and intellectual powers with success and achievement. In many ways however, it is an emotional quality that separates those who master a field from the many who simply work at a job. Our levels of desire, patience, persistence and confidence end up playing a much larger role in success than sheer reasoning powers.

Robert Greene, Mastery

Whether you set goals, write down dreams or have missions to complete, the hunger and desire must be present. It is easy to get stuck in a comfort zone, particularly after success, and coaches must be aware of this. Even the most determined players will only have so much willpower and drive themselves, so it is crucial that the coach is equally contributing drive and ambition. This must not be taken so far as to spill into being over-pushy and controlling and after all the player must bring most of the drive themselves, but a passive and carefree coach rarely stimulates players closer towards their full potential and possible successes.

Coaching is what I do. I am not a shouty kind of coach or a big speech type but I really want success. With all I have achieved so far as a coach I still want more. I want more for me and for them. I want players winning, getting higher in the rankings. I want Jenny and Laura to win more; I want Nick to get more for himself and the others. Until they stop playing, I want success if they do. It's important to drive on and improve, what's the point otherwise?

David Pearson

Social Awareness

EMPATHY AND BUILDING BONDS

People don't care how much you know until they know how much you care.

Perhaps the most powerful coaching emotional competency is the ability to empathize with a performer. Empathy is the basis of being able to accurately understand where another person is coming from emotionally and behaviourally. The power of this is extraordinary because feeling understood and listened to is a basic human need. Without it coaching will collapse, with it coaching will flow.

LIMBIC RESONANCE

Having a 'connection' with somebody else can be mapped in the brain. It is called limbic resonance. The brain's 'love centre' lights up and releases the neurotransmitters oxytocin and dopamine. Oxytocin and dopamine are fantastic natural drugs that promote feelings of harmony, love and empathy. Consequently, when a person receives information from somebody they have a 'limbic resonance' with then there is far more chance of a positive outcome. So in coaching situations this 'bond' is really important. A coach can settle a player emotionally, relax them and provide more energy for them simply by being around them.

The concept was advanced in the book *A General Theory of Love* (2000), and is one of three interrelated concepts central to the book's premise: that our brain chemistry and nervous systems are measurably affected by those closest to us (limbic resonance); that our systems synchronize with one another in a way that has profound implications for personality and lifelong emotional health (limbic regulation); and that these set patterns can be modified through therapeutic practice (limbic revision) (Lannon, Amini and Lewis, p. 170).

Simply put this is why it is difficult to laugh at a joke told by a person you do not like, yet the same joke is hilarious from someone you connect with. The reversal of this is when the bond is lacking, the love missing, then stress-related chemicals are released from the brain. People find it much harder to learn and perform in stress-related states. So rather than being productive and helpful to a player, the coach actually harms the performance and learning. The environment becomes negative underneath the surface and as time goes on coaching sessions can become counterproductive as real enjoyment and fun disappears. The magic has gone.

This can be the fault of both the player and the coach and in some cases it is just the way it is. Maybe you just haven't 'hit it off' or your time together has run its course. Realizing this and being open about it in a mature way may be a great way to help each other move on to other relationships whilst retaining some positive connection too.

Above all else, the relationship is most vital, not the coaching information being professed. Like any relationship in life, it takes work to keep things healthy. A coach must be prepared to 'connect' and open up themselves to feelings as well as facts.

I think coaches struggle with this area as much as any. Opening up yourself and forming connections is a natural thing to me. Some coaches just struggle with this. They are stiff. They can't hug a player. They go on and on and on with the information yet can't bring feelings into it, which are the real things that matter in a player's life. You've got to try and set up situations where the player can open up. Going for lunch, having a coffee together. Lots of my work is done before and after the actual squash lesson. The fun and banter before, the phone calls and exchanging gossip! It's all part of relaxing them and getting to know each other, warts and all.

Another point here is that I believe a lot of coaching is in the eyes. A lot goes on with eye contact and I am always wary of those who can't look at you in the eyes. There simply has to be a connection. It is the basis of everything. You have to have a heart and help them open up theirs. Then they open up yours too, which is all part of the bond.

David Pearson

I know when Danny and David Pearson watch me they are completely with me. They understand me, they like me and I know Danny loves me. I feel like, no matter what, they get me and are in my corner whatever happens. They can shed tears, give hugs and feel a match with me. At the end of the day we are a team and we have a strong bond, it gives me so much belief and power to train and play.

Laura Massaro

Relationship Management

When we feel safe, we humans are explorers, approaching new discoveries with delight. If people are anxious, uncomfortable, or fearful, they do not learn. That is, they do not build new connections and create new maps. Knowing how to create the conditions for learning is a key skill for coaches.

Rock and Page, p.266.

The strength and quality of the relationship between coach and performer(s) will underpin everything in the process. Both parties need energizing from each other in a two-way process that feels equal, useful and relaxing too.

DEVELOPING OTHERS

Sir John Whitmore, founder of Coaching Institute defines coaching as 'Unlocking a person's potential to maximize their own performance. It is helping them to learn rather than teaching them.' 'Helping' a person has connotations of informality, equality and support whereas teaching implies expertise and hierarchy. Having the ability to form shared partnerships and mutual respect and then maintaining them could be the greatest coaching skill of all.

COACHING AT IDENTITY LEVEL

Who do players think they are, deep down? How do they see themselves? What are their true levels of self-esteem? We are in the area of beliefs here, which ultimately links to self-identity. It is the self-identity that is tested under pressure. Who do you know you are, deep down? To the performer a belief about themselves is a fact and in the end these beliefs will surface, especially under pressure.

A key outcome of coaching at the identity level is to enable people to expand and deepen their sense of who they are and respond to the opportunities and challenges presented by life from a place of increasing presence, resourcefulness and authenticity — even during times of challenge and crisis.

Robert Dilts, p.38.

Helping a player to 'be themselves' and get rid of nagging limitations they carry about themselves is most vital in the coaching process. For squash players limiting self-identity fears could include things like 'I am slow,' 'I am not natural at concentration,' 'I am too small,' 'I am lazy,' 'I don't belong at the top,' 'I love food too much to lose weight,' 'My backhand has always been rubbish,' or 'I will never be as good as...'

Such beliefs build into a defence mechanism that makes a player shut down when really challenged. A coach's job is to help break this type of thinking and really get the player to open up to other possibilities about themselves.

> *We instinctively think of each new student as a blank slate, but the ideas they bring to that first lesson are probably far more important than anything a teacher can do, or any amount of practice. It's all about their perception of self.*
>
> *McPherson, in Coyle, p.104.*

Often our private versions of reality are not actually true. They are generalizations we make up from recreated memories and skewed interpretations we have compiled. Talking through such versions of reality with players and helping them to separate out the facts from the fictions is critical for development. It involves excellent conversational skill and deep trust. It is an ongoing process, often intimate and especially needed in emotional times when players can get really down on themselves or too high.

> *The number of conversations I have had with players that have had nothing to do with squash is unbelievable. I have had players who get blocks because of what they believe about themselves. I've seen them behaving stupidly and throwing matches away that they were capable of winning because of something other than squash. I have really tried to help players get through these stages. The things players think often borders on paranoia and madness, nobody else would ever know how they really think about themselves. We've talked about life, religion, relationships, personal things, especially parental relationship, culture, wars, everything. There's a lot of magic hidden in those conversations over the years. Players have called me up years later and said things like 'thanks for all those chats we used to have, I now know what you mean and I want you to come to my wedding!' I think I've helped them to accept themselves, grow up, get rid of a lot of rubbish and to change the way they thought they needed to behave and just be themselves.*
>
> *David Pearson*

INSPIRATIONAL LEADERSHIP
(Key words – Credibility, Respect, Charisma, Presence)

> *He did look upon me as a son. His attitude was that my family was his family. Naz demanded from me the same sort of loyalty he would have demanded of his own children. I was drawn to him because I sensed that he was very much part of the great era of the fifties, even though he had never been a world champion himself.*
>
> *Jonah Barrington, on former coach*
> *Nasrullah Khan, p.76.*

Leading by example is arguably the most powerful form of leadership as it gains instant respect. Players will constantly be thinking 'If they can't do it for themselves, how can they preach to me with confidence?' So it is important that demonstrations, decision-making skills and effort levels are up there to match your expectations of your player. Players will want to see the same sort of qualities in you that you are asking of them. Not necessarily at their level but at your own best level. If you are asking a player to push themselves harder in an agreed area of improvement it doesn't half improve the power of your message if you yourself are pushing hard in an area of your own life.

INFLUENCE

> Attention in itself is not enough for rapport. The next ingredient is good feeling, evoked largely through tone of voice and facial expression. In building a sense of positivity, the nonverbal messages we send can matter more than what we are saying. Pace and timing of a conversation and our body movements are all part of this too.'
> Daniel Goleman, p.30.

In many ways a squash coach is a salesperson. You are selling ideas and concepts to players and you are aiming to convince them in areas you believe to be beneficial. All selling comes down to the power of influence and getting 'buy in' to the product or idea on sale.

A powerful tool for influence is the use of humour. Daniel Goleman himself said, 'Laughter may be the shortest distance between two brains, an unstoppable infectious spread that builds an instant social bond.' Neuroscientist Dr A.K. Pradeep, a man who researches why people buy the things they buy, wrote in *The Buying Brain* that 'humour is one of those tools the brain is hardwired to and is key to making a message new and novel. The brain loves it.' Psychology Professor Rod A Martin and author of *The Psychology of Humour* says, 'Humour not only conveys cognitive information to others but it also serves the function

of inducing and accentuating positive emotions in others, in order to influence their behaviour and promote a more favourable attitude towards the one who is laughing.' There is no doubt that influence and humour are very closely connected and the ability to generate it in appropriate forms and frequency is yet another critical competency of the successful coach.

> There is always humour for me. You have to relax, you have to find fun and poke fun. I will laugh at myself, at others or anyone who happens to be about. We can't have it too dark, you've got to have relief. I know when a player has frozen mentally and when I need to lighten the mood. I will bring anything up just to laugh, tease a little or take the mickey. Past stories are good for it. I love seeing a player smiling whilst they're learning. It frees them up. It's often down to me to start it because generally players are so damn serious most of the time. The least I can do is add a little humour to their week. Also I like the saying 'many a true word can be spoken in jest.' You can approach sensitive areas with a bit of fun sometimes, test the waters before launching in too deeply. And I find a bit of fun brings perspective to what players see as big problems when in fact they aren't at all.
> David Pearson

COMMUNICATION AND BUILDING BONDS

> The meaning of your communication is the response you get back.

In general, coaches are good at informational output. There is a tendency to lecture instead of coach. If players do not respond in accordance with your output then surely we can not claim to have communicated very well.

INITIATION ⟷ RESPONSE

Fig. 8.5 The coaching communication cycle. (Downey, 2003, p.63)

- Facial expressions
- Gestures
- Posture
- Tone and rhythm of voice
- Accent
- Proximity
- Touch
- Appearance
- Eye movements.

Real communication involves the message being understood and acted upon, not merely delivered.

According to Myles Downey, founder of the London School of Coaching, communication is very much a two-way process that recycles. The key skill for success is 'listening to understand'. Others have termed this simply 'listening', and it is the ability to really hear what your player is or is not saying. How are they responding to information and questions that have been initiated by the coach? This checking of understanding is critical. You use acknowledgment to let them know what you 'think' they have understood.

Coach: So you are telling me that the relaxed grip leads to more speed? Is that what you're saying?

Player: Yes. It helps feel as well and stops you getting tired as much.

Coach: OK I agree, now show me in these next ten shots then. In fact, you tell me what you think of your *grip* in your next ten shots.

Player: I will try, let's go.

This example illustrates dialogue and real two-way communication. Of course this is just the verbal communication, there is much more in non-verbal communication.

This is not the place to go deep into non-verbal communication classifications but it cannot be understated how powerful the following areas are in both supporting a verbal message and ruining one.

When we used to assess coaches for advanced coaching qualifications, communication style was the biggest area we used to have to fail participants on. It was extremely difficult to explain to people that although they had the outline of knowledge, they didn't have impact on the learner. You could see they were unconfident and were edgy in themselves, making the session clumsy and staccato. You have to be able to get that instant rapport and interaction flow: a smile, a nodding head, a variety of pitch in the voice. Relaxing posture, eye contact, a bit of humour, a pause in delivery, standing at the appropriate distance and a laugh now and again. These things are so important for the whole flow.

David Pearson

TEAMWORK AND COLLABORATION

Including others smoothly into 'the coaching team' is a skill that is becoming ever more important as expertise in sport support grows. Collaboration and encouraging players to work with a wider range of people other than yourself helps reduce pressure and often sheds new learnings and insights. One person does not know it all and to think so is dangerous and not only limiting but controlling. Integrating sports science support into the coaching process is a skill in itself and will depend on how well the communications and relationships develop between coach, performer and sport scientist(s).

It is the merging of 'science and sweat' that will allow today's athletes to not only excel and compete at much higher levels, but minimize predisposition to injury and enhance career longevity. Over the years, sport science has mainly been viewed by coaches as inaccessible, too technical, or in many cases, non-applicable to the actual sport setting. With the renewed focus on prevention of injuries, on enhancing performance at the younger levels of competition, and on the extensive amount of time and financial commitment toward training and conditioning, taking a more comprehensive approach through science provides the coach, as well as the athlete, greater control, preparation, accountability and, most importantly, measurable progress.

Michael Meyers

SUMMARY

To be a coach is simply to be a person. Working on all aspects of your Emotional Intelligence will be an unfolding and hopefully oscillating experience for you. After all, this is what you wish for those people you guide, show, question and occasionally tell!

Fig. 8.6 Laura Massaro considers coaching the most important ingredient to a squash player's success.

REFERENCES

Barrington, J. (1982). *Murder in the Squash Court.* London: Stanley Paul.

Byrne, R. (2014) *Hero.* London: Simon and Schuster.

Chelladurai, P. (2006). *Human Resource Management in Sport and Recreation,* 2nd edn. Champaign, IL: Human Kinetics.

Coyle, D. (2009). *The Talent Code.* New York: Bantam.

Dilts, R. (2003). *From Coach to Awakener.* California: Meta.

Downey, M. (2003). *Effective Coaching: Lessons from the Coaches' Coach.* Ohio: Texere Thomson.

Dweck, C. (2006). *Mindset. The New Psychology of Success.* New York: Ballantine.

Epstein, D. (2014). *The Sports Gene: Inside the Science of Extraordinary Athletic Performance.* London: Penguin.

Epstein, D. www.studentdoctor.net/2013/10/20-questions-david-epstein-author-of-the-sports-gene/#sthash.UiXxO1Os.

Goleman, D. (2004). *Emotional Intelligence and Working With Emotional Intelligence.* London: Bloomsbury.

Goleman, D. (2006). *Social Intelligence: The New Science of Human Relationships.* London: Hutchinson.

Greene, R. (2012). *Mastery.* London: Profile.

Guardian (2009). O'Driscoll's tomatoes keep analysts guessing. Available at www.theguardian.com/sport/blog/2009/feb/27/rugby-union-sixnations-brian-Odriscoll (Accessed 1 June 2015).

Holmes, O.W. (1961). *Holmes-Pollock Letters: The Correspondence of Mr. Justice Holmes and Sir Frederick Pollock, 1874–1932,* 2nd edn. New Jersey Press, p.109.

International Coach Federation (2008). *Core Competencies.*

Irwin, T. (2000). *Aristotle: The Nicomachean Ethics,* 2nd edn. London: Hackett.

Lannon, R., Amini, L. and Lewis, T. (2000). *A General Theory of Love.* New York: Random House.

Lehrer, J. (2012). *Proust Was A NeuroScientist.* New York: Houghton Mifflin.

Martin, R.A. (2006). *The Psychology of Humor: An Integrative Approach.* California: Elsevier Academic.

Michael C. Meyers (2006). Enhancing Sport Performance: Merging Sports Science with Coaching. *International Journal of Sports Science and Coaching,* 1(5), 89–100.

Millman, D. (1999). *Body Mind Mastery.* California: New World Library.

Maslow, A.H. (1966). *The Psychology of Science: A Reconnaissance.* London: Regenery.

Nater, S. and Gallimore, R. (2006). *You Haven't Taught until They Have Learned.* West Virginia: Fitness Information Technology.

O'Connor, J. and Lages, A. (2007). *How Coaching Works.* London: A and C Black.

Rock, D. and Page, L. (2009). *Coaching with the Brain in Mind.* New Jersey: John Wiley and Sons.

Telegraph/GaryNeville (2014). Jose Mourinho talks to Gary Neville. Available at www.telegraph.co.uk/sport/football/managers/jose-mourinho/11170519/Jose-Mourinho-talks-to-Gary-Neville-They-wanted-us-to-be-the-clowns-at-Anfield-we-werent-having-that.html. (Accessed 1 June 2015).

Telegraph/Ian McGeechan (2014). Sir Ian McGeechan talks to New Zealand's Steve Hansen about coaching the world's best team. Available at: http://www.telegraph.co.uk/sport/rugbyunion/international/newzealand/11215758/Sir-Ian-McGeechan-talks-to-New-Zealands-Steve-Hansen-about-coaching-the-worlds-best-team.html. (Accessed 1 June 2015).

Whitmore, J. (2002). *Coaching for Performance,* 3rd edn. London: Nicholas Brealey.

CHAPTER 9

SKILL ACQUISITION IN SQUASH

Oliver Logan and Nic James, English Institute of Sport and Middlesex University

Fig. 9.1 Squash is an open-skilled sport, requiring the highest levels of technical proficiency.

WHAT THE PLAYERS THINK

Nick Matthew OBE

With your coach, as you get older and more experienced there should be a much great player input and it becomes very much a partnership. In a session I'll get a lot of information from my coach at the start, then we work together to find the key. A lot of information is good as long as you find the thing that actually makes the difference to your performance. Simple feedback is the ultimate goal as it is the easiest to process, but sometimes you have to go through all the information together to find the nugget.

Jenny Duncalf

The best coaches are extremely passionate about the sport and truly care about the player, and they bring that intensity with them in the coaching session.

WHAT THE COACHES THINK

David Pearson

If a player's technique is not right then they will not be able to deliver the tactics. When you observe tactical weakness, for example not volleying enough in the middle of the court, it is more than likely to be a technical weakness that is stopping the player from doing it. They have to be good at all aspects of technique. There is no point having one aspect functioning at 100 per cent and others at 20 per cent – all aspects of their technique need to be at least 80 per cent proficient. They need good technique to put pressure on their opponent by playing the right shot at the right time and giving themselves time. Technique is at the core of sport. There is the odd exception to the rule – but generally all the world's best players will have outstanding technique – the key is finding which is best for each player.

A coach shouldn't change a technique just because it's not what they would teach or they like to watch – technique change should be based on improving performance, not being more visually pleasing. There are of course many different techniques. Which is right or wrong? Technique is personal and the right one is the one that allows you to deliver your tactics.

Good coaches allow players to ask questions – not just tell them. A good coach listens to the player's opinions to help build the trust. Then when it comes to being told exactly what to do there is more chance the players will listen.

Fig. 9.2 Jenny Duncalf believes you have to work hard at the bond with your coach, the same as any relationships between people.

Fig. 9.3 After a successful junior career, during her early professional years Alison Waters worked tirelessly with the English Team Coaches and Sports Scientists to change her technique in order to compete in the senior end of the game.

INTRODUCTION

The topic of skill acquisition can cover a broad range of areas such as motor learning, coaching science, practice cognitive-perceptual skills, visual search skills, anticipation and decision-making. The area is applicable through the whole spectrum of an athlete's development whether they are first picking up a racket or refining a technical or tactical skill at the elite level. Knowledge of the area can assist in the acceleration of the development of the athlete and particularly in squash where execution of a multitude of skills, tactics and decision-making is crucial to be successful in the sport. In this chapter we will discuss the areas of motor learning and consolidation, expert performance, practice structure and feedback. We will discuss how coaches and athletes can best learn from the research and utilize key findings alongside their current training and competition strategies.

MOTOR SKILL LEARNING

There have been various theories and models proposed to frame the journey from an unskilled novice to a highly skilled competent athlete.

Fitts' Model

Paul Fitts (1964) developed an influential model of skill acquisition that contained three stages. He describes learning as a continuous process with gradual changes in the nature of information processing as learning progresses.

COGNITIVE STAGE
The first stage of Fitts' model is termed the cognitive stage where the learner is exposed to simple rules and verbal instruction to acquire basic understanding of the movement. At this stage, performance is variable and error-ridden as the learner experiments with different movement configurations. The learner is quite reliant on external feedback in order to improve their proprioceptive awareness as they have not yet refined their self-corrective abilities. In this stage it is important that the athlete has a clear concept of the desired movement, and when this is achieved positive reinforcement is important. This stage requires high levels of cognitive effort and the learner is very internally focused on their movement.

From a squash coaching perspective this stage is typical when teaching squash as a new sport to young children. However, older players with little or no experience of racket sports also fall into this category. Coaching drills focus on simple feeds to allow the player to hit the ball without movement difficulty so that they can focus on racket swing, body orientation and final leg movements. Typically the coach will provide immediate feedback on a single issue that needs correcting so that the task difficulty remains manageable. For a short period of time the player receives positive reinforcement when a correct movement is achieved and corrective instructions when the movement is not correct. Thus the player is encouraged to feel (proprioceptive awareness) the difference between the correct movement and the incorrect ones.

ASSOCIATIVE STAGE
The next stage is the associative stage where movement patterns become more refined and more consistent. Depending on the complexity of the task and the learner's abilities this stage can require varying lengths of practice. Here the learner has an improved ability to self-correct due to improved proprioceptive abilities as well as better motor control.

They can more clearly detect when the correct movement pattern has been achieved; however, full refinement is still to be achieved. Some cognitive effort is still required and learners can begin to multi-task with some degree of success.

When coaching squash the transition from cognitive to the associative stage can be achieved quite quickly depending on the age and ability of the player. However the transition between stages is not a clear step but rather the coach tries out coaching strategies more aligned to the latter stage, and if the strategy does not work out very well the coach resorts back to the previous coaching behaviours. During this stage of learning skills are tested under more duress to better reflect the actual demands of the game. For example typical shot sequences may be used, such as boast, drive, boast or when the player develops the simple routines well, the order of feed is varied.

AUTONOMOUS STAGE

To achieve the final autonomous stage requires extensive practice. At this stage the learner can perform the skill with minimal mental effort and few errors. The learner has a low variability in performance and can error-correct extremely quickly. They have a very clear idea of the correct movement skill and can verbalize this. The learner will now also be able to focus externally on other things without impacting on the quality or consistency of the movement pattern. Regular squash players can achieve this stage after months rather than years of practice. However, reaching the autonomous stage does not imply expertise. Rather the skill level attained can be reproduced fairly consistently, but only after years of practice can the skill level of an expert be achieved.

Coaching players at this stage of learning is more challenging than for previous

stages for a number of reasons. Firstly less than perfect technique is difficult to correct because the skill is performed automatically. A player wishing to change technique at this stage of learning needs to go back to drills performed in the early stages of learning to alter the coordination patterns already developed. Sometimes this can take months of dedicated practice with playing matches being detrimental to the progress of the change. Even when drastic changes are not required, it may require the expert eye of an experienced coach to determine the more fine-grained changes to the movement patterns. Similarly, as the player skill level increases, so too do the demands on the coach to provide adequate feeding so that the player is suitably challenged from a movement and ball placement perspective.

Schmidt Schema Theory

The variability of practice and the conditions in which they take place are implicit in the acquisition of skills. Schmidt (1975) proposed a schema theory of discrete motor learning. A schema is a set of rules concerning the execution of a movement response linked to feedback received during and after performance. Schmidt proposed the existence of generalized motor programmes (GMPs) to counter concerns that every movement would need a separate motor programme.

His theory explains how learners can produce specific movements of a given class that they have never performed previously. For example once a player learns how to lunge correctly variations of the lunge pattern are taken from the same GMP and variable practice conditions facilitate the creation of a robust, general schema than can lead to enhanced skill transfer. Ultimately the player needs to be able to cope with multiple variations of the movement in order to deal with the demands of the game on court.

Schmidt's theory offers the squash player and coach a simple theoretical perspective to explain how we refine skills. The basic idea is that each time we hit a straight drive for example, we receive feedback. The feedback is both proprioceptive (internal related to how the stroke was produced) and visual (the ball travelling to the front wall and on to the back wall). Schmidt's theory suggests that all of this information is processed by the brain subconsciously, with the individual parameters associated with the current stroke being compared against a template from which the stroke was produced (the GMP). In other words the GMP stored in the brain is used to produce the stroke, but because the ball is in a slightly different position each time, there is more or less time pressure to play the shot, the feet are in slightly different positions and so on, the brain has to adapt the GMP slightly to execute the current stroke. On this basis the GMP and the current motor programme are different. This difference forms the basis for learning. Most importantly it is the visual feedback regarding the ball trajectory that provides the brain with information regarding the success of the shot. Hence if a great shot is played the brain will decide that the current motor programme is superior to the GMP and modify the GMP appropriately.

If we consider the implications of this theory then some pertinent points can be made. First there is a lot going on in the brain that does not require direct attention by the player. Secondly it is vital that the normal process explained above is not tampered with. A classic example of tampering is not watching the outcome of the shot played. If the player does not watch the ball until the end of the shot then vital information can be missed and learning is hampered. A third point that needs to be understood is that this theory suggests that practice (sometimes referred to as deliberate practice to ensure that the conditions necessary for learning are adhered to) will lead to improved performance.

Motor Skill Consolidation

Skill consolidation is also an important part of the acquisition of skill. The consolidation of a motor skill can be promoted by ongoing training, but can also be brought about by an off-line process that is initialized by training and continues thereafter for hours and days (Stickgold, 2005). Off-line consolidation has a twofold effect on skill memories: it makes these memories resistant to interfering inputs acquired after initial training, and it induces an enhancement in skill performance at a delayed retesting.

Much of the research into this area has identified sleep as the primary mechanism for consolidation of motor skills (Korman et al., 2007) and particularly the first post-training night's sleep. Research would also suggest that daytime sleep such as napping between training sessions would also aid motor memory consolidation and that motor skill learning continues even when the performer is not practising the task. During the post-learning phase the establishment of long-term memory can be blocked by interference that refers to the disruptive effect of a later experience on the consolidation in memory of a prior training experience. However, within the research these studies have been conducted on relatively basic motor movements and not whole body motor skills or techniques.

As well as learning new motor skills and technique, technical modification is often part of an elite athlete's career for either performance or injury prevention reasons. A technical change should be seen as a distinct process from initial learning (Carson and

Collins, 2011). A technical change could be a refinement of the existing technique or may require a larger-scale change to remove an inefficiency or bad habit. In both of these scenarios the coach and athlete need to consider that there will be certain stages as there were in the acquisition of skills for the re-learning.

Firstly the athlete needs to understand and start to become proprioceptively aware of the technical change ('old way/new way', Hanin et al., 2004). This will promote a level of internal focus on the movement and coordination patterns of the limbs. This can be promoted through coach or other external feedback but this is an important first step for the athlete to understand the proprioceptive and coordination differences in the technique refinement or change. Next the new technique must be practised so that it begins to replace the old technique and the athlete moves towards the autonomous stage. Finally the new technique must be tested under increased constraints or in a pressured scenario as there will always be a tendency to revert to default if the change is not fully ingrained (Logan, 2011).

EXPERT PERFORMANCE

Research in skill acquisition with racket sports has mainly been focused on tennis; however, some of the first work in squash was investigating the visual cues in order to anticipate the opponent's actions (Howarth et al., 1984; Abernethy, 1990a, 1990b; Abernethy et al., 2001) using temporal occlusion techniques, a method in which the amount of visual information that is presented to the athletes is manipulated by editing video clips to provide varying amounts of information relative to key events such as racquet-ball contact. These studies found that the most critical time periods for extracting information about shot direction were 160–180mins prior to racket-ball contact. Experts were also able to pick up information for the early part of the opponent's actions. This method is primarily used in the laboratory setting; however this can be mimicked in the on-court setting using liquid crystal goggles to occlude vision manually (Farrow and Abernethy, 2002; Farrow et al., 2005). These studies have typically found that experts perform at a higher level than novices when the video clips are occluded prior to ball flight information becoming available. This work has been furthered by applying this in an on-court scenario in both badminton and tennis where the player is responding to pre-recorded key skills such as a serve that is viewed on a backlit projector setup, to which the player must elicit a physical response at varying occlusion points. This can be used not only to test the anticipatory skills of the player but also as a training methodology.

The early work of Abernethy and colleagues primarily considered anticipation to be a function of visual information. In other words if a player sees the opponent turn towards the back wall to hit the ball from the back corner there is a high probability that a boast will be played. It is quite obvious to experienced players and coaches that higher-level players can read their opponent's movements better than lower-level players.

However more contemporary work suggests that visual information alone may not explain the expertise advantage in terms of anticipation. Expert performers not only have better pattern recognition skills; they have a large memory bank of experiences through play and practice. These experiences help expert performers improve the probability of anticipating their opponent's next move and in the shot selection and tactical decision-making. To put this simply it seems that playing squash not only helps develop a player's motor abilities but also improves the brain's

Table 9.1 The different types of practice.			
Repetition Type	**Characteristics in repetition**	**Predictability in sequence**	**Decision-making during motor planning**
Blocked	Ten repetitions of a boast, then ten repetitions of a drive, then ten repetitions of a drop.	High	Low
Serial	Boast, drive, drop; exact sequence repeats ten times.	High	Moderate
Random	Drive, boast, drive, drop, drop, boast; performance repetitions are not repeated on subsequent trials throughout the practice session.	Low	High

capacity to understand the complex sequence of events seen in a squash match.

This type of learning is predominately associated with the autonomous stage of learning and relates to individual experiences gained on a squash court. Psychologists often refer to this ability as applying 'if then' rules (known as heuristics). For example, most squash players who have played against an opponent a number of times will tell you about their tendencies, for example, 'if' under pressure off a boast, 'then' he will hit it hard cross court. This type of summary information related to a particular player is quite naturally produced by players and coaches although attempts to recreate these insights via computer simulations have proved very difficult.

PRACTICE STRUCTURE AND FEEDBACK

Practice is an essential part of any player's development but how the practice is structured to optimize learning and skill development can potentially help accelerate the player's development. This is also a consideration whether we are discussing the general structure of a session or focusing on developing a discrete skill or technique in the game play. Research has also suggested that it is not only how much the performer practises but *how* the performer practises each repetition that is the more important variable in the contribution of practice to skill acquisition. Table 9.1 shows the differing types of practice that a performer can do.

The link between the amount of cognitive (information processing) effort that a learner puts into practice and the level of skill expertise developed is crucial. This relationship identifies a number of factors that should be considered:

- The practice context must optimally challenge the cognitive and motor capabilities of the performer;
- The performer must be able to understand relevant task-related feedback;
- The performer must be provided with the opportunity to engage and learn how to detect when errors have occurred, why they have occurred, and how to fix them;

■ The performer must also be aware of the standard they are looking to achieve, and attaining this should promote confidence in ability, reinforced through feedback, and aid retention.

Most research has shown that when people randomly practise a variety of movements, their performance is less successful than when they practise movements in a blocked fashion. However, when performers resume their performance at a later time, those who originally practised under random conditions demonstrate superior retention compared to those who originally practised under blocked conditions (Shea and Morgan, 1979). This pattern of results, termed the contextual interference effect, challenges conventional thinking about retention of skills.

In a squash context, the practice structure is perhaps the most accessible motor skill learning perspective that all relatively serious players should consider. Similarly coaches should be aware of how small manipulations in the practice format can have significant implications for motor skill learning.

Let us consider drills involving the boast, straight drive and lob. A familiar starting point could be the simple boast and drive routine where shots are played in sequence involving one player at the front of the court and the other at the back. This can be described as a blocked/serial practice (Table 9.1) requiring little or no decision-making and high predictability. This is useful for correcting technique errors including footwork and positioning but does not promote high retention of skills.

Developing this routine could include the player at the front playing a cross-court lob on each side before playing the straight drive. The routine thus becomes boast, lob, boast, drive, boast. In terms of repetition type not too much has changed although the player at the front of the court has to concentrate

on correct positioning to play the lob or drive, which increases the decision-making process. Similarly the player at the back of the court has two different shot types to return requiring extra decision-making.

Increasing the game realism slightly the next progression could require the player at the back of the court returning the lob with a drive. This could be advantageous in that the drive off a cross-court lob is a likely shot response during a match, hence increasing the ecological validity (realism) of the drill. The routine is now a boast, cross-court lob, straight drive, boast. This drill requires both players to travel along the diagonal of the court and hence requires more physical exertion. As such this drill may be too difficult for lower-level and less fit players to sustain for moderately long periods of time.

The drill is still relatively simple and does not require too much decision-making. At this point in time perhaps we should consider introducing the random nature of actual squash play into the drill. For example the person at the back of the court could have the option of playing either drive or boast. In this scenario the other player has to be ready for either shot option (a more realistic situation) and hence the predictability of the routine diminishes dramatically. One change of this nature makes the drill much more difficult for the players and thus simultaneously decreases the performance level, but increases the retention of the skill. This should be the goal of aspiring players but given the task difficulty its use is determined by the player standard.

MANIPULATION OF TASK CONSTRAINTS IN PRACTICE

The manipulation of constraints in practice has long been held by researchers as an

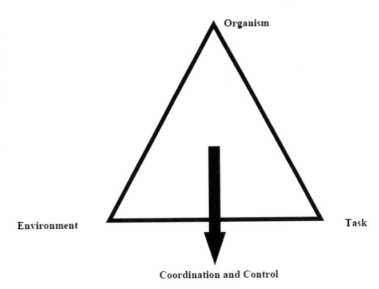

Fig. 9.4 Newell's Triangle showing the three classifications of constraints and the emergent behaviour.

Table 9.2 Examples of constraint manipulations.		
Player Manipulation	**Environmental Manipulation**	**Task Manipulation**
Weights vest;	Temperature modification	Smaller playing area;
Cognitive task while practising;	Low light	Targets placed in the court;
Serve off front leg.	Occlusion of ball flight (eyes closed).	Different ball;
		Shot rules (no drops);
		Change ball size or type.

effective method of encouraging skill acquisition as the performer is forced to adapt their action as a result of the constraint. According to Newell (1986), constraints can be classified into three categories: organismic, environmental and task. These categories provide a coherent framework for understanding how coordination patterns emerge from goal-directed behaviour (see Fig. 9.4).

Organismic constraints refer to a person's characteristics, such as genes, height, weight, cognitions, motivations or emotions. Environmental constraints are global, physical variables in nature, such as ambient light, tem-perature, altitude. Task constraints are usually more specific to performance contexts than the others and include task goals, specific rules associated with an activity, equipment, surfaces as well as boundary markings and lines. In squash here are some examples of the manipulation of constraints that are possible in practice shown in Table 9.2.

In squash, just like in other sports, the rules constrain the participants' behaviours to varying degrees and create a fair competitive context. In practice however these rules can be manipulated to facilitate a particular learning outcome or behaviour. A manipulation of the constraints-led approach is suggested by Davids *et al.* (2008) in the training of a player to return to the T-position after a shot. In practice, it is possible to mark a target area around the T that the player must touch after each shot as a requirement of the point being played. This rule should encourage players to recognize this court position as an important spatial pivotal location around which conventional shots such as the backhand or drop shot might be played. Bending the rules in this way can constrain actions where adherence to verbal instructions from the coach might not.

Good coaches will have a variety of ideas to promote a modification to behaviours, action and/or coordination in practice in order to achieve the desired outcome. Examples used during training could be: during a coach feeding session the player is required to say 'tee' when they get to the T area; or a small object is placed on the floor near the side wall during a straight drive routine to encourage the player to hit the target. Manipulations such as these provide some additional focus for the player and consequently give them feedback that they may have been unaware of previously. This type of constraints-led approach could have undesirable repercussions, however, since the natural cognitive behaviour is being modified. As such this type of manipulation is usually reserved for addressing specific issues and is undertaken fairly infrequently.

FEEDBACK IN PRACTICE

There are two types of feedback that the player can receive in practice, intrinsic and extrinsic feedback. Intrinsic feedback is the sensory information that arises as a natural consequence of producing a movement. The player is able to perceive this type of feedback without assistance from external sources. This type of feedback includes visual, auditory, kinaesthetic and proprioceptive. For example, the player hits the shot, feels the contact between the racket and ball, sees the ball travelling towards the front wall and hears it hit the wall. All of these things can be used by the player to evaluate the effectiveness of the shot. These processes take place naturally simply as a consequence of repetition as long as the player does not disrupt them by listening to music or failing to watch the outcome of the shot.

Extrinsic feedback (also called augmented feedback) is information that is provided to the player by an outside source such as the coach, video or data. This type of feedback can function in three ways. One is to facilitate the learning of a new skill by providing performance-based information that allows the athlete to determine what he or she should continue to do and what not to continue to do. Another function is to enhance the performance of well-learned skills by providing information that allows the athlete to determine how to improve performance in specific contexts and situations. Third, augmented feedback functions as motivation to continue to practise a skill or to continue to participate.

During practice these two areas can be controlled by the coach and other support staff. It is also possible that the player can become dependent on feedback so efforts should be made to ensure that feedback is reduced over time as the player's ability to self-correct improves. In squash augmented feedback is primarily a function of the coach or teammates and is gained either between games or post-event. However simple apps such as coaches' eye can turn phones and tablets into very easy-to-use feedback tools. Of course some thought is required to determine what the desired outcome is and where weaknesses lie. (Note some of David Pearson's comments at the start of this chapter.)

Coaches should consider that because feedback requires information to be remembered and used, it must be meaningful to the athlete. It therefore follows that the amount of information provided should be limited to the minimum amount of information the performer needs or can use to achieve the function that the augmented feedback is serving when it is provided. Magill and Anderson (2012) propose a rule to provide information about just one specific error observed in the performance of the activity. This may be especially critical for beginners, who have difficulty determining which errors they are making and have almost no basis for determining how to correct these errors (Fitts and Posner, 1967; Gentile, 2000). This advice is particularly pertinent for coaching between games in squash. Good coaches (again see the comments by David Pearson in this chapter) identify the critical point(s) to focus on and limit their instructions to avoid overloading the player.

When providing feedback on a technical skill the person providing the feedback should base their feedback on a priority order list of form cues that are fundamental to the movement, such as 'feet placement' or 'orientation of the hips'. By doing this the coach can prioritize how critical the part of the skill is in which the error occurred. Secondly the error that is highest on this priority list should be the one that is the basis for the feedback. When this part is improved to a satisfactory level the feedback can be directed at a subsequent form cue. This method has been suggested by Magill (2010) and research evidence supporting this process has been provided by Weeks and Kordus (1998) and Wulf, Chiviacowsky, Schiller and Avila (2010).

It has been suggested by Magill and Anderson (2012) that when the error is identified the correction information should be less specific so that the athlete is encouraged to actively search for ways to correct the error similar in a discovery learning style. The points made here primarily refer to how a coach assists the learning of skills, and the actual feedback would relate to the stage of learning of the player. This in turn determines the amount of feedback, the duration and the specificity, as advanced players would clearly be able to handle more complex feedback than novices.

Forms of non-verbal augmented feedback have also been used to improve performance. Although there is very little evidence of research in squash, this has been undertaken in netball (Helmer et al., 2010) using a wearable strain sensor and audio feedback to assist shooting accuracy; in weightlifting (Winchester et al., 2009) using video feedback on bar path trajectory and technique to improve force and power production; and in golf (Bertram et al., 2007) where video feedback with no additional verbal feedback was used by skilled players to improve swing characteristics but it impeded improvement in novices potentially due to the lack of verbal feedback combined with the video.

While there are no published studies on this form of feedback in squash it should be recognized that simply watching elite squash has the potential for providing non-verbal augmented feedback. Part of the nature of expertise in squash is knowing what to do in a given situation. Of course knowing and being able to do something are not the same but recognizing patterns of play (through watching experts as well as playing) is a component of squash expertise.

Feedback provision should also be considered based on the player's skill level and task complexity. As skill level increases and task complexity decreases, feedback can be made more specific around particular details. The player will also have an increased ability to self-correct so will have heightened levels of intrinsic feedback. However when skill level is low and task complexity is high, the player

Table 9.3 The different types of feedback.	
Type	**Description**
Summary	Feedback about a set of repetitions after the set has been completed, player required to use intrinsic feedback in between trials;
Bandwidth	Player is provided with detailed feedback only when the performance falls outside an agreed-upon error tolerance range. Ensures clarity of required standards from the player;
Faded	Decreasing the frequency of feedback provision over a series of practice trials. This promotes a transfer from augmented error correction to player self-correction skills;
Performer regulated	Frequency of feedback provision determined by the player upon completion of practice trial;
Performer estimation	Player estimates their error upon completion of an action or trial; the coach then provides the actual demonstrated by the player.

will likely need the guidance provided by augmented feedback to find appropriate ways to improve performance (Guadagnoli and Lee, 2004).

Coaches and other support staff can vary the modality of feedback based on the requirements either in a competition scenario or in a practice session. There are several types of feedback that can be employed, shown in Table 9.3.

FINAL SUMMARY

From a squash perspective the information gained from this chapter can be summarized in terms of feedback provision as follows:

■ Intrinsic feedback is very useful and always available but players need to avail themselves of all possible feedback sources.
■ Summary feedback is available not only from coaches but also video recordings can be a rich source of information.
■ The use of targets can identify bandwidth

errors and hence alert the player to errors, which in turn facilitates intrinsic feedback mechanisms.
■ Knowing what you need to achieve from a coach allows the transfer from extrinsic to intrinsic feedback to take place.

REFERENCES

Bertram, C.P., Marteniuk, R.B. and Guadagnoli, M.A. (2007). On the use and misuse of video analysis. *International Journal of Sports Science and Coaching*, 2, 37–46.

Carson, H.J. and Collins, D. (2011). Refining and regaining skills in fixation/diversification stage performers: the Five-A Model. *International Review of Sport and Exercise Psychology*, 4, 2, 146–167.

Davids, K., Button, C. and Bennett, S. (2008). *Dynamics of skill acquisition: A constraints-led approach*. Champaign, IL: Human Kinetics.

Fitts, P.M. (1964). Perceptual-Motor Skill Learning 1. *Categories of human learning*, 243–285.

Fitts, P.M. and Posner, M.I. (1967). *Human Performance*. Belmont, CA: Brooks/Cole.

Gentile, A. M. (2000). Skill acquisition: Action, movement and neuromotor processes. In *Movement science: Foundations for physical therapy* (2nd edn.). (eds J.H. Carr and R.B Sheperd), Rockville, MD: Aspen, pp.111–187.

Fig. 9.5 The skills that the world's top players display are not created by luck, they are a product of thousands of hours of targeted coaching and pertinent practice.

Guadagnoli, M.A., and Lee, T.D. (2004). Challenge point: a framework for conceptualizing the effects of various practice conditions in motor learning. *Journal of Motor Behavior*, 36, 2, 212–224.

Hanin, Y., Malvela, M., and Hanina, M. (2004). Rapid correction of start technique in an Olympic-level swimmer: A case study using old way/new way. *Journal of Swimming Research*, 16, 11–17.

Helmer, R.J.N., Farrow, D., Lucas, S.R., Higgerson, G.J. and Blanchonette, I. (2010). Can interactive textiles influence a novice's throwing technique? *Procedia Engineering*, 2, 2985–2990.

Korman, M., Doyon, J., Doljansky, J., Carrier, J., Dagan, Y. and Karni, A. (2007). Daytime sleep condenses the time course of motor memory consolidation. *Nature Neuroscience*, 10, 9, 1206–1213.

Logan, O. (2011). Considerations for Technical Modification. *The Sport and Exercise Scientist*, 29, 6–7.

Magill, R.A., and Anderson, D.I. (2012). The roles and uses of augmented feedback in motor skill acquisition. In *Skill Acquisition in Sport: Research, Theory and Practice*, 2nd edn (eds N.J. Hodges and A.M. Williams). New York: Routledge. pp.3–21.

Magill, R.A. (2010). *Motor learning and control: Concepts and Applications*, 9th edn. New York: McGraw-Hill.

Newell, K.M. (1986). Constraints on the development of coordination. In *Motor Development in Children: Aspects of Coordination and Control* (eds M.G. Wade and H.T.A. Whiting). Dordrecht, Netherlands: Martinus Nijhoff, pp. 341–360.

Schmidt, R.A. (1975). A schema theory of discrete motor learning. *Psychological Review*, 82(4), 225–260.

Schmidt, R.A. and Wrisberg, C.A. (2004). *Motor Learning and Performance: A problem-based learning approach*, 3rd edn. Champaign, IL: Human Kinetics.

Shea, J.B. and Morgan, R.L. (1979). CI effects on the acquisition, retention and transfer of a motor skill. *Journal of Experimental Psychology: Human Learning and Memory*, 5, 179–187.

Stickgold, R. (2005). Sleep-dependent memory consolidation. *Nature*, 437 (7063), 1272–1278.

Weeks, D. L., and Kordus, R. N. (1998). Relative frequency of knowledge of performance and motor skill learning. *Research Quarterly for Exercise and Sport*, 69, 224–230.

Winchester, J.B., Porter, J.M. and McBride, J.M. (2009). Changes in bar path kinematics and kinetics through use of summary feedback in power snatch training. *Journal of Strength and Conditioning Research*, 23, 444–454.

Wulf, G., Chiviacowsky, S., Schiller, E., and Avila, L.T.G. (2010). Frequent external focus feedback enhances motor learning. *Frontiers in Psychology*, 1, 1–7.

CHAPTER 10

CURRENT APPLICATIONS OF PERFORMANCE ANALYSIS TECHNIQUES IN SQUASH

Mike Hughes (Institute of Technology, Carlow, Eire)
Julia Wells (English Institute of Sport, Manchester, UK),
Stafford Murray (English Institute of Sport, Manchester,
UK), Mandie De Beer (English Institute of Sport,
Manchester, UK) and Michael T. Hughes (PGIR, Bath, UK)

WHAT THE PLAYERS THINK

Nick Matthew OBE

Quintic and Dartfish software analysis allowed me to slow down my technique – it is a simple process of capturing the shot you are working on and then with the coach working out what needs to be changed. Some things it is not possible to see with the naked eye. It's not rocket science what we used to do on court, but there is no doubt that having real-time visual feedback during coaching sessions massively sped up and enhanced the process of technique change.

Changing my technique with my coach using analysis has allowed me to properly deliver tactics; you cannot deliver your tactics if your technique is not right. Real-time video feedback allowed me to create a technique that became a weapon that can hurt my opponents – not just something that looks nice. The key is having the video not only allows you to look at the aesthetics of the swing but where the ball goes and the result of using that technique. Having the camera on court allows me to see the effect a technique change has on the flight of the ball, which in the end is the most important thing, you shouldn't just change technique for change's sake – there should be a clear performance purpose for technique change.

Having a tactical plan simplifies the game

for me. Some people think that doing tactical analysis can complicate your mind. The key is to find two or three things you can apply in reality. Performance analysis between matches and tournament allows me to look at my individual differences and see what I am getting tactically right and wrong.

Performance analysis provides real numbers and that gives you confidence in your game plan – these are facts, not just what you think. Having a gut instinct about your plan is a good thing, but performance analysis reinforces your gut feeling whilst at the same time telling you where your gut instinct may be wrong! Having a clear visual image of what I need to do helps me to clear space in my mind.

Not every match or opponent will have clear patterns, that's the nature of sport. In the British Open in the 02 I had lost to Ramy four times in a row. All these matches were close, 3–1 or 3–2, but I kept just losing at the end, not down the physical stuff. So I sat down with the analyst who had analysed loads of Ramy's matches and we came up with a new plan based on what the profiles of the matches I had played against him. On the day the plan worked and I won 3–0 in the final to win the tournament. Winning the British Open at the 02 was pretty much down to having a plan on not only how to beat Ramy but also to get myself better so I could beat everyone else. Most importantly I went away and practised the plan; I tailored my practice and training sessions in order to be able to deliver the tactics.

In the future I would love performance analysis to provide physical information on things like distance covered, number of steps, amount of turns and how many times you lunge during a match. This would give me and my S and C information to ensure the training we are doing is sufficient enough to replicate the demands of my matches. If I knew exactly what happens in a match then I could make sure my training and practice is even more specific for the sport – which is how it needs to be.

During events having real-time motion information on players would really help make the sport a better spectacle for the public and show exactly how hard the sport is.

James Willstrop

Tactical analysis is a great example of how the player, the coach and the scientist can come together to give clarity on the game plan. That working together as a team is vital for success in my eyes. I would not have won the TOC in 2010 without opposition profiles of the three Egyptians (at the time world numbers 1, 2 and 3 respectively) I played in the quarters, semis and final.

Laura Massaro

At a young age Quintic sessions enabled me to see things that you would normally not be able to see. Technical video analysis has helped not only change my technique but also understand it. In the CWG 2014 tactical analysis was huge for us as an England team. You have to be adaptable on court with your tactical plan – sometimes you have to just do what it takes to get through a match.

Jenny Duncalf

Real-time visual FB was absolutely vital for improving my technique. Trying to mentally paint a picture of your swing in your head is impossible. Video analysis took this problem away for me and sped up my learning curve. I have built up a database of ideal technique clips for each shot. I use this as a reference when I am travelling and may feel my swing needs tweaking. I have used video analysis to create the optimal swing model which I can reference and compare my swing to at any time.

Opponent profiling is very useful, but it's interesting that often a player's area of strength is also their area of weakness – that's why you shouldn't look at winner or error distribution in isolation. Opponent analysis is very useful – but the key is working out with you and your coach how you will expose the weaknesses and defend against the strengths. Visual tracking work massively improved how I read my opponents game. Analysis refreshes the way I look at opponents. We play each other all the time and you can easily fall into the trap of thinking you know all your opponent's tactics.

Fig. 10.1 During his early professional career Nick Matthew used performance analysis interventions to completely reshape his backhand technique, which he credits for his success.

WHAT THE COACHES THINK

David Pearson

For me as a coach performance analysis has been the most important and influential aspect of sport science provision. It is the key ingredient a coach needs to use to improve players' performance.

During the CWG in 2006 Peter Nicol did what is pretty much unheard of and significantly changed his technique between the semi-final and the final. This was done to enhance his forehand counter drop technique and try to break down David Palmer's movement in and out of the front left corner by reducing his recovery time – getting onto the counter drop as soon as possible. Without performance analysis and statistics we would not have seen this and Peter may not have won the gold. Real-time on-court video feedback was absolutely integral in totally reshaping Nick Matthews' technique and movement patterns. If Nick didn't use video analysis he would never have been a world champion or world No. 1.

For me Performance Analysis will never replace coaching – but it definitely cuts down the learning curve by half – it speeds up and enhances the retention levels of the learning. When you are trying to get a technical point across it is very difficult without a player being able to see for themselves exactly what they are doing wrong.

Profiling opponents is absolutely vital; for me the profiles are the most important area that Performance Analysis covers. Where possible a player should have a plan going onto court based on a performance profile. It gives a player confidence and helps stop any little doubts they may have in their heads.

A good analyst will break all the complex stuff down into very simple messages that the player and coach can readily use. In a very open-skilled sport like squash I think it is vital the analyst has a background in the sport to put the numbers into real-life context.

Paul Carter

One coaching session with a camera is worth ten without – having instant visual feedback massively speeds up and enhances the learning process. As a coach having visual feedback enables you to get your point across much quicker and provide the truth – the player can't hide behind the visual images – it's fact!

If you are not careful you can suffer from paralysis by analysis. You can't forget this is a human thing and you need to coach! You need to be aware of the limitations of the player you are working with: it consistently needs to be contextualized – sometimes the 'ideal' swing would not work with a certain individual.

The key is to focus on the outcome of the ball – sometimes the technique might not look good but the outcome is! You need to make sure the intervention of the analysis is done at the right time and for the right reason, not just because modern technology allows you to do so easily! The technique of the best player in the world might not be suitable for all players – we need to be careful we don't just copy without rationalizing why.

You need to make the message from the complex data simple for the players to understand. If you focus too much on opponents' strengths it can become a worry for the player you are working with. You need to know your player to understand how much and what type of tactical information will work best with them.

Malcolm Willstrop

Performance analysis, properly utilized, is an asset for today's players. A prime personal example was when James, at the Tournament of Champions in New York, watched an analysis of his opponents each morning. The process was not over-long or over-emphasized, but definitely helped him to beat three top world-class Egyptians in a row – Amr Shabana, Karim Darwish and Ramy Ashour – something that had never been done and has not been done since.

Too much analysis could lead to being obsessive about it – I'm excluding physio and fitness training, which are vital. Players should not be over-concerned about opponents, but rather seek to impose themselves.

Fig. 10.2 James Willstrop viewed opposition profiles before each match during the 2010 Tournament of Champions in New York, enabling him to emerge victorious.

Fig. 10.3 Laura Massaro values performance analysis, but is also acutely aware that you can sometimes over-analyse opponents and stop playing to your strengths.

INTRODUCTION

This chapter offers information about performance analysis by presenting a brief form of overview of the research work already published in this field. Although this is written for, and by, sports scientists, it is hoped that anyone with an interest in this rapidly growing area of practice and research will find it interesting and rewarding.

It is not possible to trace the work of all those coaches and sports scientists who have contributed in one way or another to notational analysis. A large number of these innovative people did not see the point of publishing the work that they did, regarding it as merely part of their job, and consequently cannot receive the just acclaim that they deserve here in this compilation. There

is no doubt that all the published workers mentioned within the following chapter could cite five or six other 'unsung' innovators who either introduced them into the field or gave them help and advice along the way.

Squash and soccer were the first sports to be analysed in Britain by way of analysis systems, and squash in particular has been a precursor to the analyses of all those other sports in terms of the development and involvement of computerized notational analysis. This is due to many of the first designers of analysis systems choosing squash as the sport to analyse – squash was seen as a simple game and one that could easily be recorded because it was played indoors and in a well-lit and defined area.

It is the aim of this chapter to trace the development of performance analysis in squash. But as a consequence of early researchers using squash as their template, this process will effectively trace the development of performance analysis across sport as a whole (see Hughes, Hughes and Behan, 2007). Squash has not only had the most advanced performance analysis support systems available, but, most importantly, these have been adopted and applied by the coaching staff of Squash England and the Welsh Squash Federation, which led to an interactive approach to the development and application of performance analysis in squash.

DEVELOPMENT OF SYSTEMS

The first-hand notational analysis system published in Britain was in fact for tennis (Downey, 1973). This system was never actually used to gather data, however, due to its complexity. Not only did this system enable the user to record such variables as shots used, position on the court, and the result of the shot, but also the type of spin used in a particular shot. This system was significant as it provided other researchers with a wealth of ideas.

Early research, in the 1970s, at Liverpool Polytechnic led the way in developing notational analysis in both soccer and squash. Because two of the staff there were advanced coaches, the work in squash progressed very rapidly in the development of systems and presentation of complex data analyses. Sanderson and Way (1977) reported devising a system for notating squash in real time, as the match happened, which seems to be based on the work by Downey (1973). Their hand notation system was created to analyse successful and unsuccessful patterns of play in squash and was further developed by Sanderson (1983) to include symbols to represent shots that were placed upon a diagram of a

court (Figs 10.4 and 10.5). All shots in the match were recorded, together with the position of the point of contact of the racket head and the ball. If the shot was the last shot in the rally the outcome was also recorded. It was difficult to execute in real time. Results obtained from matches were presented using longitudinal and lateral summations next to the different areas of the court. However, it took five to eight hours to learn how to use this system at full match speed, and a further forty to fifty hours to analyse the data from one match.

Table 10.1 The shot codes, or suggestive symbols, used by Sanderson (1983) for his data gathering system for squash.	
Shot Codes	
Drive	|
Xdrive	/
Drop	•
Boast (B'hand)	⊂ ; (F'hand) ⊃
Volley	V
Lob	L
Serve	S
Combinations	
e.g. Xdrop	/•
Volley-Lob	VL

Most of the data that Sanderson and Way presented were in the form of frequency distributions of shots with respect to position on the court. This was then a problem of presenting data in three dimensions – two for the court and one for the value of the frequency of the shots. Three-dimensional graphics at

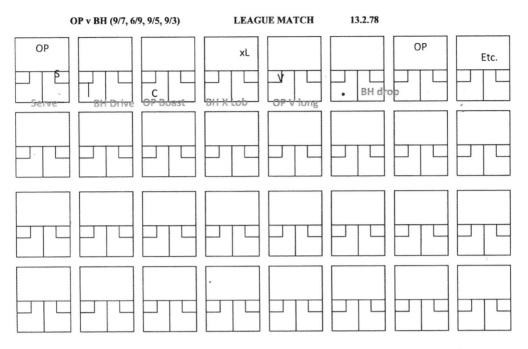

Fig. 10.4 The data gathering sheets and example data of the shot codes, or suggestive symbols, used by Sanderson (1983) for his data gathering system for squash.

that time were very difficult to present in such a way that no data were lost, and that could be easily visualized by those viewing the data. Sanderson overcame this problem by using longitudinal and lateral summations (Fig. 10.5). Not only were the patterns of rally-ending shots examined in detail, but also those shots (N-1) that preceded the end shot, and the shots that preceded those (N-2). In this way the rally ending patterns of play were analysed.

The major pitfall inherent in this system, as with all long-hand systems, was the time taken to learn the system and the sheer volume of raw data generated, requiring so much time to process it. Because of these problems inherent in using more sophisticated hand notation systems, computers were used to minimize learning time and process the data gathered. Hughes (1985) began this progression by computerizing the processing of the data gathered by hand with the system of Sanderson and Way, and then transferring it to PCs, which were only just coming on the market.

Pioneers

Hughes also at this time was working with Chris Robertson, the then National Coach at Welsh Squash, and together they devised a number of 'in-event' hand notation systems to gather data answering simple tactical questions about the game. One of these, the Squash Winner/Error Analysis Tactics System (SWEAT), became a very important part of the development of profiling in squash.

From the start of the rally (the serve), the user counts the number of shots in the rally.

At the end of the rally, they notate the following:

	1	2	3	4
	5	6	7	8
	9	10	11	12
	13	14	15	16

Fig.10.5 Example of sixteen-cell division of squash court.

- Number of shots (from the serve to the final rally ending shot)
- The outcome of the shot: winner, error, let or stroke
- The type of shot that was used to end the rally: (Drive, Cross Drive, Lob, Cross Lob, Drop, Cross Drop, Volley Short, Volley Long, Cross Volley Short, Cross Volley Long, Volley Boast, Trickle Boast or Back Boast)
- Where on the court the shot was played *from* (the cell where the racket face made contact with the ball), indicated on a sixteen-cell grid placed over the court, Position 1 being the front left corner and Position 16 being the back right corner of the court (Fig. 10.5).

This process is then repeated for each of the rallies until the end of the match. The information notated is collated by the software in a data file that can be exported to statistical processing software such as Microsoft Excel for further analysis and subsequent interpretation.

Various notations systems for squash have been developed over the years with many similarities between them. Most emphasize the collection of data to form a picture of visible 'patterns of play' for a particular player or opponent. What is critical about these systems is that they are all based on objective data. This means that they are founded on impartial measurement without bias or prejudice. The system developed by Sanderson and Way (1979) used a series of suggestive symbols that a user could then learn and remember, subsequently notating the various actions and events during match play. This was a rather time-consuming system and processing the data could take a further forty hours of work. Now, however, thanks to the development of modern computer systems and software, the time it takes to notate a match and further processing of the data to produce a match report has significantly decreased.

Studies by Hughes (1986) and Hughes, Wells and Matthews (2000), using these systems or updated versions of them, distinguished between playing patterns of different standards of players of both genders. There were significant differences, not surprisingly, both between and within the groups, due to the differing physiological factors that exist between the two sexes, for instance being able to retrieve the ball, and also other factors that might contribute to the variance in playing patterns, such as quality and style of coaching.

Armed with information of this type the coach can then analyse any technical deficiencies of their players when playing in these particular areas of the court or when playing a certain shot. This in turn will inform the player of tactical considerations of shot sequences. This can be executed live in training, or with use of video feedback. Seeing technical faults in the past was quite difficult on video due to the frame rates. However with the introduction of high-speed cameras for feedback purposes, technical analyses of the racket swings and individual player movement can now be examined to the minutest detail. Individual match analysis at elite-level senior squash is based on the same principles that the early pioneers of notational analysis employed. This can be applied in both real-time and lapsed-time analysis if used by a skilled operator.

Use of systems

DATA COLLECTION

Individual match analysis in its simplest form is based on events that occur in each rally ending shot. A template can be set up using modern notation software such as Dartfish Pro, Focus, Siliconcoach, Quintic, Sportscode or any of the many generic systems available on the market these days. They enable buttons to be created and activated in a sequence in which the operator would enter the information (called tagging), with a pen and paper table, observed during play. A good analyst can design data gathering systems to collect the data necessary to answer whatever questions the coach has about their sport. These are based on recording the position of the action, the player executing the shot, the shot itself and then the outcome, either rally continues or rally end (Winner, W; Error, E; Let, L; or Stroke, S). It can be beneficial to also record the time of the action but this can be difficult. This process is then repeated for each of the rallies until the end of the match. The information notated can be collated by the software in a data file that can be exported to statistical processing software such as Microsoft Excel for further analysis and subsequent interpretation.

REAL-TIME ANALYSIS SYSTEM

The real-time system (SWEAT – Simple Winner and Error Analysis Tactics) was based on a hand notation system designed by Hughes and Robertson (1995) and later computerized to speed up both data collection and processing. This system analyses the distribution, frequency, and type of the rally ending shot.

If more than the rally ending shot is analysed then the lapsed-time system is needed. The data are entered using a QWERTY keyboard and mouse. The data are gathered into a Microsoft Access Database using a visual basic interface (Fig. 10.6). The data are processed in real time and available for viewing between games. The analyses present the data in 3-D graphs, with the options to filter by game, players, outcome and shot (Figs 10.7 and 10.8).

LAPSED-TIME ANALYSIS SYSTEM

The lapsed-time analysis system (Brown and Hughes, 1995; but based on the systems of Sanderson, 1983; Hughes, 1985) collects much more complex performance data than the real-time system. The position on the court, the time and type of shot is entered for every shot in the match. The data collection for this system has around a 1:4 (real time : notation time) ratio for a trained user (that is, a 30-minute match = 2 hours data collection).

From this, certain key performance indicators are derived and then used to compile a match report. This system produces data analyses based upon the examination of the respective W/E ratios as Performance Indicators. The example in Fig. 10.8 shows the W/E frequencies in each game of the match. They also clearly demonstrate the importance of errors in squash – Cassie Jackman won the first and the fifth and final games, despite Natalie Grinham having won considerably more rallies in each game, because of the relative numbers of errors. The example in Fig. 10.9 demonstrates the distribution of W/E frequencies from the SWEAT system with respect to length of rally. Lee Beachill had a very poor ratio (high numbers of errors) in rallies shorter than five shots – perhaps too anxious to create pressure too early in the rally? The system offers other options for analysis – shot types, position on court, and so on.

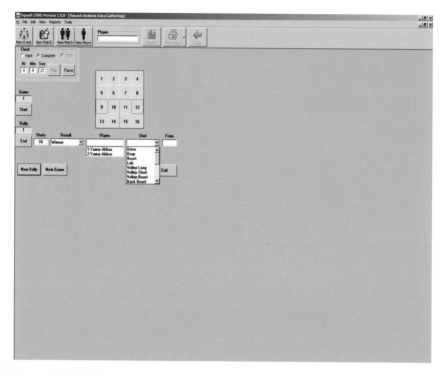

Fig. 10.6 Squash **SWEAT** data gathering interface.

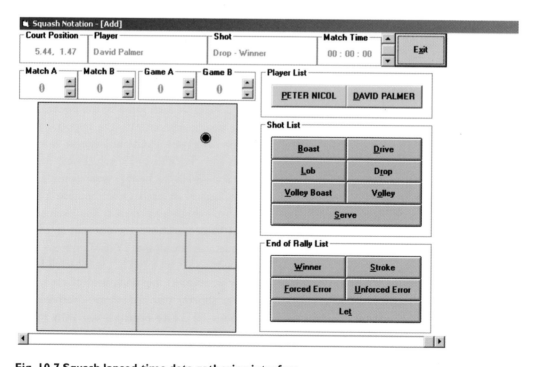

Fig. 10.7 Squash lapsed-time data gathering interface.

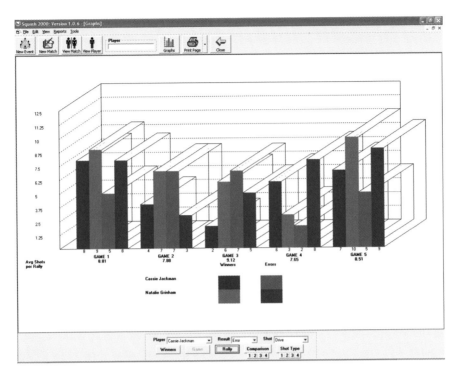

Fig. 10.8 Winner/Error (W/E) frequencies from the **SWEAT** system within each game.

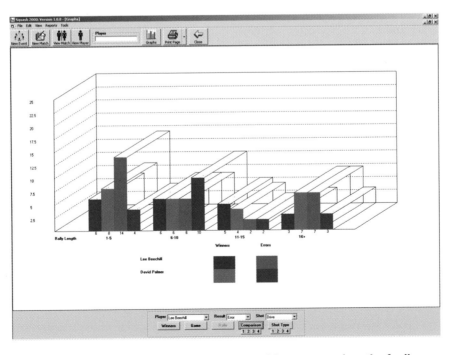

Fig. 10.9 W/E frequencies from the **SWEAT** system with respect to length of rally.

The full analysis system firstly provides simple winner and error ratios and average rally length data (Fig. 10. 10). The next set of data produced (Fig. 10.11) analyses the shot options taken (therefore patterns used) by both players. These two sets of data provide the coach and the player with the patterns used in a specific match, a simple thumbprint of the players' patterns – a combination of five or more matches are used, when possible, to provide enough data to define a 'stable' profile (Hughes, Wells and Matthews, 2000). The final four lines of the data in Fig. 10.9 further process the shot type into straight, cross court, short and long; this simplifies the data further for easier understanding by the players. Fig. 10.11 shows the distribution graphs produced by the full system. The three examples demonstrate the possible combinations (around 300) that the system produces.

The data from matches are processed and analysed in arrays ranging from simple winner and error ratios to complex rally ending patterns.

There are and were many other systems designed for analysing squash. These two systems formed the basis of a lot of applied work later, but also serve as good examples of the methodology.

PROFILING

Individual and opponent profiling

These data gathering systems produced hundreds of pages of data for one match. As a result of initial feedback from the coaches and players, and years of experience in interpreting these figures at the top level of squash, these sets of data were then further analysed and summarized into a briefer format (about sixteen sides of A4) outlining the major strengths and weaknesses of the player. The coaches and players

asked us to condense these data into bullet point form, in order to simplify the information, and therefore avoid overload and confusion. Further, these bullet points were then used as a storyboard for the accompanying edited videos assembled to support the performance data. Fig. 10.13 is an example of the bullet point data initially given. The feedback from the players and coaches was positive about this summary form of data, and coupled with the edited video made a very powerful tool.

As a result of some more feedback from the players, it was decided to combine the data from the five matches into one figure, again reducing the complexity level of the data. Also the data was normalized, and put into percentage form (Fig. 10.14). Areas of the court that had unusual data in the analysis were further examined with respect to the shot types. The court was also split into forehand/backhand, front/back and the four quarters of the court. These more simple sets of data can more easily be put into tactical plans.

Additional depth was given to the profiles by analysing the distribution across the court of not only the winners and errors, but also the distribution of shots that preceded the end shot – (N-1)W and (N-1)E. The full analysis system (see Fig. 10. 15 right-hand screen) also enables the analyses of the shot that preceded these shots – (N-2)W and (N-2)E. Using these we could then present the positive profiles of shot distributions, from winners (W), (N-1)E, (N-2)W (see Fig. 10.15 as an example); and negative profiles from errors (E), (N-1)W and (N-2)E. These overall distributions were also further analysed to examine which shot types were contributing most to the frequencies in the important areas of the court. It was found that player profiles 'stabilize' after five matches (Hughes, Wells and Matthews, 2000) – that is, if another match is added and all the performance indicators are recalculated, they will not change significantly.

Squash Match Summary Details

	Total	Player A Serving	Player B Serving
Total Shots	760	345	415
Total Rallies	122	56	66
Shots / Rally	6.23	6.16	6.29

	Total	Player A	Player B
Winners	69	22	47
Errors – Forced	6	3	3
Errors – Unforced	34	12	22

Player A Serving	Total	Player A	Player B
Winners	26	6	20
Errors – Forced	3	1	2
Errors – Unforced	19	8	11

Player B Serving	Total	Player A	Player B
Winners	43	16	27
Errors – Forced	3	2	1
Errors – Unforced	15	4	11

Print Screen ▷ Exit

Fig. 10.10 Example of initial winner/error data produced from the computerized full analysis system.

Squash Match Shot Summary Details

	Player A	Player B
Serve	56	66
Drive	126	116
X – Drive	82	56
Drop	30	44
X – Drop	11	14
Boast	31	52
Lob	0	1
X – Lob	20	7
Volley – Short	11	22
Volley – Long	18	23
X – Volley – Short	2	8

	Player A	Player B
Straight Long	144	140
Cross Court Long	144	104
Straight Short	41	66
Cross Court Short	47	74

Print Screen ◁ ▷ Exit

Fig. 10.11 Example of shot frequency summary data.

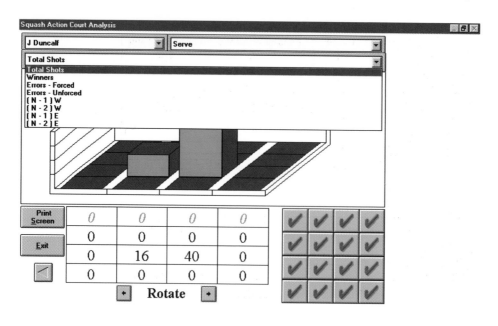

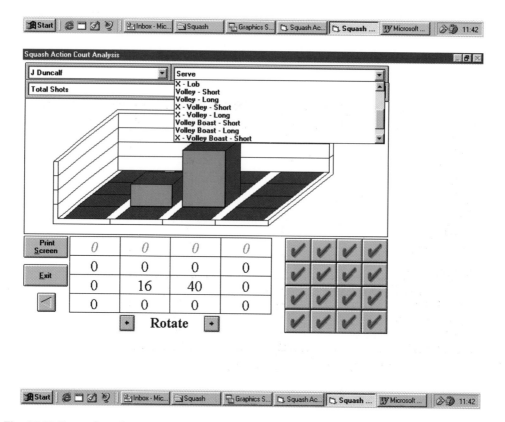

Fig. 10.12 Examples of various screens of data available.

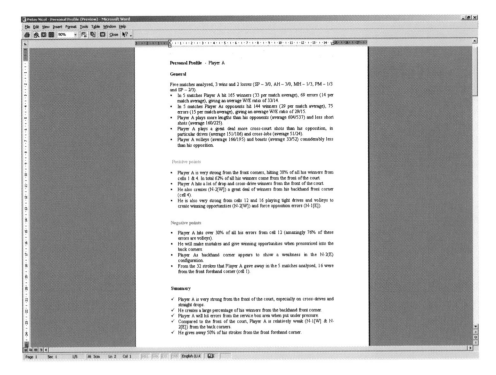

Fig. 10.13 Summary of data used as feedback and storyboard for edited video.

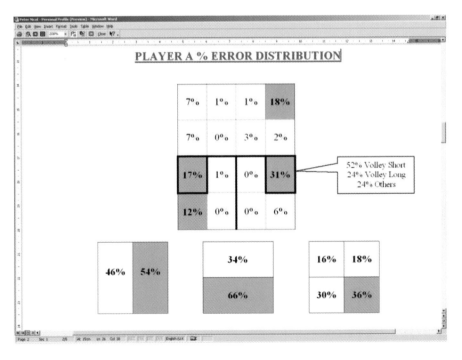

Fig. 10.14 An example of normalized distribution data.

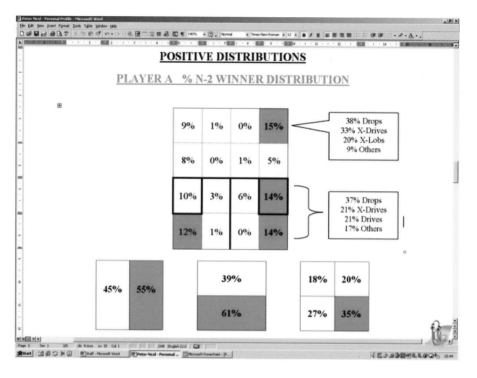

Fig. 10.15 Distribution of shots that were two shots before a winner by Player A–[(N-2)W].

These profiles were then given to the players at a national squad, and again the feedback was positive and ideas from the players were often very perceptive and always practical. The British champion at the time suggested that we go one layer deeper in the analysis and analyse the shot selection of the top players from the four corners of the court (Fig. 10.16). This form of analysis assists the players in building a constructive rally and anticipating the opposition's next shot.

Using the match report, a player or coach can identify the relative strengths and weaknesses of a player. These can then be used to support any interventions during practice or for tactical planning in preparation for the player's next match. What were also compiled were profiles of all the top players in the Top 20 of the world, potential opponents that the English players might meet in a tournament. In

this way tactical plans based upon the profiles of the player and that of the opponent would be drawn up by the coach and the player.

These profiles were used to highlight a player's strengths and weaknesses, and would form the basis of the plans for player development both in-season and out of season. In addition all players in the Top 20 in the world, both men and women, were profiled, so that an English player going to a tournament had the profiles of the players that they were likely to meet. So, in conjunction with their coach, they could prepare an appropriate tactical plan for the match.

Momentum analysis

IN SINGLES MATCH PLAY

In a discussion with the SRA psychologist during a top-class tournament, she highlighted

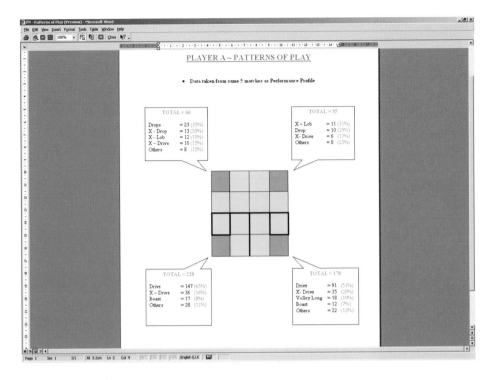

Fig. 10.16 Example of shot option analysis.

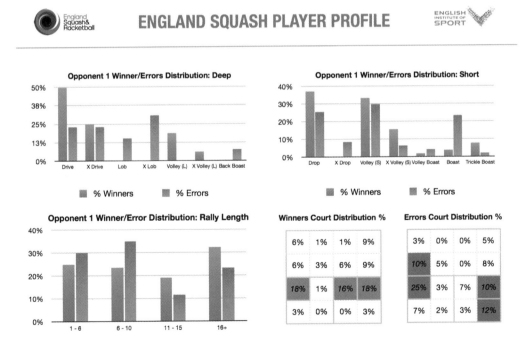

Fig. 10.17 Example of England Squash player profile.

her interest in extremes of body language and the resultant outcomes of the next three or four rallies. We realized that we had the outcome data in the computer from the SWEAT analyses. By writing another analysis program we calculated a running score (momentum) for a player during a game. We gave a winning shot by a player a '+1' score, an error a '−1' score, and if the opponent hit the rally end shot, or it was a let, the score stayed the same (Fig. 10.18). This would also show any swings in momentum during the match, and then the video could be used to analyse the body language and try to understand the reason for these swings.

With the data processed by the software, it was possible to present the two sets of data for both players at the same time (see Fig. 10.19). It is possible to examine these curves and see where the 'turning points' in the match occurred, so the coach and/or the team psychologist could discuss with the player

what happened at these turning points, which would enhance insight into each respective performance.

Fig. 10.20 shows another way that we could present these data; we termed this form of presentation a 'cumulative' momentum graph. In this graph the momentum of each player 'interacts' – so that a winner by a player will move the graph upwards, whereas an error by the player moves it downwards. The opposite applies to the other player – a winner moving the graph downwards and an error moving it upwards. In this way one curve represents the interactive momentum of the match, with each player having their positive areas on each side of the abscissa and the turning points can be seen clearly.

Figs 10.21, 10.22 and 10.23 show a clear example of these different forms of presentation. Fig. 10.21 is the impressive profile of PM, showing a positive increasing curve throughout the match. Fig. 10.22 shows a

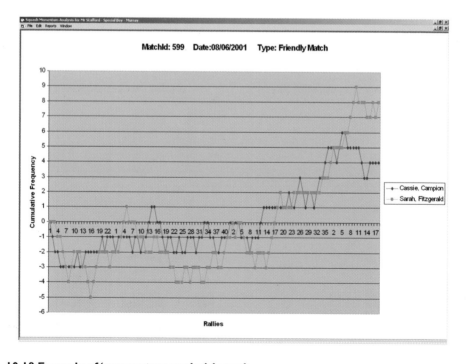

Fig. 10.18 Example of 'momentum analysis' graph.

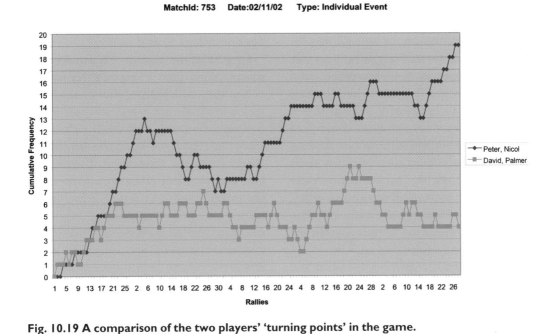

Fig. 10.19 A comparison of the two players' 'turning points' in the game.

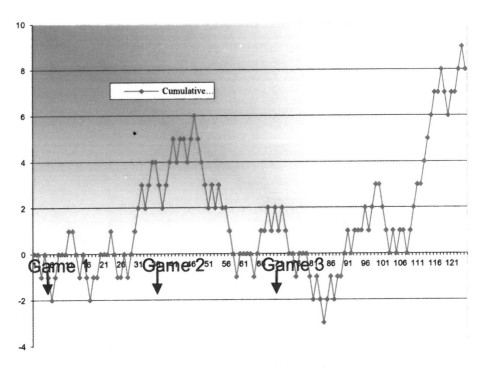

Fig 10.20 Example of a cumulative momentum analysis graph.

similar profile for DE, apart from a big trough at the start of the match. Looking at these two profiles, it is difficult to see who won the match and where the turning points occurred. Although DE's curve does not reach as high as PM's at the end, this is not the important factor – it is the slope of the curves that is important, so perhaps we could divine from this that DE won the match. But if we examine the cumulative 'interactive' momentum graph of the two players (Fig. 10.23), the patterns of momentum become much clearer. By marking where the end of each game occurs, it is clear to see that PM won the first game easily, just lost the second, won the third again very easily, but then lost momentum losing the fourth and fifth games. A coach would be very interested in talking about concentration and application at some of these critical points in the match where the momentum shifted so starkly.

In Fig. 10.22 the x-axis represents the number of rallies in the match. The y-axis on

the right side represents momentum: +1, +2. −1, −2, etc. The y-axis on the left side represents number of shots in each rally.

In Fig. 10.23 the graph of momentum is now superimposed onto a graphical representation of the respective lengths of the rallies in the match. These data were requested by the physiologist working with the English squash players to see if we could see any fatigue effects – losses of momentum, or otherwise, by players after long rallies in the latter stages of a match.

IN DOUBLES MATCH PLAY

Momentum analysis was originally implemented within the singles games; however, it has recently been shown to greatly benefit the doubles game that is played at the Commonwealth Games. The concept works in a very similar fashion to momentum analysis of a singles match, but in this case, two line graphs with different running scores are

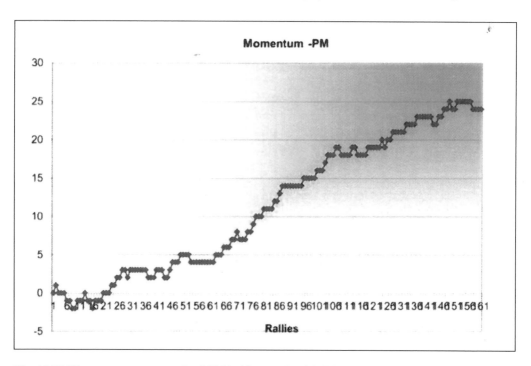

Fig. 10.21 The momentum graph of PM in his match with DE.

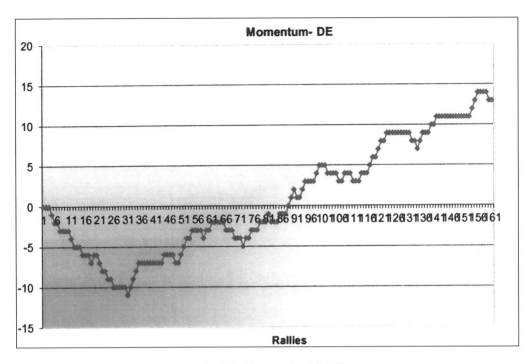

Fig. 10.22 The momentum graph of DE in his match with PM.

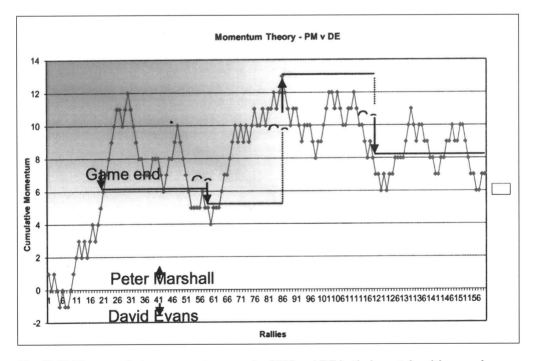

Fig. 10.23 The cumulative momentum graph of PM and DE in their match, with game by game analysis.

207

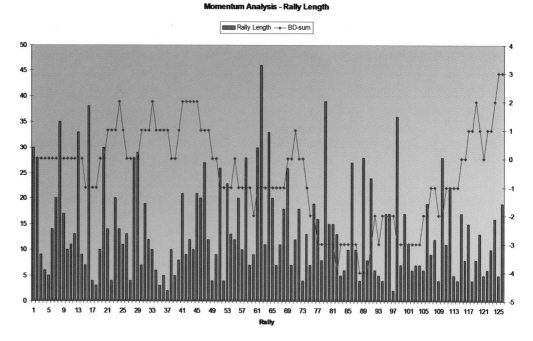

Fig. 10.24 Example of 'momentum analysis' for doubles squash.

presented at the same time, with one complementing the other. The example in Fig. 10.24 shows this.

We are still exploring the potential of the 'momentum graphs' as they have only recently been developed. But they do seem such a strong indicator of the mental strength of a player during the different stages of a match and it is felt that there could be more that can be explored with these analyses. The exciting part is how the analyses are pulling together all the different parts of the sports science support team.

PERTURBATIONS

Dynamical system theory was developed from physical principles of pattern formation to explain how order emerges in open systems without regulation being imposed by

some executive. Squash is a sport that lends itself strongly to the dynamical system theory as the game is nearly always played between two players, therefore the behaviour of one directly affects the behaviour of the other.

An integral aspect in the tactics of squash is the control of the 'T' area (near the centre of the court), and players will circle each other rhythmically during a rally, as they attempt to gain supremacy, control of this area. This movement generated the idea that the spatial temporal data that describe the interactions within squash are the result of a coupling relation between players oscillating on a common locus (McGarry, 2006). In order to control the rhythm of the game, it is essential to attempt to keep your opponent under pressure and not in control of the 'T' (Pearson, 2001). Squash match play intermittently alternates between stable and unstable behaviour, and it is at the boundaries or transition

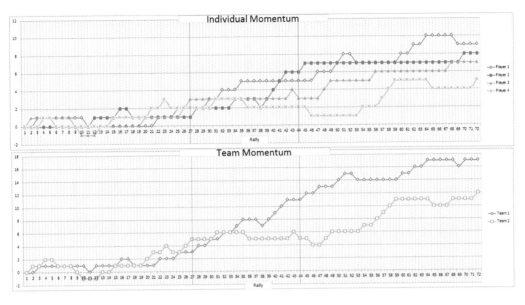

Fig. 10.25 Oscillation of players around the 'T' in a squash game (McGarry, 2006).

points of these behaviour states that perturbations and 'critical incidents (rally-end shots in this sport)' are most likely to be detected (McGarry et al., 1999). These system transitions are key behaviours within the system that cause a change from a stable rhythm to unstable behaviour. These system transitions can also be called perturbations, and can be used to provide a useful system descriptor and possibly provide information related to winning performance (Hughes et al., 1997).

A perturbation exists in an open system where the usual stable rhythm of play is disturbed by extreme elements of high or low skill, which consequently result in a particular outcome (Hughes and Reed, 2005). Concentrating on the aspects of the match that are by definition critical would make analyses not only easier but far more relevant to sports performers. Analysing whole game patterns in sport may submerge the important events in that sport under the vast amount of general data gathered (Hughes and Franks, 1997). The perturbation theory is attractive since it

can mean that analysts can focus on a much smaller body of data, so that instead of examining thousands of bits of data that make up a match, attention can be centred on what are considered to be the important events in a match.

These ideas have been pursued so that distributions of shots that caused perturbations ('pressure') were charted; they give similar pictures to the distributions of W and E, but they are different and enable a different perspective of the performance. Fenwick, Hughes and Murray's (2006) study of momentum in elite players shows there is conclusive evidence that management of this momentum by elite squash players correlated strongly with the world rankings of the players.

Winners and errors

Hughes et al. (2006a) examined the winners and errors of a number of players' matches from which they calculated each player's momentum profile. It is recognized by most coaches in squash that it is not the last shot in the rally that is the most important, hence the complex rally analyses of Sanderson and Way (1977) and most subsequent researchers (Hughes, 1986; Hughes and Robertson, 1998; Hughes et al., 2000). By recording the perturbations in rallies, the 'pressure shots' are being entered into the database; it seems logical then that profiles drawn up on these shot data will present more informed ways in which a player puts his or her opponents under pressure, and conversely, how they themselves react to these types of pressure situations.

It was not deemed appropriate to compare or collate the data by gender – the studies of the men and women are analysed and discussed separately. Conclusions are drawn, however, on the general effects of perturbation profiles on the forms of feedback in sport. Considerable time and experimentation was expended on the forms of presentation of these data, and it is clear that the form of presentation for data as complex as these is critical to their being understood and/or accepted (Willis, 2004).

In this section, on the women's data, the momentum graphs were placed in the following order, for each player's four matches:

INTERACTIVE MOMENTUM FROM WINNERS (W) AND ERRORS (E)

If the subject hits a winner then the momentum increases by one, if the subject hits an error then her momentum decreases by one; if her opponent hits a winner then the subject's momentum decreases by one, and if her opponent hits an error then the subject's momentum increases by one. If it is a 'let' ball, the momentum stays the same.

INDIVIDUAL MOMENTUM FROM WINNERS (W) AND ERRORS (E)

If the subject hits a winner then the momentum increases by one, if the subject hits an error then her momentum decreases by one; if her opponent hits a winner or if her opponent hits an error then the subject's momentum remains the same. If it is a 'let' ball, the momentum stays the same.

INTERACTIVE MOMENTUM FROM PERTURBATIONS

If the subject hits a perturbation then the momentum increases by one; if her opponent hits a perturbation then the subject's momentum decreases by one.

INDIVIDUAL MOMENTUM FROM PERTURBATIONS

If the subject hits a perturbation then the momentum increases by one; if her opponent hits a perturbation the subject's momentum remains the same. Each of the three subjects were analysed for four matches; the momentum graphs for one player for one match are presented as an exemplar.

These graphs give a clear indication of the turning points in a match and also show which are the most important stretches of positive and negative momentum with hitting winners and errors. The subject is always the positive side of the x-axis (the ordinate) – the opponent is on the negative side. Positive momentum is determined by the slope of the graph, not where the graph points are – so the graph can be in the positive but because the curve has a negative slope the subject player has negative momentum. It should also be noted that although the graphs all look to have the same amounts of data, their scales are all different, so that there are sometimes very different amounts of data in the graphs.

INTERACTIVE MOMENTUM (W AND E)

This match of Nicol David, presented in Fig. 10.27, against Vicky Botwright, is interesting. Vicky was ranked considerably lower than

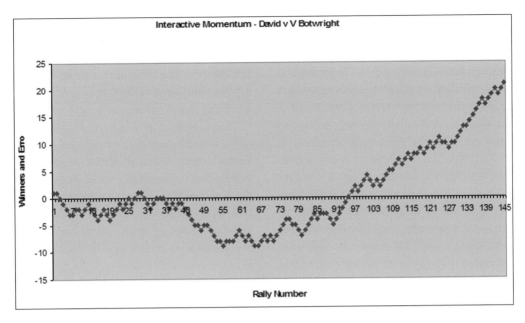

Fig. 10.26 Interactive momentum (W and E) for Nicol David.

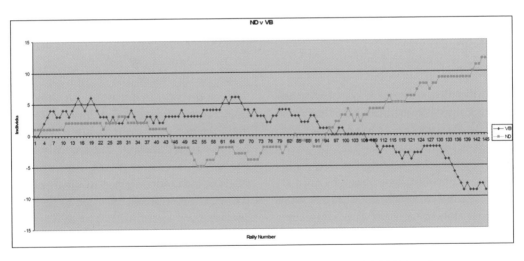

Fig. 10.27 Individual momentum (W and E) curve 1 for Nicol David (–■–) and opponent.

Nicol at the time and won each of the first games, both of which lasted 50 rallies. Then Nicol won the next three games with a very positive surge – the third game was 19 rallies, the fourth and fifth both 30 rallies. Did Nicol change her tactics? Was Vicky tired?

Whichever, this curve clearly picks out the turning point. These curves give a very clear idea of where the changes of momentum occur and would certainly help the coach and athlete to return to the video and analyse why there was this swing in momentum (Murray and Hughes, 2001). The curves do not readily help identify whether it was one player playing really well or the other playing badly. There do seem to be repeated patterns – particularly in the profiles of Nicol David and Natalie Grinham, the two top players in the world at this time – and even the winning and losing patterns of Rachel Grinham are repetitive.

INDIVIDUAL MOMENTUM (W AND E)

The individual momentum curves reflect only the performance of that player and can be instructive when used in conjunction with the interactive curves. They show how aggressive the player is in terms of hitting rally-ending shots and how consistent they are (Hughes et al., 2006b).

Many of the players' curves look to be similar in shape and form. But this is deceptive as there are different scales (different numbers of rallies in different matches) on the graphs.

INTERACTIVE MOMENTUM (PERTURBATIONS)

The interactive momentum graph from perturbations is simply calculated for a particular player – when that player hits a perturbation then their momentum increases by one, if their opponent hits a perturbation then the interactive momentum decreases by one.

These curves are generally more difficult to interpret than some of the others, but some do give definite indications of how aggressive or passive players are in certain stages of the matches, and this is an important part of the skills in match management (Pearson, 2001). Certainly, used in combination with the individual momentum from perturbations, they will give an insight into the respective shot-making of each player.

The curve (Fig 10.29) shows Nicol dominating the perturbation profile between her and Vicky Botwright, even though she lost the first two games. Perhaps she was not playing too tight or Vicky was working very hard to reverse these pressure shots (Pearson, 2001). But the pressure told, and she sustained her number of perturbation shots through the last three games to win the match.

These profiles give an insight into how players are attempting to manage their attacking and, conversely, their defensive strategies. In a number of matches players were turning the pressure from their opponent's perturbation into an opportunity to turn the tables and were winning rallies. These insights into the importance of this form of tactical competence are very rewarding – the balance of pressuring the opponent, usually by playing short (Hughes et al., 2006a), but doing so without offering too much of an opportunity to then hit a free shot. Using these curves in conjunction with all the others helped to make them understandable, because they are not immediately clear some of the time. But their value cannot be underestimated because of the more in-depth view they give of in-match tactics (Murray and Hughes, 2001).

It can be concluded that there is shown to be no comparison between the momentum using winner and errors and the momentum using perturbations. Nevertheless, after conducting a case study on some of the subjects, indications started to emerge from the momentum graphs of usage patterns of perturbations within matches which identified specific styles of play. Adding the data from different matches was deemed to be counter-productive to the true value of using these graphs, and also conflicted with the sequential nature of the data involved. There is evidence to indicate that momentum using perturbations can further the analysis in squash. This study can also conclude that the physiological characteristics of physical conditioning have an effect upon the amount of perturbations caused. This could be attributed to a player

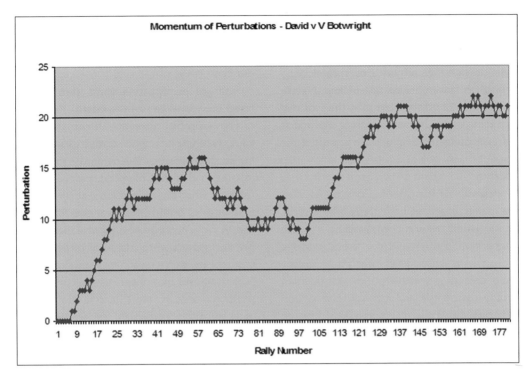

Fig. 10.28 Interactive momentum (perturbations) curve I for Nicol David.

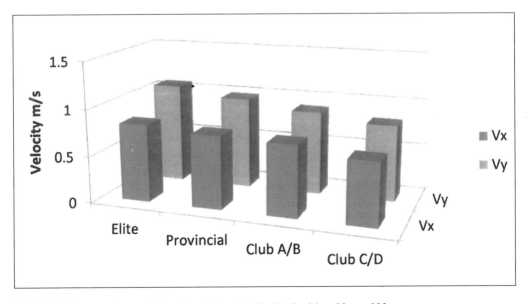

Fig. 10.29 Comparison of lateral and longitudinal velocities, Vx and Vy.

becoming more urgent towards the end of a match and performing more high-risk shots, as evident through rally lengths imposed with the momentum graphs using perturbations.

Further research into the points of critical momentum shift could be investigated to examine whether situations of the match, for example refereeing decisions, caused the some critical swings in momentum within matches. This could be analysed qualitatively by interviewing the players and coaches after the match to see whether there where areas of the match where they thought that the momentum shifted and for what reasons. From the results the interviews could be analysed correspondently with the momentum graphs to identify and confirm the critical incidents within the match and what created momentum instabilities. An extension of this research could also involve an alternative method for identifying perturbations. Rather than a trained analyst recognizing them by eye it could be possible to use tracking hardware or software to highlight them automatically using kinematic variables.

TIME-MOTION ANALYSIS

Measuring position with respect to time

The aim of this type of performance analysis work is to analyse and compare the dynamic motions of squash players of varying technical abilities. Hughes and Franks (1994) used the system developed by Hughes, Franks and Nagelkerke (1989), which utilizes current developments in notational analysis and video technology. Players in a match were tracked from video using a digitization pad calibrated to 'match up' to the squash court. Because of initial poor accuracy of repeatability, the images of the stylus on the pad and that of the player were mixed, which, after training, gave accuracy repetition figures of over 95 per cent.

Four groups of squash player were categorized: Elite (international standard), Provincial (players who had represented their province), Club A/B (players who played regularly at either the A level or B level in the inter-club leagues in British Columbia) and Club C/D (players who played regularly at either the C level or D level in the inter-club leagues in British Columbia). Six competitive matches of different players were analysed for each of the groups. Each game in each match was analysed separately and means-per-rally calculated for: positional data, X and Y; lateral and longitudinal velocities, Vx and Vy; average velocities, V; distances travelled, D; and accelerations, A. An Analysis of Variance was completed on the data to test for inter-game and inter-group variation.

The groups exhibited different average positions on court reflecting the developing tactics employed by each group. It was also found that the dynamic profiles (average distance covered, velocity and acceleration per rally) all increased significantly from group to group. None of the players showed signs of slowing down; that is, there were no decreases in either velocity or acceleration as the matches went on. The lateral velocity profile was significantly higher than the longitudinal profile for each of the groups except the C/D players, those at the lowest ability. The values obtained for the accelerations, and the associated standard deviations, would seem to indicate that the game is more anaerobic than has previously been suggested.

This study changed the subjective views of players and coaches to training for squash, long regarded as a principally aerobic sport, and focused our attention on short bursts of high-intensity activity, involving a lot of turning.

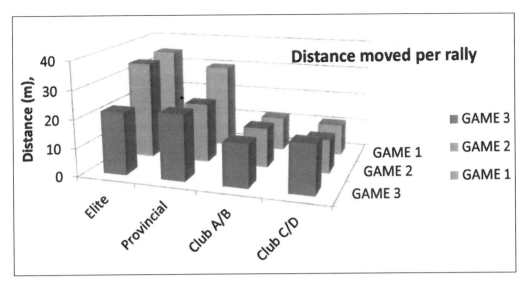

Fig. 10.30 Comparison of distance moved per rally.

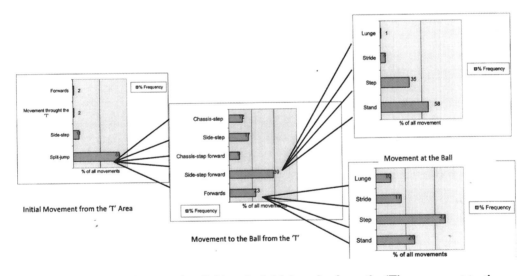

Fig. 10.31 Percentage frequencies, linking the initial modes from the 'T', movement to the ball and movement at the ball to form the most occuring sequence of when to play a drive shot from the back of the court.

Squash-specific movement

Squash has such a high demand on physical fitness (Sharp, 1997) that efficient and economical movement within the court is vital to generate less energy wastage and to approach a ball giving yourself plenty of time to make contact. This increases the pressure upon your opponent, while giving the player time to recover back to the 'T' looking to attack the following shot. 'The great players are the great movers,' says McKenzie (2002, p.39)

Table 10.2 An example of the designed spreadsheet used.									
ID	Match	Game	Server	Score	Movement	Player	T Position	Left Foot	Right Foot

From T	To Ball	Shot Start	At Ball	Lead Foot	Side	Shot Played	From Ball	To T	Shot Finish	Outcome

referring to Geoff Hunt, who moved rhythmically around the court. When Jansher Khan first appeared on the World scene, it was his movement, not his racket skills, that singled him out, and all the top squash experts held him in awe (Pearson, 1999).

There has been no research into 'squash-specific' movement analysis in elite squash. By 'squash-specific' was meant those movements that are used on a squash court: split step, lunge, stride, side skip, and so on. This study aims to rectify this by producing a performance profile of elite women's movement patterns. Perreira, Wells and Hughes (2005) hoped to produce a detailed collection of results indicating feet positioning and movement to and from the ball in different parts of the court, for different shot selections.

The Microsoft Access package was used to input the data via the computerized notation system devised for this study. Code representations were taken for the following aspects: shots played, the server, the receiver, the game, the match title, the side the shot was played from, the foot movements, the player's movement from the 'T', recovery back to the 'T' and the outcome of the rally.

There were representations using the layout of cells, by dividing the 'T' area into twenty cells (lettered A to T). This represented the feet positions of the subject before moving to play a shot. The court was split into sixteen cells, which Hughes and Knight (1993) had similarly developed studying patterns of play. This was used to indicate when the player made contact with the ball and where the ball landed in the court.

The design of this system was produced in the Microsoft Access package. Table 10.2 displays an example of the design spreadsheet used within the study.

LINKING A SEQUENCE MOVEMENT PATTERN FROM THE WHOLE COURT

The researcher decided when looking at movement patterns that the information gathered did not show how each movement follows onto another. Therefore an actual sequence of movement patterns should be gathered. Fig. 10.31 shows the percentage frequency taken from ten elite women players, linking the initial movements from the 'T' area, movement to the ball and movement at the ball from the most occurring sequences, when playing a drive shot in the whole court.

As the split-jump occurs 79 per cent from all of the initial movements from the 'T' area, the split-jump was significantly greater than any other initial movements. From the split-jump the side-step forward movement occurred 36 per cent and forward movement occurred 28 per cent of the total percentage

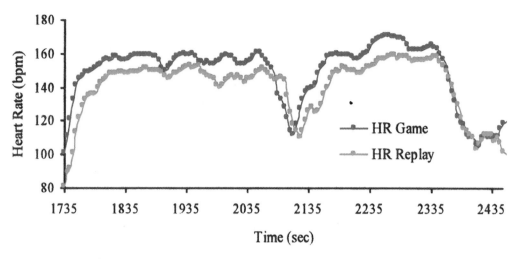

Fig. 10.32 Heart rates in the actual match and that of the same player executing replication ghosting of the match.

of all the other movements to the ball. Due to having insignificant difference between the two movements to the ball, both movements were continued to gather data at the ball. The split-jump occurred 79 per cent followed by the side-step movement to the ball (36 per cent), then standing at the ball was 58 per cent and stepping at the ball occurred with 34 per cent. Though when compared to split-jump (79 per cent), forwards (28 per cent) and stepping at the ball 39 per cent and striding being 27 per cent, then standing creating 21 per cent of the total movements at the ball, there is a difference between both the sequence movements.

It is difficult to judge these sequences as true movement patterns that occur because these movements are looked upon as a sequence in the whole court. Fig. 10.31 refers to a percentage frequency of where the drive shot is played the most in the various areas of the court. From this it could be said that the front court and the back court could generate different movement patterns.

BACK AND FRONT COURT SEQUENCE MOVEMENT PATTERNS

The first graph is Fig. 10.31 refers to percentage frequency taken from ten elite women players, linking the initial movements from the 'T', movements to the ball and movements at the ball to form the most occurring movement sequence patterns when playing a drive shot from the back half of the court (see Fig. 10.6, cells 9–16). The split-jump occurs in 85 per cent of all initial movements from the 'T' area, and is therefore significantly higher than 15 per cent of 'other' initial movements. The split-jump occurs more frequently than any other initial movement from the 'T' area, hence the movement to the ball occurred with side-step forwards generating 39 per cent and forward movement to the ball 23 per cent of all movements to the ball from the 'T' area. These two types of movement patterns occur with standing and stepping at the ball capturing the highest percentage frequency.

These sequence movement patterns are different compared to the second part of

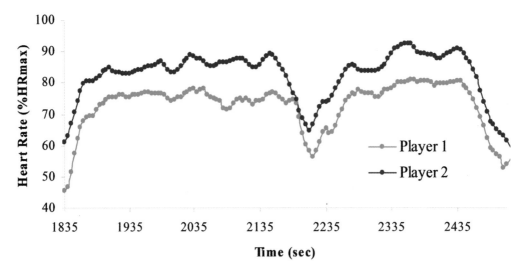

Fig. 10.33 Heart rates (normalized by the HRmax of each) of Player 1 replicating a top-class match and a junior player (Player 2) trying to replicate Player 1's movements and shot execution.

Fig. 10.31 concerning movement patterns in the whole court. The graph displays the percentage frequency taken from ten elite women players, linking the initial movements from the 'T', movement to the ball and movements at the ball to form the most occurring sequence pattern when playing a drive shot in the front half of the court (cell 1–8). The forward movement has the highest percentage frequency concerning the initial movement from the 'T' area. Linked with the initial movement from the 'T', the side-step forward movement to the ball occurs 98 per cent compared with the 2 per cent of forward movement to the ball. As the side-step forwards is significantly greater than the forward movement (0.005) the movements at the ball from the 'T' linking the side-step forwards occur with the lunge (28 per cent), striding (25 per cent), standing (4 per cent) and stepping at the ball (43 per cent). Compared to the fourth graph in Fig. 10.31 stepping is also the greatest movement to occur at the ball though lunging is significantly greater in the front of the court than

compared to the back of the court. Occurrence of standing at the front ball is lower in the front court (4 per cent) than in the back of the court (58 per cent). These sequence patterns could be viewed in all other shots rather than just the drive shot; however it could not be completed in time.

Due to the limitation in time and space not all the shots' analyses could be presented here, just this one example in the depth that the movement sequence patterns produced for the drive shot. However, the methods used to conclude the four movement patterns in each corner of the court could be applied to any shot.

Replication Ghosting

What is replication ghosting? It came from an idea of Paul Carter, England Squad Coach and also a personal coach to Cassie Jackman (World No.1). Cassie was making a comeback after more than twelve months out with a serious back injury, and although Paul felt that she was back to full fitness Cassie did not believe it. Paul suggested to the analysts (Murray and Hughes) that they record on a notation sheet the 'choreography' of the previous World Championship final between Cassie and Natalie Grinham (the then World No.1), which Cassie had won, so that they could get Cassie to replicate the movement patterns she executed in the final, and the specific shots, at the speed that she executed them in the final. In that way she could begin to believe that she was back to full fitness.

Murray and Hughes came up with the suggestion that, in order to fix a correct time scale to movements, they project the video of the match onto the front wall from a projector either on the balcony or above the back wall (if a glass-back court). The image is big – covering the front wall. The script is dictated to the player – cell number and shot to be played as she returns to the 'T' after the previous shot. Random ghosting has long been a part of the squads' preparation for match play, enhancing fitness, speed, stamina, balance in the shot, preparation of swing and returning to the 'T'. This form of ghosting enabled:

- Replication of specific match play movement patterns;
- Movements done without the ball;
- Repetitive patterns of movement to cover all areas of the court at match speed.

CURRENT LIMITATIONS OF GHOSTING

- Not loaded towards match-specific game play (distribution of movement and individual variation);
- Not situation/player-specific (patterns of movement);
- Weaker patterns are not emphasized;
- Consistency of training (boredom through repetition = low adherence)

POSITIVE USES

In order to examine what we were achieving in spite of the limitations, a series of tests was set up. The first was to compare heart-rates, blood lactates and distance covered in the real match with those covered by the same player replicating the match on court. The only difference was that the HR was about 5 per cent less in the replication exercise compared to that in the match (see Fig 10.34). There were no differences in lactate levels nor in the distances covered.

The next step was to examine the effect of a player trying to replicate a better player's movement and shot patterns, to see how much of a 'learning' experience it might be. The World No.1 male (Player 1) replicated one of his top matches, this was then repeated by a young member (Player 2) of the U21 squad.

Although the junior player was very fit and trained with the World No.1 regularly, his heart rate was on average 10 per cent higher throughout the replication exercise. Afterwards, he spoke of not realizing how much more often Player 1 volleyed the ball than him, and how this meant staying further forward on the court and moving more quickly but often not as far.

So overall it was a positive experience and an exercise that was applied for a number of years.

USES OF REPLICATION GHOSTING:

- Replay specific strengths and weaknesses;
- Replay specific situations/opponents;
- Play a higher level of match play (juniors understand the hard mentality required);
- Test Squash-specific Fitness;
- Stimulate the training environment, NM, for example.

Fig. 10.34 The accuracy of the analysis and feedback provided is vital, as is the timing at which it is administered. The photograph shows David Pearson in 2001 using Quintic, one of the first commercially available analysis softwares, to work on technique with then world champion Peter Nicol. (Photo: Sarah Murray)

On-court technical feedback in training

The profiling techniques applied to the W/E analyses will highlight the strengths and weaknesses of players, usually rooted in problems of technique in the swing or perhaps the approach movement to the shot. These technical improvements are tackled by the coach and players usually in the short 'out of season' period in the summer, not wishing to intrude changes in a player's game during the competitive season.

Video analysis feedback systems (such as Dartfish in the action) are used for live real-time feedback sessions conducted by the coach with a specific technique and/or intervention. During these sessions the feedback is enhanced by using big-screen displays on court for the athlete to review performance. Technological developments over the years have made the amalgamation of data and video footage far quicker and more user-friendly.

The digital revolution has had a huge impact upon feedback provision and it has allowed for the real-time presentation of video and data. There are a number of these general computerized analysis software packages available, enabling users to conduct their own technical analysis: Dartfish, Quintic, SiliconCoach and Focus all have similar packages on the market.

Accurate quantification of such movements is only possible with a consistent and precise set-up, which is covered in the following articles. All of the software packages allow the user to edit video clips, to compare them in split-screen and to add angles and drawings to the video.

The image that is being analysed within the software is two-dimensional and, as such, caution needs to be used when calculating body angles and velocities, as the direction of motion is unlikely to be completely linear. As motion will be taking place in other planes, literal interpretation of the values obtained could be dangerous, but relative comparisons of results are useful as long as the same protocols have been followed. If this is the case, then valid comparisons can be made of an athlete's technique pre- and post-injury, pre- and post- a coaching intervention or between an athlete and a role model. This has obvious benefits for rehabilitation or for a developing athlete looking to improve.

> *The use of technical feedback greatly speeds up the coaching process and increases the rate at which an athlete can develop and modify techniques.*
>
> Paul Carter,
> England National Squash Coach

ANGLE OF FILMING

There are two aspects to look at here. The first aspect relates to the angle of elevation, which is particularly important in invasive sports such as football, where opponents are mixed together in the playing area, and

for tactical analysis. For these sports, the more elevation the better, as this allows for a greater perspective of distribution and playing patterns. For technical analysis, it is preferable to have the camera at the same level as the performance indicator you are analysing.

The second aspect relates to the angle of the camera in relation to the flow of performance. Generally, the camera is best positioned in line with, or at 90° to, the performance. This is particularly critical if you are performing technical analysis and looking at changes in limb position and joint angles (such as the vault in gymnastics). A note of caution when using video to quantify joint angles and velocities is that the values achieved are only in two fields of motion and can only be seen as relative, not absolute. Obviously, the information given here is the best-case scenario and allows for repeatability. However, if this is not achievable, then try to get the angle as near to optimum as possible.

COMPARISON

One of the most powerful messages is given by comparing the performance of a skill on court today (a swing, a particular shot, recovery movement, swing preparation, and so on) with another performance of that skill:

- By the same player last season;
- By another player, same standard but ranked higher;
- By a world ranked player;
- Before and after injury.

All of the software systems enable playback and some enable overlays with synchronization systems so that a direct comparison of the differences can be assessed. The use of higher-standard players introduces a motivational spur for players to keep working, particularly if the player is a 'hero' of the player being coached – what is termed ' gold standard examples'.

It is the responsibility of the analyst to provide the material quickly and clearly, without intruding on the coaching session, so it requires a lot of preparation, planning and forethought, which is best done in conjunction with the coach. The widespread use of iCloud databases, iPads and iPhones has made the dissemination of video material easier and more acceptable to players and coaches.

COACH DEVELOPMENT

Behaviour of coaches

The term 'behaviour' is used to explain the actions and comments of the coaches and the way they are presented during the sessions. A coach can be seen as the individual responsible for the climate of the learning environment for athletes; hence the coach needs to perform their behaviours in the most appropriate manner to help develop the athlete.

One of the obvious and frequent behaviours a coach uses during training sessions is comments to their athletes. More and Franks (1996) suggested that the majority of comments made by a coach should be positive in nature to increase effectiveness of learning environment. Tharp and Gallimore's (1976) investigation of a top sports coach found that the coach did not provide this, as the coach used more scolding rather than praise/ positive comments to athletes by a ratio of 2:1, therefore going against the theory of helping athletes by increasing the effectiveness of the learning environment.

Cushion and Smith (2006) aimed to examine the coaching behaviour of professional youth soccer coaches during matches. They used the Arizona State University observation instrument to analyse their defined behaviours, the frequency of them, as well as the amount of time each one was performed. Coaches were all from professional backgrounds, which can indicate they are experienced and knowledgeable in the area. The investigation showed that two themes emerged in the coaches' behaviours: firstly the coaches were seen to help develop performance, and secondly they showed support and encouragement. This second finding relates to the claim of More and Franks (1996) about positive comments being used in the coaching set-up. With academic research involving professional and elite subjects providing results that differ, this would suggest that it is not established that positive comments, maybe involving reinforcement and encouragement, are an important part of effective coaching, therefore the results in this investigation may be able to help provide a definitive answer.

Hughes and Franks (1997) went one step further, however; they explained that motor learning literature (Schmidt, 1988) states augmented feedback produces learning through the information given about the previous actions. Due to this they suggest that coaches should therefore ensure that the feedback given goes beyond just praise or scold ('good work'), and should include some informational content ('good work but get more pace on the ball'), or information about why the performance was correct or incorrect. This information should be given to reinforce the particular aspects of performance that are correct so they help develop learning, or to highlight incorrect aspects so they can be modified and corrected.

Another investigation which was carried out analysed the coach of a highly rated youth team performed by Jones (2006). It involved the analysis of one qualified and experienced university soccer coach over three of the team's training sessions (one as a pilot) and used systematic observation with the coach analysis instrument (CAI) to record the frequency of defined behaviours of the coach. The results gave more depth into the comments made by the coach, in terms of when comments were made and the technical claims in them. The majority of these comments made were non-skill-related (57 per cent). Of the 43 per cent that were skill-related comments the majority (33 per cent) were instructional, which coincides with Tharp and Gallimore (1976) who also discovered in their experiment that over half the comments of a top-level sports coach were instructional.

Other data collected showed 61 per cent of the overall comments made were during performance, with 30 per cent made by stopping the performance first and 9 per cent after the performances were complete. This information shows how the coach behaves, and can help with evaluating their abilities and how it may affect the athlete's performance. Although the analysis was only a case study of one coach, which may not provide results for a population – other coaches, other sports may use different techniques in their performance when coaching due to the demands of the game, whether a team sport, individual sport or use of highly skilled technique. However, the reasoning of the investigation and the methodology behind the research show an insight into the subject, and a way to compare how that experiment was performed when related to this investigation.

Harris-Jenkins and Hughes (1995) observed the behaviours of three female lawn tennis coaches (all with the same grade qualification) in three sessions each. A computerized coaching analysis system (CCAS) was used to record the data, each comment the coaches made was coded into the programme and chi square was used to analyse significance (significance being less than 0.05).

The data from the experiment produced a couple of results.

Firstly there was no significance in the data of behaviour patterns between the coaches; this meant that all of the coaches showed a consistent and similar profile of behaviour. This would be related to the research done by Rushall and Siedentop (1972; cited in Harris-Jenkins and Hughes, 1995) who suggested that behaviour becomes more consistent with experience, so for example the very experienced/elite coaches would know how to coach the situations, therefore produce the same results every time in that circumstance as long as it is successful. This may explain the literature on elite coaches, as Ericsson and Charness (1994) who found that to become an expert would take at least ten years of deliberate practice, and from those years of experience, they could relate to their coaching situations and produce the correct actions. From this research and these results it would propose that the current investigation also using elite, highly qualified coaches would therefore provide results showing all coaches to have similar/consistent behaviours due to their vast experience in the field.

The second set of results produced from the Harris-Jenkins and Hughes (1995) research found that the coaches made more organizational comments in their sessions compared to skill-related knowledge. These results further support Tharp and Gallimore (1976) in their conclusion that the coaches provide a lot more instructional comments. However the tennis coaches involved in Harris-Jenkins and Hughes (1995) were working with youngsters, which could explain why more organization and instruction was needed than when compared to top-level players who would already know basic organization and technique and consequently not need the instruction. Also the experiment only took place over two sessions (with another session as a pilot), which may not be enough to gather the coaches' range of behaviours.

Research has suggested that differences occur in coach behaviour between winning and losing coaches (the winning coaches being defined as the more successful, that is, their team winning the matches or tournaments) during game play as well as in practice sessions (Lyle, 2002). This therefore suggests that different people act in different ways to help coach their athletes – some successfully, some unsuccessfully, using different methods.

Douge and Hastie (1993; cited in Smith and Cushion, 2006) when looking at coach effectiveness suggested that the more effective coaches frequently provided feedback, along with prompts and hustles of encouragement and work rate. The coaches provided high levels of correction and re-instruction and used high levels of questioning and clarifying in their behaviours. They were predominantly engaged in instruction rather than the skill-related information and managed the training environment to maintain considerable order.

Markland and Martinek (1988) also found that the behaviour of successful coaches was to give more immediate feedback, which is also supported by Jones (2002). Magill (1998) agreed with the research described earlier and suggested that skill-related information given to athletes is best provided when they are free from performance demands (not during competition) and able to process coaching information effectively, such as the training sessions, which would suggest that practices involve lots of skill and performance information which would come from coaches and therefore be expected in the investigation being studied here. This is supported by Phillips and Carlisle (1983), and Mustain (1990; cited in Hughes and Franks, 2004) who believe more effective coaching occurs when performance-related information and feedback are maximized, therefore

again suggesting a lot of skill terminology and knowledge is used when in a training environment.

Hughes, Archer, James, Dancs and Vuckovic (2010) examined the behaviour patterns of elite coaches working with elite student athletes. The studies that have been produced mostly come from America, and little is known about British coaches. The aim of this work was to analyse the behaviour of elite coaches and add to the theory and knowledge in Britain and enable the comparison of their behaviour patterns.

The analysis of four elite coaches involved in football, basketball, pole vaulting, and squash working with elite athletes in university was performed through four hours of recording the coaches in their training sessions. The investigation used a combination of the behaviours used by More and Franks (1996) and Tharp and Gallimore (1976) and after hand notating the recordings, the total amounts of time for each behaviour were calculated and then compared against each other. The results showed the coaches performing consistently throughout their four sessions, and surprisingly there were no significant differences ($p < 0.05$) between the behaviours of the four coaches. Instruction, organization, positive demonstration and praise were the behaviours that were consistently used more by all coaches. From the findings it was able to produce times for a set behaviour pattern for elite coaches.

Although the statistical tests showed no significant differences between the coaches, diversity was seen throughout the data sets, suggesting how coaches may be different and that universal behaviour sets are not possible. The results stimulate many questions for discussion and further research, including: why coaches are similar, why they are not, how testing procedures many affect the findings and how future research should be performed.

RULE CHANGES

In May 1988 a new scoring system was introduced to the game of squash by the Squash Rackets Association in an attempt to make the game more attractive to television viewing audiences. This system, initially known as 'American scoring', was renamed 'point-per-rally scoring', and differed from the traditional scoring system in that a point is scored at the end of every rally regardless of whether the winner held serve or not. A game was decided by one player reaching 15 points; if a 14–14 tie is achieved they play on until someone wins by two clear points. The purpose of the study by Hughes and Knight (1994) was to establish whether or not the introduction of this new scoring system produced any difference in the patterns of play exhibited in competition by elite male squash players when compared to the traditional 'English' scoring, and whether or not any reduction in both the average rally length and the number of let and stroke appeals occurred. Performance analysis has been used in many sports (soccer, rugby union, rugby league, badminton and so on), to quantify the changes wrought in the actual game brought about by the rule changes made. Quite often these changes have the exact opposite effect to those declared by the rule makers.

It was found that point-per-rally scoring, in comparison to English scoring, produces no significant difference in the average length of the rallies. This was surprising, as the original belief was that the rallies in the new system would be shorter and therefore more interesting to the general public. There was no reduction in the time of one game (about 20 mins). The reasons for this may be the extremely high levels of fitness of the elite players, enabling retrievals when under great pressure, and developed strategies by the players to minimize errors.

Significantly more winners were observed with point-per-rally scoring. It was hoped that this would be a product of the new system, that players would attack more, irrespective of who was serving, thus removing the defensive 'boring' play that players adopt under the old rules when receiving serve. No significant difference between the two systems of scoring were observed in the number of errors. It was thought that the number of errors would increase if players were playing more attacking shots. It would seem that players have developed strategies and tactics that minimize the errors while enabling more winners. Significantly fewer let/stroke appeals were found with point-per-rally scoring. This factor should help to make the game more entertaining to the general public, often confused both by the appeals and the ensuing decisions. Further analysis of the different shots and the positions from which they were played showed that point-per-rally scoring produces a more attacking style of play amongst elite male players than does English scoring.

Hughes (1995) analysed the scoring structures in tennis and squash, using the phrase 'activity cycles' and 'critical points' to describe events leading to exciting points in each system. In tennis these activity cycles last about three minutes and the scores were always close because of the nature of the system. Hughes recommended a new scoring system in squash to try to make the game more attractive. He recognized the need to shorten the cycles of play leading to 'critical' points in squash – currently it takes about fifteen to twenty minutes to reach a game-ball. By having more, shorter games, more critical points will arise and this will raise the levels of excitement and crowd interest. Badminton has the same problems with its scoring systems and the ensuing activity cycles. He also demonstrated quantitatively that there is an imbalance in the game when the winner of a rally is given the serve at the start of the next rally – the lesser player is being penalized. Analysis of the effects of rule changes in sport has frequently been the subject of research in notational analysis, usually by creating statistical norms or models of performance pre- and post-rule changes. This kind of work (Hughes, 1995) is relatively unusual in being proactive rather than reactive.

CREATING A TACTICAL MODEL

Creating a database of a competitive sport and extracting from this database a tactical model of the game is one of the most desirable outcomes of notational analysis. Many coaches seek the template of tactical play at the highest level for preparation and training of elite players, and for developing players who aspire to reach the highest levels within the game. Particular databases, aimed at specific individuals or teams, can also be used to prepare potential opponents for match play. The aim of this work was to utilize computerized notation systems to create, firstly, a structural archetype of the game of squash at the elite level, and then to extend this to a tactical model of the game. The second aim was to develop hand notation systems for use by coaches and players, with the intention of providing not only immediate feedback to the competing players but also an educational tool for those players using the systems.

Development of database and models

Five matches of elite players (ranked in the World Top 20) were videotaped at the finals of the 1996 British Open by Hughes and

Table 10.3 This model is based upon data taken from five matches involving players who were in the top twenty in the world at the time (1995–96 season).

Average number of shots/match	1089
Average number of shots/game	351.2
Average number of rallies/game	26
Mean rally length (19" tin)	13.52
Mean rally time	21s
Time between rallies	10s
Average number of winners/game-winning player	9 (8.9)
Average number of errors/game-winning player	5 (4.7)
Average number of winners/game-losing player	6 (6.2)
Average number of errors/game-losing player	6 (6.3)

Robertson (1997). All these matches were analysed using a comprehensive computerized notation system (Hughes and Knight, 1995), which was used post-event. Chi-square and t-tests were used to test for significant differences when appropriate.

The length of the rallies agrees with research (Hughes and Knight, 1995) but differs from other earlier research (Hughes, 1985). This is attributed to lighter rackets with increased power. In the tactical model a performance indicator, the ratio of winner to errors, W/E (Sanderson, 1983) showed significant differences ($P<0.01$) between the profiles of all the different categories of shots of winning players and losing players at elite level. The highest ratios of W/E for both sub-

Table 10.4. Analysis of winners and errors for winning and losing players; the totals for the winners and errors in the columns are for five matches.						
	WINNING PLAYERS			LOSING PLAYERS		
Shot	Winners	Errors	W/E Ratio	Winners	Errors	W/E Ratio
Drive (D)	23	22	1.05	20	29	0.69
Drop (d)	41	21	1.95	32	24	1.33
Boast (B)	8	9	0.89	8	19	0.42
Lob (L)	1	7	0.14	2	10	0.2
Volley Long (VL)	9	2	4.5	2	0	-
Volley Short (VS)	22	9	2.44	19	14	1.36
Volley Boast (VB)	0	1	0	0	1	0
Cross Drive (cD)	29	1	29	11	2	5.5
Cross Drop (cd)	12	6	2	6	5	1.2
Cross Lob (cL)	3	1	3	0	4	0
Cross VL (cVL)	2	1	2	4	1	4
Cross VS (cVS)	10	4	2.25	8	2	4
TOTAL	160	84	1.90	111	114	0.97

sets of players was for the cross-court drive; the lowest ratio, of those shots that were played with significant frequency, were the boast and the straight drive. The shots that had the highest frequencies of errors were the straight drive and the straight drop.

Five matches of elite players (ranked in the world top twenty) were videotaped at the finals of the 1996 British Open by Hughes and Robertson (1997). All these matches were analysed using a comprehensive computerized notation system (Hughes and Knight, 1995) which was used post-event. Chi-square and t-tests were used to test for significant differences when appropriate.

The length of the rallies agrees with recent research (Hughes and Knight, 1995), but differs from other earlier research (Hughes, 1985) – this is attributed to lighter rackets with increased power. In the tactical model a performance indicator, the ratio of winner to errors, W/E (Sanderson, 1983), showed significant differences (P<0.01) between the profiles of all the different categories of shots of winning players and losing players at elite level. The highest ratios of W/E for both sub-sets of players were for the cross-court drive; the lowest ratio, of those shots that were played with significant frequency, were the boast and the straight drive. The shots that had the highest frequencies of errors were the straight drive and the straight drop.

Seven models, and nine associated notation systems, were developed that encompassed all parts of the game from serve and return to awareness of the opponent when playing a short shot or long shot, from patterns of volleying to responses to short or long shots.

Development of the systems

All these tactical models were used as a basis for creating nine systems for notating squash in-match in a simple, visual way, that require little or no data processing. The tactical ideas on which the systems are based are:

- Service and return
- Positioning of shot: straight-long or -short, cross-long or -short
- Winners and errors
- Winners and errors + and rally length
- Volleys
- Response to a short shot
- Response to a long shot
- Awareness of opponent when volleying
- Awareness of opponent when playing short.

There is a deliberate tactical progression within this list of systems and it has been found that this progression is useful when using the systems with squads of players that are of different standards. This list of systems offers two or more systems that could be used for a squad session, no matter what the theme of the session may be.

The systems are designed to be used by the players, for the players, and are all visual and therefore can provide immediate feedback. Learning time for the players is minimal, particularly when they operate in pairs. This use of the systems by the players has an extra

benefit for them, as it heightens their awareness of the importance of the tactical reason for the particular system. The ideas behind the systems and progressions of tactical development involved in the systems can easily be extended to other racket sports.

The most recent change has been in the Professional Men's Circuit, where the games are still played PPR, but reduced to 11. There was a belief that a goal of 15 led to no real urgency in the battle for the first few points, whereas condensing the game meant a sprint to 10 was almost a necessity. A further requirement for a two clear point margin if players reach 10-all, was aimed at creating more 'critical points' in matches.

The main aim of a study by Hughes, Watts, White and Hughes (2009) was to analyse any changes in the game structure or differences in the patterns of play occurring amongst the elite of men's squash (inside Top 12 in the world), whilst playing in competition under two different scoring systems. This study analysed six matches from both scoring systems played by male players ranked in the Top 12 in the PSA World Rankings. The analysis of the data gathered entailed such comparisons as rally lengths and the amount of winners and errors played. The study also attempted to determine if matches were shorter and if more 'critical points' were created through the new scoring system, hence making it more attractive to the television media.

The data produced by the system were placed into Microsoft Excel to be analysed in greater detail. The first page of results that are produced by the system are the total amount of shots, total rallies and shots per rally for both players individually and collectively, as are total winners, forced errors and unforced errors.

These figures were totalled for all matches under each scoring system. From these results

Table 10.5. Average distribution of shot types per 500 shots and P value from Mann-Whitney statistical test.

Variable	Scoring System		% Difference	Asymp. Sig. (2-tailed)
	PPR to 15	PPR to 11		
Serve	43.7	41.7	−4.52	0.630
Drive	195.2	221.3	13.42	0.631
X-Drive	112.6	112.6	0.05	1.000
Drop	39.7	36.9	−7.23	0.630
X-Drop	8.9	7.3	−17.64	0.262
Boast	22.0	24.5	11.28	0.521
Lob	11.5	14.6	26.45	0.631
X-Lob	19.8	19.1	−3.52	0.631
Volley – Short	20.5	25.0	22.07	0.337
Volley – Long	32.8	38.8	18.60	0.749
X-Volley – Short	4.4	3.6	−18.39	0.521
X-Volley – Long	40.8	37.2	−8.81	0.522
Volley Boast – Short	0.1	0.0	−100.00	0.317
Volley Boast – Long	0.1	0.1	12.78	0.902
X-Valley Boast – Short	1.2	1.4	18.15	0.630
X-Volley Boast – Long	0.1	0.1	12.78	0.902

an average frequency of shots per rally was calculated for both systems showing very similar results. PPR to 15 averaged 12.67 shots per rally, with PPR to 11 averaging slightly higher with 12.99, both rounding to 13 shots per rally (Table 10.5). Hughes and Robertson (1998) found an average of 13.52 shots per rally, which is surprisingly close given the changes in rackets over the last decade and these rule changes that have occurred. It might have been expected that shorter rallies were played under the PPR to 11, because of the implied urgency to attack, but this is not the case. The same argument was used when the rule change from traditional scoring (English) was made to PPR to 15 – but Hughes and Knight (1995) demonstrated that there was no significant change in rally length then.

Performance indicators (Hughes and Bartlett, 2002) were used to assess the changes in performance between the two scoring systems. The main performance indicators defined were the amount of attacking and defensive shots, shot selection, shot distribution, winners, errors and rally length. Attacking shots in squash are mainly linked with

Table 10.6. Average shots, rallies and time of games and matches for both scoring systems.			
Variable	Scoring System		% Difference
	PPR to 15	PPR to 11	
Avg. Shots per Match	1503.0	1376.3	−8.43
Avg. Shots per Game	354.6	233.82	−34.09%
Avg. Rallies per Game	28	18	−35.71%

taking the ball early to put the opponent under pressure, which can be achieved by volleying the ball. The PPR to 11 shows 22 per cent more short volleys played, compared to PPR to 15. There was also 18 per cent more long volleys under PPR to 11, showing players are taking the ball earlier, placing their opponents under greater pressure. The amount of defensive shots such as lobs were used 26 per cent more in PPR to 11 (Table 10.6). This could mean that the players are being placed under greater pressure so are required to use the lob more often to recover. The overall shot selection changed slightly under the new scoring system. PPR to 11 showed a greater number of straight shots, such as drives, lobs and short and long volleys (Table 10.6). This showed that even though the game may be played at a higher pace, a safer game is adopted – a poor cross shot can place the shot maker under extreme pressure on the next shot (Hughes, 1985; Pearson, 2001).

In PPR to 15, the average number of shots played per game agrees with previous research by Hughes and Robertson (1998). There have been no significant changes in average amount of rallies per game or the average amount of shots per rally. The average time taken between rallies in PPR to 15 has increased from 10 to 11.55 seconds compared to Hughes and Robertson's (1998) findings, and to 12.71 seconds in PPR to 11. Using 10 per cent change as 'important', this shows PPR to 11 creating an 'important' increase in rest time between rallies, although this was found as not significant using a t-test. This large difference may be caused by the increase in intensity of the rallies.

The overall average game time is six minutes less under PPR to 11, but the overall match-time averages are the same (Table 10.6). This may be due to a number of factors, the first being two matches in the data sample for PPR to 11 lasting in excess of 90 minutes, compared to an average length of *fifty-six* minutes for the remaining four matches, thus possibly causing the data to be skewed. A second factor is in the PPR to 15 matches, where there were only twenty-two games played in the six matches, compared to twenty-five games in the six matches in PPR to 11. To compensate for this imbalance in the number of games, consider that an average score of an elite match is 3–1 (Hughes, 1995). Extrapolated results were produced by multiplying the average game time under each rule system by four. This produced results showing PPR to 15 matches lasted on average just under seventy-five minutes, as compared to fifty-three minutes under PPR to 11. This shows that the introduction of the new scoring system should create shorter match times, retaining audience attention.

The new scoring system was introduced to make the game more attractive to television audiences. One major failing in this respect has been the low number of critical points – game points or match points. Tennis produces a critical point every three minutes, which keeps the attention of its audience (Hughes, 1995). This study has shown that a critical points occurs every seventeen minutes in PPR to 15, which agrees with Hughes (1995), and every 11.24 minutes in the new scoring system PPR to 11. The option to calculate critical points was decided post-analysis, so a critical point has only been recorded at known game points in the matches. The main reason why PPR to 11 produces more critical points is the introduction of the two clear points should 10-all be reached. This is similar to 'deuce' in a game of tennis, where two points in a row are required to win the game. PPR to 11 has improved the frequency of critical points, but does still not create as many as in a match of tennis.

SUMMARY AND CONCLUSIONS

In writing this chapter we were initially surprised at the volume of work in the area, but then when you do the sums, over thirty-five years of work, and count up the number of contributors, some of whom are still clinging on, it seems logical.

What is surprising though is that the basic 'profiling' ideas of data collection and data presentation of Frank Sanderson in the late 1970s still form the basis of our work today. The systems are fundamentally the same – based on frequencies of W/E distributions round the court. The computing technology has changed (every two years or so) and the data presentation incredibly so. The interesting developments in this area have been the ways that analysts, coaches and players have sought different ideas of analysis to complement the frequency distributions, using different ways of analysing the shots of opponents. Without a doubt, the attitude of the coaches and players in squash contributed immensely to the success of the discipline in this sport, and later other sports.

The ideas on momentum were developed and rapidly taken up and applied in different sports. Perturbations were first explored in squash (McGarry and Franks, 1996), and then extended to soccer, rugby, field hockey and so on. Time–motion analysis defined the fitness demands of the sport and the overall game structure.

Similarly the advances in presentation improved with innovative ideas like the 'ghosting' training. Advanced use of graphics and VHS video editing took us all down the road to digital video. Now we have the challenge of iCloud, iPads and iPhones and a whole new generation of 'digitally aware computer nerds' – it can only get better?

From a coaching point of view performance analysis brings home things that are so often missed in real-time. It is an invaluable tool for coaches and athletes as the results from the data are brought home visually.

David Pearson

Fig. 10.35 Performance Analysis is now commonplace in most sports, giving athletes objective information that helps enhance their movement, technique and tactics.

REFERENCES

Brown, D., and Hughes, M.D. (1995). The effectiveness of quantitative and qualitative feedback on performance in squash. In *Science and Racket Sports* (eds T. Reilly, M. Hughes and A. Lees). London: E. and F.N. Spon, pp. 232–236.

Cushion, C.J. and Smith, M. (2006). An investigation of the in-game behaviours of professional, top-level youth soccer coaches. *Journal of Sport Sciences*, 24(4), 355–366.

Downey, J.C. (1973). *The Singles Game*. London: E.P. Publications.

Ericsson, K.A., and Charness, N. (1994). Expert performance: Its structure and acquisition. *American Psychologist*, 49, 725–747.

Fenwick, M.E., Hughes, M.D. and Murray, S.R. (2006). Expanding normative profiles of elite squash players using momentum of winners and errors. *International Journal of Performance Analysis in Sport*, 6(1), (in press).

Harris-Jenkins, E. and Hughes, M. (1995). A computerised analysis of female coaching behaviour with male and female athletes In *Science and Racket Sports* (eds T. Reilly, M. Hughes and A. Lees). London: E. and F.N. Spon, pp. 272–278.

Hughes, M.D. (1985). A comparison of patterns of play in squash. In *International Ergonomics* (eds I.D. Brown, R. Goldsmith, K. Coombes and M.A. Sinclair). London: Taylor and Francis, pp. 139–141.

Hughes, M.D. (1986). A review of patterns of play in squash at different competitive levels. In *Sport Science* (eds. J. Watkins, T. Reilly, and L. Burwitz). London: E. and F.N. Spon, pp. 363–368.

Hughes, M.D. (1995). Using notational analysis to create a more exciting scoring system for squash. In *Sport, Leisure and Ergonomics* (eds G. Atkinson and T. Reilly). London: E. and F. N. Spon, pp. 243–247.

Hughes, M.D. and Franks, I.M. (1994). A time-motion analysis of squash players using a mixed-image video tracking system. *Ergonomics*, 37, (1), 23–29.

Hughes, M.D. and Franks, I.M. (1997). *Notational Analysis of Sport*. London: E. and F.N. Spon.

Hughes, M.D. and Knight, P. (1995). A comparison of playing patterns of elite squash players, using English scoring to point-per-rally scoring. In *Science and Racket Sports* (eds T. Reilly, M. Hughes and A. Lees). London: E. and F. N. Spon, pp. 257–259.

Hughes, M. and Reed, D. (2005). *Creating a performance profile using perturbations in soccer*. Proceedings of 4th International Scientific Conference on

Kinesiology, Opatija, University of Zagreb, Croatia, September.

Hughes, M.D. and Robertson, C. (1998). Using computerised notational analysis to create a template for elite squash and its subsequent use in designing hand notation systems for player development. In *Science and Racket Sports II* (eds T. Reilly, M. Hughes and A. Lees). London: E. and F. N. Spon, pp. 227–234.

Hughes, M.D., Franks, I.M. and Nagelkerke, P. (1989). A video system for the quantitative motion analysis of athletes in competetive sport. *Journal of Human Movement Studies,* 17, 212–227.

Hughes, M.T., Howells, M., Hughes, M. and Murray, S. (2006a). Using perturbations in elite men's squash to generate performance profiles. In *Science and Racket Sports IV* (eds A. Lees, J.-F. Kahn and I. Maynard). London: E. and F. N. Spon.

Hughes, M., Hughes, M. T. and Behan, H. (2007). The evolution of computerised notational analysis through the example of racket sports. *International Journal of Sports Science and Engineering,* 1, 3–28.

Hughes, M.D., Wells, J. and Matthews, K. (2000). Performance profiles at recreational, county and elite levels of women's squash. *Journal of Human Movement Studies,* 39, 85–104.

Hughes, M., Watts, A., White, C. and Hughes, M. T. (2009). Game structures of elite male squash under different rules. In *Science and Racket Sports IV.* (eds A. Lees, J.-F. Kahn and I. Maynard). London: E and F. N. Spon, pp. 227–231.

Hughes, M., Archer, B., James, N., Dancs, H. and Vuckovic, G. (2010). Behaviour patterns of elite coaches working with elite student athletes. In *Research Methods and Performance Analysis* (eds M.D. Hughes, H. Dancs, K. Nagyvaradi, T. Polgar, N. James, G. Sporis and G. Vuckovic). Szombathely: WHU, pp. 162–171.

Jones, R. (2006). How can educational concepts inform sports coaching? In *The Sports Coach as Educator: Reconceptualising sports coaching* (ed. R. Jones). London: Routledge.

Lyle, J. (2002). *Sports Coaching Concepts.* London: Routledge.

Magill, R.A. (1989) *Motor learning: Concepts and applications.* Iowa, USA: Wm. C. Brown.

Markland, R. and Martinek, T.J. (1988). Descriptive analysis of augmented feedback given to high school varsity female volleyball players. *Journal of Teaching in Physical Education,* 7, 289–301.

McGarry, T. (2006). Identifying patterns in squash contests using dynamical analysis and human perception. In *Performance Analysis of Sport VII* (eds M. Hughes and H. Dancs). Cardiff: CPA, UWIC (in press).

McGarry, T., Khan, M.A., and Franks, I.M. (1999). On the presence and absence of behavioural traits in sport: An example from championship squash match-play. *Journal of Sports Sciences,* 17, 297–311.

McKenzie, I. M.(2002). *Ian McKenzie's Squash Skills.* Marlborough, Wilts.: Crowood.

More, K.G. and Franks, I.M. (1996). Analysis and modification of verbal coaching behaviour: The usefulness of a data driven intervention strategy. *Journal of Sports Sciences,* 14, 523–543.

Murray, S. and Hughes, M. (2001). Tactical performance profiling in elite level senior squash. In *pass. com* (eds M. Hughes and I.M. Franks). Cardiff: CPA, UWIC, pp. 185–94.

Mustain, W.C. (1990). Are you the best teacher you can be? *Journal of Physical Education, Recreation and Dance,* February, 69–73.

Pearson, D. (1999). Movement is the key. http://uks-quash.hypermart.net/movement.htm

Pereira, A., Wells, J. and Hughes, M. (2001). Notational analysis of elite women's movement patterns in squash. In *pass.com* (eds M. Hughes and I.M. Franks), Cardiff: CPA, UWIC, pp. 223–238.

Rushall, B.S. and Siedentop, D. (1972). *The Development and Control of Behaviour in Sport and Physical Education.* Philadelphia: Lea and Febiger.

Sanderson, F.H. (1983). A notation system for analysing squash. *Physical Education Review,* 6, 19–23.

Sanderson, F.H. and Way, K.I.M. (1977). The development of an objective method of game analysis in squash rackets. *British Journal of Sports Medecine,* 11, 188.

Schmidt, R.A. (1988). *Motor Control and Learning,* 5th Edn. Champaign, IL.: Human Kinetics.

Tharp, R. G. and Gallimore, R. (1976). Basketball's John Wooden: What a coach can teach a teacher. *Psychology Today,* 9, 8, 74–78.

Wells, J., Robertson, C., Hughes, M. and Howe, D. (2004). Performance profiles of elite men's squash doubles match play. In *Science and Racket Sports III.* (eds A. Lees, J.-F. Kahn and I. Maynard), London: E. and F.N. Spon, pp. 196–201.

CHAPTER 11

WHAT LEARNING CAN WE TAKE FROM THIS BOOK?

Over the last thirty years or so, there have been major changes that have markedly influenced match play. Some of these influences have tested rules because combined and in common with several other sports, players were outstripping the dimensions of courts and governing rules. The design and construction of rackets from wood to composites increased the speed of balls; different rubbers designed to reduce the bounce and speed of balls were introduced; materials were used to increase the quality and durability of squash courts, and for international-standard squash in particular, there was a reduction in the height of the front-wall's tin from 48.3 cm (19in.) to 43.2 cm (17in.) and 'slower' televisual all-glass courts.

As standards of play increased, changes in scoring systems attempted to reduce lengths of matches and increase attacking play from conventional point-only-when-serving to point-a-rally with variations in first-to-fifteen now first-to-eleven for international match play. These structural changes were mapped by the analysts (Hughes, 1995; Hughes and Knight, 2004; Hughes, Watts, White and Hughes, 2008). Simultaneously, attempts by administrators to reduce stoppages in play because of 'lets' became increasingly robust. Players occupy the same playing space, so collisions and obstructions are inevitable. However, the onus is clearly on players to make every effort to play the ball and then clear to allow their opponent(s) to do likewise.

Of note is the buoyancy and increased interest in the UK of masters' squash both for men and women. Five-year age groups begin at thirty-five and go all the way to over-seventies for men and even over eighty in some tournaments. Similar five-year divisions apply for women. Age might have a slowing effect but it is difficult to see that effect in the best age-group players whose abilities are remarkable. These abilities are an indication of the application of training principles that enable older players to continue to enjoy their squash. What changes little is the competitiveness of age-group players.

TRAINING

If training programmes are to be effective, they must be based on sound physiological rationale. However, programmes have to be designed, implemented and evaluated in conjunction with coaching staff and other members of the scientific support team. That team includes psychologists, nutritionists, performance analysts, physiotherapists, physicians (and perhaps surgeons), strength-and-conditioning staff and, of course, players. All this is for the benefit of those players both now but perhaps more importantly, in the future. Assembling the scientific support team is challenging. Ideally, but not essentially, members should have a knowledge of the game so as to empathize with players. As sport and exercise science is firmly embedded in squash, increasingly players are fully accustomed to such support. It is essential principally for professional-standard players but permeates to all standards and ages. That looks set to continue.

Training activities for the physical development of squash players should be prescribed using an objective needs-based approach rather than following traditional accepted practice. Prescription should be guided by fundamental principles and the programme should be monitored and modified according to the individual's response to the training stimulus imposed.

A long-term developmental view should be taken with the progression of loading and intensity built upon a foundation of movement competence. Developing all-round athletic potential rather than just adopting a narrow sport-specific focus best supports sustainable improvements in squash performance. There are many essential physical qualities that affect squash performance and any significant deficiencies will limit the player's potential.

Strength and conditioning

The evolution of strength and conditioning support for squash continues. Potential areas for further development of practice are:

- A range of interventions targeting the progressive development of movement competence, strength and mobility of junior players should be applied broadly across the junior squash population.
- Improvement in time-motion, metabolic and kinematic competition data should be used to further inform more individualized prescription of training activities.
- Bespoke individualized recovery protocols have previously been implemented by several players at major events but the application of optimal recovery activities during tournament competition is currently under-developed for many players.

Physiotherapy

Injuries either acute or through repetitive micro trauma can have career-ending implications for squash players if not managed correctly. Consequently the physiotherapist plays a pivotal role in both preventative strategies and fast tracking return to play following injury. As with any aspect of performance, it is essential that the physiotherapist works in conjunction with the rest of the multidisciplinary team including the athlete themselves to provide a holistic approach to the athlete's performance management.

Nutrition

Squash is a high-intensity sport, requiring multiple bouts of vigorous sprint activity (Wilkinson, McCord and Winter, 2010). A squash player's ability to perform high-intensity, variable movements is a key determinant of success at the elite level of competition (Wilkinson et al., 2012). The body composition of a squash player may affect athletic performance and carrying excessive body fat may increase injury risk and impair agility and speed. However, minimal body fat levels may negatively impact endurance and immunity (Meltzer and Hopkins, 2011), which may result in reduced performance and increase the risk of illness. Athletes who wish to optimize athletic performance by reducing their body fat levels and maintaining lean mass are advised to follow a structured nutritional intervention that promotes a gradual body-mass loss of 0.5–1kg per week. Moreover, preservation of lean body mass (LBM) is desirable to a squash player in order to prevent unwanted losses of strength, speed and power. In consideration of this, achieving an appropriate energy balance is essential, as adequate nutrient intake will support health, training load and performance. In addition, as squash is predominantly an indoor sport with little structured outdoor training, players may be at increased risk of vitamin D deficiency (Angeline, Gee, Shindle, Warren, and Rodeo, 2013), due to the lack of exposure to ultraviolet radiation from the sun.

PLAYERS

It is important to believe in what you are doing, to understand why you are doing it, to learn from every experience and to ultimately feel like you have done all you can to prepare when you enter the court. Being effective in your daily training environment, from the moment you wake up in the morning to when you leave the club at the end of training, helps you stay in control of your destiny and believe in the journey you are on.

Working on your mental performance is an integral part of your daily training. The body and mind do not exist in isolation; therefore as you train physically, technically and tactically remember to integrate aspects of mental training and performance lifestyle to your programme. Develop your growth mindset and embrace opportunities to push your boundaries. Be relentless in training, especially when under pressure. Set challenging, effective goals and create a deliberate practice approach to every session. Be optimistic in all aspects of your squash game as well as your life. A positive outlook will engage parts of the brain that keep you focused, present, mindful and emotionally in control. This allows you to get the best out of yourself every session. You have the opportunity every day to build mental resilience in performance and life.

COACHES

Including others skilfully into the 'Coaching Team' is a skill that is becoming ever more important as expertise in sport support grows. Collaboration and encouraging players to work with a wider range of people other than yourself helps reduce pressure and often sheds new learnings and insights. One person does not know it all and to think so is dangerous and not only limiting but controlling. Integrating sports science support into the coaching process is a skill in itself and will depend on how well the communications and relationships develop between coach, performer and sport scientist(s).

> It is the merging of 'science and sweat' that will allow today's athletes not only to excel and compete at much higher levels but to minimize predisposition to injury and enhance career longevity. Over the years, sport science has mainly been viewed by coaches as inaccessible, too technical, or in many cases non-applicable to the actual sport setting. With the renewed focus on prevention of injuries, on enhancing performance at the younger levels of competition, and on the extensive amount of time and financial commitment toward

training and conditioning, taking a more comprehensive approach through science provides the coach, as well as the athlete, greater control, preparation, accountability and, most importantly, measurable progress (2006).

Michael Meyers

To be a coach is simply to be a person. Working on all aspects of your emotional intelligence will be an unfolding and hopefully oscillating experience for you. After all, this is what you wish for those people you guide, show, question and occasionally tell!

When providing feedback on a technical skill the person providing it should base their feedback on a priority order list of form cues that are fundamental to the movement, such as 'feet placement' or 'orientation of the hips'. By doing this the coach can prioritize how critical the part of the skill is in which the error occurred. The error that is highest on this priority list should be the one that is the basis for the feedback. When this part is improved to a satisfactory level the feedback can be directed at a subsequent form cue. This method has been suggested by Magill (2010) and research evidence supporting this process has been provided by Weeks and Kordus (1998) and Wulf, Chiviacowsky, Schiller and Avila (2010). It has been suggested by Magill and Anderson (2012) that when the error is identified the correction information should be less specific so that the athlete is encouraged to actively search for ways to correct similar errors in a discovery learning style.

Forms of non-verbal augmented feedback have also been used to improve performance. Although there is very little evidence of research in squash this has been completed in netball (Helmer *et al.*, 2010) using wearable strain sensors and audio feedback to assist shooting accuracy; in weightlifting (Winchester *et al.*, 2009) using video feed-

back on bar path trajectory and technique to improve force and power production; and in golf (Bertram *et al.*, 2007) where video feedback with no additional verbal feedback was used by skilled players to improve swing characteristics, but it impeded improvement in novices potentially due to the lack of verbal feedback combined with the video.

Feedback provision should also be considered based on the player's skill level and task complexity. As skill level increases and task complexity decreases, feedback can be made more specific around particular details. The more advanced player will also have an increased ability to self-correct so will have heightened levels of intrinsic feedback. However when skill level is low and task complexity is high, the player will likely need the guidance provided by augmented feedback to find appropriate ways to improve performance (Guadagnoli and Lee, 2004).

Coaches and other support staff can vary the modality of feedback based on the requirements either in a competition scenario or in a practice session. There are several types of feedback that can be employed, shown in Table 11.1.

The physical, psychological, tactical and technical demands of squash look destined to continue to increase, therefore requiring players to prepare even more thoroughly than ever to achieve success. Already high standards of match play show little if any sign of doing anything other than continue to improve. Moreover, the number of players of such standard also continues to increase. Conversely, margins that define success reduce. These reductions highlight the need for strategic, detailed and sustained scientific support to gain a competitive edge. The battle remains primarily between players; however, in this modern era the impact of the support from the team of coaching, scientific and medical staff is vital, perhaps even decisive.

Table 11.1 The different types of feedback.	
Type	**Description**
Summary	Feedback about a set of repetitions after the set has been completed; player required to use intrinsic feedback in between trials.
Bandwidth	Player is provided with detailed feedback only when the performance falls outside an agreed-upon error tolerance range; ensures clarity of required standards from the player.
Faded	Decreasing the frequency of feedback provision over a series of practice trials, which promotes a transfer from augmented error correction to player self-correction skills.
Performer Regulated	Frequency of feedback provision determined by the player upon completion of practice trial.
Performer Estimation	Player estimates their error upon completion of an action or trial; coach then provides the actual demonstrated by the player.

Fig. 11.1 The physical, psychological, tactical and technical demands of squash look destined to continue to increase, therefore requiring players to prepare even more thoroughly than ever to achieve success.

INDEX

acceleration/deceleration 47
achievement orientation 164
adaptation & evolution of players 157
aerobic fitness & training 47–8, 57–9, 71
age groups 26, 234
agility 43, 47, 63–6, 70
anaerobic fitness 47–8, 57
ankles 51
antioxidants 100–1
ATP-PCr systems 57

Barnes, Dr Kirsten 24
Barrington, Jonah 23, 24, 167
Bioelectrical impedance analysis (BIA) 106
body composition assessment 106–7
body mass 92, 105–6, 236
bond-building 168–9
bone health 101–2
Botright, Vicky 210–12
breathing exercises 123–4
British Open 1996, analysis of 226–8
Brown, Damon 24, 25

caffeine 99
calcium 98
calf injury case study 82
carbohydrates 24, 92–5, 100
cardio-pulmonary function 34–5, 48, 57
Carter, Paul 218–19
Chelladurai, Packianathan 161
circuit training 42
coach behaviour analysis 222–4
coaching, qualities needed 152, 158–63, 236–7
cognitive effort, in practice 179–80
collaboration 169–70
communication 168–9
competition calendar, accommodating 43, 46
competitions, recovery help & support during 66, 80–1
connective tissue 49–50

constraints, manipulation of in practice 180–2
court design & structure 26, 31, 234
Cowie, Alex 25
Craig Sharp, N.C. 24
creatine 98–9

data collection, performance analysis 191–8
    momentum analysis 202–8
    player profiling 198–202
database, development 226–8
David, Nicol 210–12
deliberate practice 116–17
densitometry 106
detraining/reversability 46
dietary supplements 98–100
direction, change of (COD) 63–4
Downey, Myles 169
drugs testing 100
Dual energy X-ray absorbtiometry (DXR) 106
duration of play 32–3
Dweck, Carol 163
dynamic system theory 208

elite level training 43, 63
emotional intelligence 158
empathy 165
endurance 57
energy system output 57–8
Epstein, David, The Sports Gene 155–6
ergogenic aids 98–100
exercise
    capacity 43
    definition 30–1
    rehabilitation 81–5
eye injuries 76

fascia 49–50
fat levels 92, 105–6
fatigue 35, 102, 103
Fick Equation 35
Fitts, Paul 175
flexibility 47, 48–54

active & passive 49
physiotherapy for 80
techniques 54–6
tests 70
fluid intake see hydration
focus/refocus 121–4, 137–42, 144
Functional Movement Screen 70

Galen 23
Galileo Galilei 23
game length 230–1
generalised motor programmes (GMP) 176–7
genetics 155–6
Gerschler, Dr Woldemar 23
ghosting 58, 83
    replication 218–19, 231
glycogen 92–4
goal setting 118–21
Goleman, 168
Greene, Robert 164
Grinham, Natalie 212, 219
growth mindset 115, 163–4

Hammond, Matt 25
Harbig, Rudolf 23–4
Harris, 'Bomber' 24
heart rate 33, 57
Hill, Archibald Vivian 23
hips 51, 76
Hughes, Mike, data systems development 25, 193ff, 209ff
Hunt, Geoff 216
hydration & dehydration 33, 96–7, 101, 103–4

illness, avoiding 100
initiative 162–3
injury, common 76, 81
    during competitions 80–1
    early identification & screening 78–80
    factors & rates 76
    recovery schedules 81
    rehabilitation 81–5
    screening for 76–9

investigative tools 157
iron 98

Jackman, Cassie 218–19
joint stiffness, contributions to 50
jump training 63–4
junior players 44–5, 61

Khan, Jansher 216
Khan, Nasrullah 167
knee injury, case study 84

labrum 76
lapsed-time analysis 195, 198
leadership behaviour 161–2, 167–8
Leonardo da Vinci 23
Libet, Benjamin 138
life outside sport 129–31
lifestyle needs 156–7
lighter rackets, effects of 226–7, 229, 234
limbic resonance 165–6
Liverpool Polytechnic research 192–3
lunges 52–4, 79

Marcus Aurelius 23
Martin, Rod 168
Maslow, Abraham 161
Massaro, Danny 159
Massaro, Laura 163
matchplay, psychology of 137–46
Matthew, Nick 162
McClusky, Mark, Faster, Higher, Stronger 157
McQuillan, Colin 25
meal size 103
measurement, performance 157
mental training 114–32, 236
metabolic conditioning 57–9
Meyers, Michael 170
Millman, Dan 159
Mindfulness, Acceptance, Commitment (MAC) 117, 123
'mindlessness' 141
minerals 98
mobility see flexibility
momentum analysis 202–8, 210–14
motivation 118–2, 175–8
motor skills 175–9
Mourinho, Jose 152–3
movement analysis & patterns 215–18
Murray, Stafford 25, 209, 219
muscle type & activity 30–1, 33–4

neuromuscular control 78
neuroplasticity 150
neurotransmitters 165
notation systems 192–8 , 228–31
nutrition 92–109, 235–6
    balanced 92–6
    & bone health 101–2
    & fatigue 102
    & illness & recovery 100, 103
    pre- & post-exercise 93–5
    supplements 98–100
    & travel 101

Olympic Games 23
optimism 117, 162–3
oxygen uptake 35, 36–7

Pearson, David, on coaching 25, 154–5, 159ff
Perception, Decision, Action (PDA) cycle 139–40
performance analysis, development of 191–8
'periodization' 45
personality types 156
perturbation analysis 208–14, 231
physical assessment tests 69–71
physiotherapy 76–87, 235
    prehabilitation 79–80
    in competitions 80–1
player profiling 198–208
    momentum analysis 202–8
practice structure 179–80
    feedback in 182–4, 237
    manipulating constraints 180–2
Pradeep, Dr A K 168
prehabilitation 79–80
pressure, handling 124–7
    coping strategies 126–7
pressure feeding 58
probiotic 100
Progressive Overload 45
protein 93, 94, 95–6, 97–8

racket, changes in 26, 31, 226–7, 229, 234
rally statistics 228–9
range of motion, improving 48–56
Rate of Force Development (RFD) 61
rating of perceived exertion 57
real time analysis 195
recovery training, during competitions 66
rehabilitation 82–5
Reindel, Dr Herbert 23
relationship management 166–70
resistance training 42–3
Robertson, Chris 139, 140, 193
rotation 45
rule changes 225–6
rules, manipulation of 181–2

Saltin, Bengt 24
Sanderson & Way data analysis 192–3, 194, 195
sarcomere 49, 50
Schmidt schema theory 176–7
scoring system , changes in 26, 31–2, 225–6
    effects of 228, 229–31, 244
self-assessment/belief, coach's 159
self-awareness 118, 144, 159
self-belief/confidence 127–31, 141 142–4
self-control, coach's 160
sensory perception 138
service orientation 164
short & long stretch shortening cycles (SSSC & LSSC) 63
skinfold measurement 107

sleep 177
social awareness, in a coach 165–6
Specific Adaptation to Imposed Demands (SAID) 45
Specific Multiple Sprint Ability (SSMSA) 47, 69
speed 47
    training 63–6
    tests 70
spine injury 76
Sports Council Education Programme 24
sports drinks 96
sports science, history of 23–4
squash, physical characteristics needed 32–3
    scientific & medical support for 24–5
    state funding 24
Squash Rackets Association 24, 25
Squash-specific movement analysis 215–18
squash-specific needs, in individuals 156–7
Squash-Specific Repeated Speed Test (SSRST) 47
squash-specific speed & agility 47, 63–4
    interval training 57, 60
squats 79–80
Star Excursion Balance Test (SEBT) 79
stoppages 234
strength training & tests 43, 44–5, 47, 70–1, 59–63, 66, 69–71, 235
    in rehabilitation 83
stretching 48–54, 80
supercompensation 45–6
SWEAT (Squash Winner/Error Analysis Tactics System) 193–4, 195–7, 204
sweat rates 33, 96

T area, control of 208–9
tactical model, creating 226–31
tart cherries 99, 100
teamwork 169–7
technique, refinement & change 178
tendons 33
time-motion analysis 214–22
training preparation/reflection 130
travel 101
trust & reliability 160–1

urine, assessing 96, 97, 103–4

vegetarian diet 97–8
video feedback 220–2, 231
Vitamin D 92, 101–2

weight loss 104–5
whey supplements 95, 96
Whitemore, Sir John 166
winning, importance of 142–4
Winter, Prof. Edward 24, 25
World Class Performance Plans 25
Wright, Paul 25